MARJORIE I

*T*H*E*

Maggie Kelly

The **Hallamshire** Press 2000

By the same author:

The Tali Stone
The Reluctant Traveller
Abe's Legacy

Published by The Hallamshire Press Limited
Broom Hall
Sheffield S10 2DR
England

Typeset by The Hallamshire Press Limited, Sheffield
Printed by The Cromwell Press, Trowbridge, Wiltshire.

British Library Cataloguing in Publication Data:
  A catalogue record for this book is available from the British Library

ISBN 1 874718 58 X

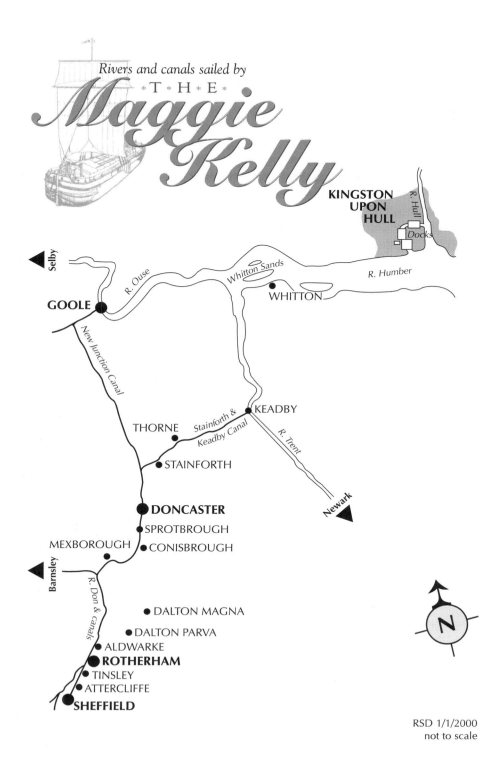

Rivers and canals sailed by
*T*H*E*
Maggie
Kelly

KINGSTON
UPON
HULL

R. Hull

Docks

Selby

R. Ouse

Whitton Sands

R. Humber

GOOLE

WHITTON

New Junction Canal

KEADBY

THORNE

Stainforth & Keadby Canal

R. Trent

STAINFORTH

Newark

DONCASTER

SPROTBROUGH

MEXBOROUGH

CONISBROUGH

Barnsley

R. Don & canals

DALTON MAGNA

DALTON PARVA

ALDWARKE

ROTHERHAM

TINSLEY

ATTERCLIFFE

SHEFFIELD

N

RSD 1/1/2000
not to scale

To Cai Pettitt, my grandson

ACKNOWLEDGEMENTS

Acknowledgements and thanks to:

Roy Bullen for the loan of his research material on keels.
Phillip Marshall once more, for reading and correcting the draft manuscript.
Colin S. Screeton for allowing me to board the keel *Comrade* and for his help.
Special thanks to my husband Bob for his patience and skill in refining the text.
Sheffield City Library, Local Studies Library.
Kingston-upon-Hull Central Library, Local History Library.
The staff of the Old Black Boy, Hull, for their hospitality. (The conditions described in the book bear little resemblance to this hostelry as it is today.)

FURTHER READING

Geoffrey Tweedale, *The Sheffield Knife Book*, The Hallamshire Press, Sheffield. ISBN 1 874718 11 3.

Simon Ogden, *The Sheffield & Tinsley Canal*, The Hallamshire Press, Sheffield. ISBN 1 874718 26 1.

Mike Taylor, *Memories of the Sheffield & South Yorkshire Navigation*, Yorkshire Waterways Publication, 1988.

The Art-Journal Illustrated Catalogue of the Industries of All Nations, The Great Exhibition - London - 1851: David & Charles Reprints.

Chapter 1

*T*he day could not have been a more miserable one, nor the swollen River Don less attractive than it was now in a March squall. Rain lashed the deck of the keel with as equal a force as it did his face, and Michael stood numb with cold, tightly holding the tiller of his vessel. He was grateful that no-one could see the tears of frustration which mingled with the stream of rainwater pouring down his face from the neb of his cap. His leg ached far worse than ever before, aggravated as much by the cold, damp day as by his old injury. How long he could carry the burden placed upon him he knew not, and the future loomed black and forbidding. Not only was loading and unloading the keel becoming a trial but he now found that standing for hours on end at the tiller, especially in bad weather, took its toll. Even climbing in and out of the cabin sent pains shooting through his leg. The discomfort had always been there but this winter the icy winds had really increased the problem.

He guided the *Maggie Kelly* against the swift current of the river towards the bank, just short of the lock at Mexborough, where he would leave his mast and sails in a storage trap. There he joined the other vessels waiting for horses to haul them beyond this point and he recalled how, in hard times, both his parents had taken turns to haul the keel themselves to save paying the hauling fees. To have constantly lowered and raised the mast and rigging in order to pass beneath the numerous low bridges ahead would have taken up far too much of their precious time, indeed they would not have been able to pass under the bridge at Bacon Lane in Sheffield at all if the mast had been still on board.

Today, however, he was going only as far as Rotherham, four locks up the river, where he could leave the keel in safety before visiting his mother at her home in Dalton. She lived there with his sister and her husband, a blacksmith and wheelwright, a man to whom Michael's life on the canal was as foreign as were the unhealthy factories of Sheffield. They were all at this time, of course, unaware of the terrible news he was bringing them.

Giving a blast on the keel's foghorn to draw the attention of the lock keeper who was sheltering in the toll-cottage, Michael drew alongside the bank and waited impatiently for someone to appear. At last the man scuttled along the tow-path towards him, sheltering beneath a thick waterproof coat. He caught the rope which Michael threw and tethered the keel to a mooring-post.

'What a terrible day!' Michael shouted, complaining in a loud voice so as to penetrate the buffeting wind. That same wind which had, in fact, guaranteed their arrival under sail.

'You can say that again,' the man hailed back. He indicated the line of waiting craft and called, 'There'll be a long wait for a tow!'

Michael climbed carefully off the *Maggie Kelly*, wincing with pain, and spoke in a quieter voice as he reached Joe Marshall. 'I'm only going as far as Rotherham this time, Joe. Sheffield will have to wait a day or so for this load.'

Joe looked at him in surprise. 'It's not like you to delay your journey, Mike!' he commented. 'I'm afraid all this rain has muddied things up and the horses are making heavy work of it, so everyone needs two animals today.' Then, seeing that Michael was quieter than usual, he asked, 'Is there something amiss? You're later than usual as well, what kept you?'

Michael sighed deeply. 'It's my father, Joe. He's dead!' he said this bluntly, lacking in feeling, for his heart was as numb as were his limbs.

'What?' Joe exclaimed, in disbelief. 'Say that again!'

'Dad's dead!' Michael repeated, flatly. 'Two days ago he was as fit as you and me, then yesterday he simply never woke up.'

'Hey, Mike, I'm sorry to hear that,' the other man said, shaking his head sadly and gazing down at the keel.

Seeing this, Michael nodded. 'Yes, he's still on board, and I've got a full load with only my sister to help. She's near distraught with grief and shock.'

'What'll you do?' Joe asked, really saddened at the unexpected news.

'I'm hoping the family will help me get to Sheffield and back, then I'll have to hire a keelman in Thorne, or Hull. I suppose I can manage under tow with the help of a horse marine for the remainder of this trip, but I'm thinking in the long run I may have to get rid of the *Maggie*' he mumbled, lapsing into his mother's dialect. It had been some time since he'd spoken with an Irish lilt, something which both surprised him and took him off guard.

'I'll take Maggy off your hands,' the lock-keeper rejoined, his face impassive.

Michael stared at him, questioning the feasibility of the offer, then said, 'I'm serious, Joe, I might have to let her go. I'm in trouble with my leg, but what I'll do for a living if I quit the canal I don't rightly know. Surely you can't afford to buy the keel in your position?'

Joe laughed softly. 'No, not the vessel, Mike! I mean your sister, Maggy! I'll take her off your hands any day.' He saw the look of disapproval on Michael's face, then remembered the dead man on the keel and murmured apologetically, 'But perhaps now is not a good time to joke about things.'

'No matter,' Michael replied, letting the matter drop, for normally he would have seen the funny side of it all. 'It's just that everything seems to be working against me, and standing there at the tiller for hours in the cold and rain hasn't helped.' His face was drawn and miserable. 'I'll lower the rigging and give you a yell when I've done, then if you'll help me off-load and put the lot away in the storage trap, I'll see you right.'

'Fine, give me a call when you're ready.' Joe replied, anxious to make amends and glad to have the opportunity to earn a few more coppers.

The two parted company and once back on board, Michael summoned Maggy from where she sat waiting for him in the small fore-cabin, so that she could help him lower and lash the square-rigged sail. The wet flapping canvas seemed heavier and stiffer than ever before, and the lively wind hindered every movement. He fully realised that things would be impossible without the help of an experienced keelman, especially when sailing on the currents of the Humber. Nevertheless, he would have to manage somehow until he could find a buyer for the keel. Had his father been a less stubborn man Michael would have left the keel for other work some time since, because of the problem with his leg, but the harsh way of life on the water had hardened the old man, and he seemed unable to understand his son's physical limitations. He'd say, 'Don't give in to it, lad!' And that was it. Well, his father was gone, but he'd left him with a mother and sister to provide for, even if they did live with his brother-in-law's family most of the time.

Even with his sister's help, it took half an hour of hard battle against the wind and canvas before they'd finished dismantling the rigging and the mast. He knew Maggy was doing her best to help but she didn't have the strength of a man and the shock of their father's death had shaken her badly. Once the mast was down he turned to her. 'Thanks, Sis. Now go back below and get warm. I'll finish here and then bring something from the aft cabin for us to eat.' Murmuring her thanks she went for'ard, leaving him to tidy up the rigging ready to off-load into the storage trap until it was needed on the return journey—and when that would be only God knew! Finally, Michael went aft to the main cabin which he had shared with his father whilst Maggy was on board and using the fore-cabin.

It was starkly cold below deck and he quickly gathered up the items needed to provide a meal of sorts for them both. He glanced at the shrouded body on one of the bunks in a recess of the small yet well planned cabin, and shivered. He'd told Maggy to stay in her cabin where it was warm, having warned her not to light this stove for fear of the effect the heat might have on his father's body. With some relief he climbed back on deck and walked the length of the keel to hand the provisions down to Maggy. 'Get the water boiling,' he said, 'I'll be as quick as I can.' With that, he went to give a short blast on the horn to draw Joe's attention to the fact that he was ready for him.

It wasn't long before the pair of them had removed the unwanted items from the keel and finished stacking them safely into storage. As they stood in the shelter of the trap, Joe said awkwardly, 'I'm sorry if I sounded a bit callous earlier, I'd a great deal of respect for old Jim, and meant no harm. I still can't believe he went so suddenly.'

Michael accepted Joe's apology and smiled understandingly. 'I know he could be a strong-minded old coot but everyone admired him, it was his dependability I suppose. It's left me in a difficult situation, though. I'd been trying to tell him for some time that we'd need help because of my leg, but he just said we couldn't afford a three-man crew, not with trade declining as it is. However, if I'm reduced to carrying coal, Joe, it will be the death of me. I can't afford to travel 'light' on return journeys to Hull, and if I have to take coal and pay fees every time I need help, I'll go broke. Where's the sense in that?'

Joe nodded his understanding, and felt a bit guilty as he took the coppers Michael gave him for helping. 'Thanks, Mike' he said, 'it's a great shame, but the railways are certainly making a dent in canal trade.'

Michael changed the subject and asked, 'Have you seen the *Mary Ann* lately?'

'They came through yesterday,' Joe replied, 'but you won't have seen them. They couldn't get a cargo in Sheffield and said they were going to try for a load of coal along the Dearne canal. It seems there's not much doing in Sheffield at the moment.'

'It'll be coal or nothing on the return journey for us all soon.' Michael grumbled bitterly, dreading the time when he might find himself out of work. Everything was beginning to get on top of him. In his present condition he'd need to pay men to shift the stuff on and off while he stood idly by, and he just couldn't afford it. Would he be able to find alternative cargoes though, that was the crucial point?

He regretted missing the *Mary Ann* on her return trip, he'd hoped that the keel would pass him before he was obliged to see to family affairs in Dalton. It wasn't that he knew the Captain all that well, they saw each other occasionally and just had a pint together when they docked at the same place. However, in recent months, 'Swifty', as the Captain was known from his habit of being quick to get a load-up, had started bringing his family on board and Michael quite looked forward to seeing his ship coming into view. He tried to tell himself that it wasn't because of the bright young woman who sometimes sat on deck and waved to him, but it was a lie. It was hardly likely that she noticed him any more than other men on the canal. Why should she? There was nothing extraordinary about him. He was of average height and build, though perhaps a bit fairer than most, in fact a watered down version of his 'carroty' sister's complexion. The original Maggy Kelly, his grandmother, had been a stunner by all accounts and turned every head, though he remembered her vaguely as seeming always to have a drink in her hand. Yes, that part he would never forget or forgive. It had been during one of her less sober times that she'd carried him upstairs, stumbled and dropped him from top to bottom, fracturing his leg and damaging his knee. At the time he'd been too young to understand the cause of the incident but, whenever the ache worsened, it never allowed him to forget what had happened.

'Well, I'll be off then,' Joe said quietly, seeing that Michael's thoughts were far away and that he was no longer in a mood to talk. 'I'll let you know when I can get you a horse-marine and horse.'

'Thanks, Joe!' Michael said, returning to the present. 'Thanks for helping.'

When he finally joined Maggy in the cramped for'ard cabin which was full of supplies and equipment, she was sitting despondently on the locker, huddled beneath a shawl and looking utterly miserable. 'I've got the water ready,' she said in a subdued voice. 'There's a mug of tea for you.'

Michael removed his dripping oilskins and hung them over a bucket to drain off. 'We've got to wait some time,' he explained. 'There's not a horse or man available to tow us at the moment and, because we're only going to Rotherham, some marines might not like to take such a short haul.' Maggy passed him his tea which he drank immediately, feeling the heat of it coursing through him. That was better! He also realised just how hungry he was when she passed him some bread and cheese. 'Thanks, Maggy,' he said, smiling kindly at her, 'it's not been a good day, has it?'

Maggy looked at him solemnly. 'What will you do, Michael?' She always called him by his full name especially when they were low in spirits.

He shook his head. 'One thing at a time. We'll think of something.'

'You're in pain again, aren't you?' she said, her face softening with concern.

He reached for a bottle of brandy which he kept behind a tin in the cupboard for emergencies. 'Here, Maggy, get some of this down you,' he said, and poured a drop in her tea.

'I thought you didn't drink the hard stuff,' Maggy chided, eyeing him with suspicion. 'Not after you learned the truth about grandma!'

'I don't,' he replied hastily, 'I only keep it for when I'm really cold or in pain, nothing else helps me enough to carry on. I've not touched it in weeks.'

'Good!' Maggy said, firmly.

They ate quietly on, each immersed in their own thoughts and memories, only exchanging the occasional word when called on to do so. 'You've not had a really hot meal in two days,' Maggy commiserated, 'but it's not my fault you know, and I realise we dare not light the big stove in the other cabin.'

'No, we couldn't, Sis, but when we get to Dalton they'll give us a good meal. If we'd much further to go we'd have been forced to eat at an Inn, but I can't bear to leave him here on his own.'

They waited nearly two hours for a tow. 'Don't forget,' Michael said, when Joe had knocked to warn them that they were next in line, 'as soon as we get to Aldwarke you get off, Maggy, close the lock after me and go to John's. I'm afraid Ma will know there's something amiss when she sees you, so perhaps you'd better go to the forge and talk to John first before going into the house.' Maggy wept openly now and stared down at her feet, her hands clasped loosely on her lap. There wasn't much he could do to help her, except to say quietly, 'It's a horrible day, so wrap yourself up well and walk home as quickly as you can. You'll be fine once you get there.'

He observed her fondly, for she was not as coarse or as rough and ready as some of the river folk. She was lively and quite pretty, but not suited to the lonely and sometimes monotonous days spent on the keel, for she was also a bit of a dreamer. 'I've no choice but to go on and berth at Rotherham,' he continued, 'the cargo's too valuable to leave moored along an unguarded stretch of the river.'

There was a sudden sharp knocking on the side of the keel's hull as Joe gave them the signal that a marine was finally available. Michael rose, pulled his oilskins on again and went on deck from where he saw the horse marine waiting to harness his beasts to the keel. Once the ropes were in place they were ready to move forward.

'Catch!' Joe called as he threw the last mooring rope towards the *Maggie Kelly*. 'And the best of luck, Mike!'

'I've got it,' Michael called back, 'and thanks for your help.' He secured the rope and grasped the tiller. 'Right, haul away!'

Slowly the horses on the tow-path started forward until the ropes seemed almost at breaking point, then, gradually, the vessel began to glide forward and move into the lock. Once inside and with the gates closed firmly behind him, he felt for the first time in his life strangely trapped in the dank, green-walled cavern, trapped indeed with the body of his father. It was an eerie feeling, as though they had both been lowered into the grave at the same time.

He was very relieved when the water level rose, and happier still when he realised that the rain had almost ceased. For the rest of the journey he was content to let the horses take the strain under the care of the marine whilst he controlled the tiller, leaving Maggy to watch pensively from the bows and take over from him when he needed a rest.

When finally they reached Aldwarke, where the lock permitted boats to by-pass the weir, Maggy got off, closed the heavy gates then waved to him before heading towards the tiny isolated hamlet of Dalton Magna. Suddenly she was gone, and he waited whilst the marine adjusted the harnesses on the horses ready for the onward journey to the wharf-side at Rotherham. Here, his brother-in-law would meet him with a wagon with which to collect his father's body. He stood at the tiller thinking of his strange predicament. Maggy thought he didn't care about their father's death, but he did; they'd been working together as a team for sixteen years, since he was twelve in fact, and that had created a strong bond between them. Since yesterday he'd pushed sentiment to the back of his mind in the need to bring the keel and his sister home safely, but now he faced a momentous turning point in his life, one which hurt him more than she would ever know. At least in dying his father had been spared the knowledge of being let down by his son, and for that Michael was grateful.

Maggy walked carefully along the rutted track towards the scattered dwellings of Dalton Brook. The rain had stopped but thick clouty mud sucked at her boots, slowing her progress past the old windmill, its sails flapping in the wind and making a sound similar to that of the keel's sail. There were no leaves on the trees this early in the year and the hedgerows were bare of growth, exposing a few birds' nests and rabbit holes.

After reaching the Grapes Inn she crossed the Rotherham to Doncaster coaching road, passed the old smithy and made her way up Far Lane towards John's house. Gypsies were camped in the lane again, as they did each year at this time, and their horses stood wet and bedraggled nearby. She heard the cry of an infant from within one of the caravans and wished there had been time to pay a call.

Walking on, she came to a small quarry where several men were attempting to lift a large stone onto a wagon. A mile further on she arrived at the hamlet and stood for a moment contemplating her next move. She knew the news she was about to impart would cast a veil of deep sadness over the entire hamlet, and was afraid to go directly into the house where her mother would be. So, taking Michael's advice, she walked round to the forge where she could hear her brother-in-law at his work.

In spite of the noise of his hammer ringing on the anvil as he shaped a piece of hot metal, John was immediately aware of her presence by the open forge door. He looked up and, seeing Maggy's drawn face, knew that there was something seriously wrong.

'Is there trouble with the keel?' he asked, in an anxious voice, and put the hammer down, knowing he would have to reheat the metal before he could start working it again later. 'What is it?' he repeated.

'It's Dad, John—he's dead!' she cried. 'And I daren't go in to tell Ma!'

'Oh God!' John exclaimed, hardly believing her. 'How? When?'

Maggy swallowed hard. 'Yesterday! He was dead when Michael tried to wake him. He's taken the keel on to Rotherham and needs you to find an undertaker and take a wagon there as soon as possible. He daren't leave the keel.'

By this time, and without realising it, John had removed his strong leather apron which was tied firmly round his thick girth and moved towards her. 'I'm sorry, lass,' he said, kindly. 'Look, I'll go in the house and tell Ma and the others. You warm yourself by the hearth and come in when you're ready.'

'Thanks, John,' she said, going towards the fire. 'I couldn't face them right now. But don't forget Michael will you? He's had a tough journey and daren't leave the keel unattended with a full load on board.'

John shook his head, 'Now don't you go worrying your head about it, we'll sort things out straight away.' With that he left Maggy and went into the house.

Some time later, when Michael finally heard the wagon rumbling along the wharf towards the keel, it was almost dark and he waved a lantern to attract John's attention before climbing from the keel onto the wharf side.

Seeing him, John drew up close by. 'I came as soon as I could get an undertaker,' he said, pulling on the reins to keep the horse still. 'This is Mr Cooper of Cooper Brothers.'

The sombrely-dressed man sitting with John raised his hat politely in the half light. 'I'm pleased to be of service, Mr Havercroft, and offer my condolences on your sad loss.' He peered through the gloom, his voice full of respect.

'Thank you for coming at such short notice,' Michael said, helping the man down with his bag. 'I've done the best I could, but we'll have to lift him out of the cabin onto the dock before we can place him in a coffin.'

The older man nodded gravely. 'I've done one of these before, Sir. Have you had a doctor to him, and do you have a death certificate?'

'It's down below. The doctor examined him in Doncaster, but I've brought him home to Ma.' A tremor of emotion caught Michael's throat.

'I understand,' the man said, kindly. 'Just show me where he is.'

Helping the man aboard, Michael then led him to the aft hatchway and pointed down into the cabin where his father lay on his bed covered by a piece of canvas. 'I was hoping that now the new graveyard's finished at Dalton he could be put there,' Michael said, quietly. With that he left the undertaker to his job and waited on deck as his brother-in-law tied the horse to a post where there was no risk of the animal falling into the canal, taking wagon and all with it. Holding his own lantern carefully, John boarded the keel with some trepidation for he was neither mariner nor boatman.

'I'm sorry, Michael,' he sympathised, 'it's still hard to take in, everything's in turmoil back home, but I came as soon as I could find Mr Cooper. What happened?'

'Nothing startling, really,' Michael said quietly. 'I woke up as usual and found him gone. Just like that—no warning at all! It was a shock, I can tell you, and I seem to have been in a daze ever since.'

John nodded. 'That's understandable. You must be exhausted. Maggy says you've got to stay with the keel?'

'I'll have to, John. I've got a load of ivory for Parker's on board, so there's no way I dare risk leaving the keel unattended. I've had time to think about it and the best thing I can do is leave for Sheffield at daybreak and drop this lot off, along with some hemp and other stuff, as soon as I can, then come back 'light'. I should be back by late afternoon. Can you cope with things until then?' However, before John could reply he continued, 'How's Mother taken it?'

'Excuse me,' a voice called from the cabin. 'Can you come down?'

Startled, Michael went immediately below and saw the man struggling to tie his father into a shroud.

'It's very awkward managing in here,' Mr Cooper said in a quiet voice. 'Would you be kind enough to help me?' Michael swallowed hard. 'I've seen to everything,' the man continued, 'but I can't lift him on my own, and I'll have to ask you both to assist me while we get him up through the hatchway.' He waited whilst Michael helped John down into the cabin. 'I've bound some ropes round your father so that we can lift him more easily, and it is more dignified in the long run.'

Steadying himself, Michael grasped the rope around his father's shoulders and eased him gently out of the bed until the three of them could lift him up the vertical ladder onto the deck. They then carefully moved onto the wharf where they placed him in the undertaker's coffin.

'What an undignified state of affairs,' John said, mortified at having to handle his dead father-in-law so roughly.

Michael patted him comfortingly on the shoulder. 'He was used to this way of life, and there's no other way to have got him out without unloading first. The bulkhead door is blocked by the cargo. At least it's dark and there is no one about to gawp at us. Besides, other boatmen have seen it all before.'

'We'd better go,' John replied, shaken by the experience. Then he remembered the pot of stew his wife had placed under the seat of the wagon. 'Oh, I forgot, our Mary's sent you something to warm up on the stove, and Ma says you're to come home as soon as you can.'

'That's good of her! But how's Ma taken the news?' Michael asked again, his earlier question having been interrupted by the undertaker.

'I don't think it has hit her yet. I left her with the women folk, she's not always capable of taking things in, as you know, but she understands this alright.'

'Thanks for looking after her,' Michael said, taking the cooking pot and parcel of food for which he was more than grateful. 'I must admit a hot meal is really something I need right now, so thanks again. I'll get back as soon as I can.' He shook hands with Mr Cooper and helped him onto the wagon. It was fully dark now, and it was with sadness that he watched the flickering light of the lanterns on the wagon, as it rolled out of sight.

The thought of spending the night alone in the cold cabin from which his father's body had just been removed did not appeal to him, nor did lighting its stove to heat up his supper. Collecting a few items that he might need later, he closed and locked the hatch and retired to the smaller, cramped forecabin. It was quite some time before the pot of stew on the stove top was piping hot, ready to eat, but when it was he ate with relish. Now, for the first time in two days, he felt that at least some normality was returning to his life. Once having eaten, he lay back on the locker and thought over the day's events, wondering just what lay ahead for him. He must have dozed off into a deep sleep because he was not aware of the tapping on the hull until suddenly it grew louder and more impatient. 'What the devil?' he cried, springing up with a start. He grasped his shotgun, climbed up the ladder and cautiously opened the hatch a fraction. Peering out he shouted. 'Who is it? What do you want?'

'It's me,' a voice called out. 'I'm back from the pub.'

'Oh God! I'd forgotten about you,' Michael laughed, 'I thought I was being robbed. Hang on a minute!' He put down the shotgun, grasped his lantern and opened the hatch cover fully. He'd arranged earlier that the marine would take him all the way to Sheffield the following day, and had given him money for something to eat and drink before taking one of the horses to the depot, the weather having improved considerably. It didn't do to invite strangers below deck, and normally he wouldn't have done so, but it was cold outside and the man had hauled him on many occasions in the past. It was part of the payment for services rendered that he should feed and house the marine in his employ, but usually such men would eat and sleep on deck when the keel was moored for the night.

He knew this man was respectable enough and found himself asking, 'Do you want to spend the night in the fore cabin here with me, or do you want to camp on deck?'

Somewhat relieved at this, the man replied, 'I wouldn't mind coming down, it's drizzling again and it's right cold'. He lost no time in accepting Michael's invitation and was soon sitting on the end of the locker, looking tired but cheery.

'I'll fetch a couple of blankets,' Michael offered, 'but you'll have to curl up on the floor as it's so cramped in here.' It was good to have someone other than Maggy to talk to. 'I can't come to terms with sleeping in my father's cabin yet,' he admitted, hoping the man understood.

The marine nodded. He must have been in his mid-thirties, rugged looking and browned, like Michael, by the weather. 'Making much of the funeral?' he asked politely, as he pushed some tackle to one side to give himself more room.

'No, just the family up at Dalton, I expect. It's a bit too late now for word to get around. The best way anyone can pay their respects to Dad is to remember him kindly.'

The two men chatted on for some time but as an early start was needed in the morning, they decided to turn in and were soon fast asleep, oblivious to anything beyond the cabin walls.

Usually, out of habit, Michael woke at four o'clock each day and this morning was no exception, he had work to do. Slipping his boots on, he went to the main cabin to wash in readiness for whatever the next few hours might bring. By four-thirty he'd cooked the bacon John had brought, and made tea for himself and the marine, who said he had enjoyed a surprisingly good night's sleep.

Once breakfast was over the man stood up. 'Right, thanks for the hospitality,' he said. 'I'll wash on deck then finish getting the horse ready to move as soon as it's light enough. Let me know when to pass the towing rope.'

As had been arranged with the other waiting captains, due to his circumstances, and their knowing that Michael had no intention of jumping the line for the sake of a return-load, the *Maggie Kelly* was allowed to go ahead first.

Reaching Tinsley, they started to ascend the first of the two flights of locks which would raise them seventy feet up to the level of the canal leading to Sheffield. This was the most tedious and time-consuming part of the whole navigation system and by the time the keel arrived at the strangely castellated lock-house eight locks up, Michael's leg ached badly. He knew then that he would need more than just an ordinary keelman to assist him if he were to stay on the water to make his living.

Waiting at the tiller as yet another lock began to fill, he tried to estimate what the keel was worth should he have to sell it and make a fresh start. His father had struggled for years to pay off the loan on the vessel, and had finally managed it. She was a Dunstan Keel, built at Thorne twenty years before at a cost of £100, and still a good craft, fettled and re-painted during the harvest some months before. There was little trade at that time of year when man-power was needed on the land, but it gave waterfolk a chance to overhaul their gear. The keel might still fetch a £100 to £125 from the right man at the right time. If he could hold on until the end of summer and not be panicked into parting with it, then he might even get more. Although the keel didn't entirely belong to him, it was his responsibility to decide what to do with her and, provided he took care of his mother and his sister, until she wed, the choice was his.

Climbing the last flight of four locks seemed to take an eternity but finally they were able to enjoy the smooth, lock-free, three and a half mile journey to where the canal ended in Sheffield

The day was turning out to be brighter than he'd expected but there was still quite a strong breeze as they passed through the flat rural landscape towards the village of Attercliffe. Gradually, over the years, he'd seen that same area slowly being spoiled by small coal mines and tall factory chimneys belching out smoke. Sheffield was stretching out its grimy reach and it wouldn't be long before the remaining green fields would disappear forever.

With such a good wind and someone to help him he could have sailed the keel on this last stretch but there were too many low bridges beneath which it was impossible to pass with full rigging. Even if the mast had been lowered to lie along the length of the keel these were impassable, which, of course, was why it had been left behind in the trap. He felt quite relaxed as the keel moved slowly along the stone aqueduct over Darnall Road, before entering the deep cutting at Attercliffe. However, when they reached Bacon Lane bridge he noticed that the water level was higher due to the previous day's heavy rain, and this meant he had to wait and watch as an unladen vessel was eased slowly towards him under its arch.

One thing became clear to him, and that was the futility of paying to have the *Maggie Kelly* hauled back down the lock system empty, plus the trouble of taking in water as ballast to pass under the arch, only to return again after the funeral to collect a cargo. Far better to leave her empty in the Sheffield basin and go back to Rotherham on the train, thus saving both money and time. Once he'd dealt with his father's affairs he could return and take the *Maggie* to Hull, hopefully with a good cargo. When they were at last ready to pass under the low bridge it was like passing through the eye of a needle. Many times in the past, he'd helped his father work the keel through it with the aid of a crowbar to ease their passage.

He looked over the side of the keel. Here the canal was a vivid yellow, coloured by the water pumped from the underground workings of Nunnery Colliery to guarantee an adequate depth in drier conditions. The sight was far from pleasant. The closer they got to the end of the canal and into the bustling town, the dirtier everything appeared to be and the thought that he might one day have to find a job thereabouts depressed him. The slow loss of canal trade since the coming of the railways was, he supposed, the result of rapid expansion in ideas, mechanisation being the most powerful. It was progress, but manufacturers didn't seem to appreciate that transportation by water was the cheapest way to haul bulk cargo. Yes, the only way to survive now was to transport coal from the mines to the steam ships in Hull—but he was incapable of the heavy physical effort needed to make such a thing possible. He couldn't deceive himself any longer; even with the improved weather conditions his leg was still giving him a great deal of trouble.

Forward progress was now considerably easier and he actually looked forward to escaping from the water for a while. Soon they approached Parker's Wharf which was built specially to receive the tusks and horn of which he carried a supply in the hold today. This was a commodity he particularly enjoyed carrying as, since childhood, he had watched his grandfather Havercroft carve precious broken pieces of ivory into works of art. Whether these fragments of tusks had been bought, or 'half-inched', Michael never knew. Whenever the keel was fast in ice, or during the long, dark winter evenings his grandfather would work away with great dedication, priding himself that for an untrained man he could produce a fairly presentable piece of work. Seeing Michael's fascination he had even begun to teach him the craft, explaining that a worthwhile side-line was an asset which could swell the coffers in times of shortage.

The family had owned two keels in those days, often travelling together. Sometimes, when following each other and reaching a certain point, Grandma, in the first keel, would leave a mug of tea in a niche of a tight bridge for his father, on the second keel, to pick up minutes later. At first, Michael had been too young to travel on the keels, instead he'd stayed in the small family house in Doncaster with either Grandma or his mother until he was old enough not to be at risk on the canal. When he did spend more and more time afloat he was passed from one keel to the other, learning the ways of the river and the waterfolk, but with no proper education.

As soon as Michael saw his mooring up ahead he warned the marine. 'Hello there,' he called, then released the hauling rope and manoeuvred the keel across the canal with a long pole until it was almost level with the arched opening in the wall of Parker's warehouse. 'Hello,' he repeated, his voice echoing beyond the entrance, giving him no need to use his foghorn, as he secured the keel to mooring rings in readiness to unload.

'Who's there?' a voice called back. A man appeared and, seeing Michael, said, 'Oh, it's you, Mike—how's things?'

'Not too good, Jack!' Michael replied, knowing that he had to be discreet in case some other enterprising captain might suspect there could be a future for himself with Parker's.

'How so?' Jack asked, looking round and obviously wondering where Michael's father was.

'I'm sorry to say my father's dead,' Michael said, aware that he would have to repeat the statement many more times before the day was through. 'I'm going to need help to unload your delivery this time, but I'll have someone with me in future.'

There was a moment's silence as the man let this information sink in. Then, with genuine sincerity he said, 'Oh, I am sorry to hear that. We've got used to the pair of you delivering over the years. This won't change things will it?'

'No!' Michael quickly reassured him, although he felt a little uncomfortable at not being completely honest with the man. He also wished that he'd been a little more careful at Mexborough Lock when, in his misery, he'd hinted to Joe that he might sell the keel. It wouldn't take long for that kind of message to pass along the whole length of the waterway. 'I may be a day or two late next time, but I will be able to collect your next shipment from Hull. Just tell Mr Parker that once the funeral's over I'll hire a man and be off again.' He drew back the hatch covers and together they carefully removed the large tusks of African ivory from the hold, but it took Michael a considerable effort to conceal from Jack the pain he was experiencing from the continual lifting.

Thinking him subdued by the loss of his father, Jack worked quietly on until in the end he said, in a friendly manner, 'Y'know, your dad was a good man. He called a spade a spade but never tried any tricks. If you were late we knew there'd be a good reason for it. Mostly we could tell by the weather how things would be.'

'Thanks, Jack. Let other people know will you? The sooner it gets around the better it will be. It just makes you realise that you can never tell what'll happen next.'

Nodding, Jack grimaced. 'You're lucky though. You'll live a lot longer at your job than the poor devils on the grinding hulls.'

They fell silent again for a while, and Michael contemplated the other man's words. It wouldn't be easy getting work without having served an apprenticeship, nor did he fancy labouring amongst the dirty, damp and harsh conditions in most of the factories he'd seen.

When finally they lifted out the last sacks of animal horns and tusks from which the handles of Sheffield's quality knives were made, he poled the keel along the towpath to where the marine had been chatting to passing boatmen, and was soon under way again.

It wasn't long before they reached the terminal basin where its seven-storey warehouse dominated the skyline. Everywhere he looked activity of some kind or other filled the scene, both visually and with noise, as he waited for a space at the wharf to unload the hemp which made up the rest of his cargo.

With the keel secured fore and aft against the wharf side, he paid off the marine—who was already keeping his eyes open for another vessel to haul back to Mexborough, so as to avoid the long return tramp with the horse unhired.

The cobbled areas around the wharves were strewn with piles of boxes, sacks and casks, ready for loading or already unloaded from other vessels, some of which had overtaken him during his stay at Parker's and were now half empty. Michael hurried over to one of the stone-arched warehouses beneath the railway sidings.

'I've got a consignment of hemp for Mudford's,' he told the warehouseman, 'but unfortunately I'm not able to off-load it by myself. There's been a death in the family and I'm alone.' By this time he was fed up with explaining his predicament and wanted nothing more than to finish his business and catch the next train back to Rotherham.

'You'll have to pay for someone, of course,' the man stated, not at all pleased to have his routine disrupted.

'I know that and I'm sorry. Just let me know how much,' Michael said, wearily. 'It won't happen again. I suppose you'd better know, my father's just died and I shall have to employ a man again after the funeral, when I pick up the usual load of ropes for Thorne.'

'Oh,' said the man, in a rather disgruntled tone which was completely lacking in sympathy. Michael's father had never liked him and had been content to collect the ropes and cast off as quickly as possible. 'We can't hold this consignment much longer, you know, the ropes are always needed at the other end.'

'Two days, that's all I need,' Michael said, with more confidence than he felt. 'I can't afford to lose more time either.' He didn't add that two days lost on a journey was nothing when tides and weather conditions were taken into account. 'I'll wait by the keel until you send someone,' he added, pointing to where it was moored.

When the last bundle of hemp was stacked on the wharf side he went to the Canal Company's Office to hand in his receipted bills of lading, and to pay his wharfage and toll fees. He explained once more about his circumstances and obtained permission to leave the keel at a vacant mooring, out of the way, where it would stay until his return. He locked everything of value away and walked to the railway station, where he ate what had remained in the *Maggie Kelly's* larder whilst waiting for a train to arrive. It was much later in the day than he had planned, very late in the afternoon in fact, and although he had been hungry at the wharf side he'd been acutely conscious that his family was waiting for him to return. In his haste to leave he'd simply thrown his belongings and the food into his canvas bag ready to eat when he could enjoy it.

Michael boarded the train after what seemed an eternity of waiting and was not impressed by this mode of travel, as the carriage rattled and lurched its way along the Don valley from the Wicker Station towards Attercliffe. He'd never been on a train before, although he'd admired and watched them with great curiosity as they passed by. However, he was now becoming convinced that although it might be a quicker way of travelling, transport by water was more pleasant. He wondered, though, if there might perhaps be an opening on the railway for him if he quit canal life? Not as a clerk; he knew he wasn't illiterate like his grandfather who, when making out his books, drew an onion because he couldn't spell the word; his education nevertheless was poor. What use had canal men for literature? Just as long as they could keep their accounts in order, they needed nothing more from the pen. However, the world was changing, even on the water, and Michael wished now that he'd been given more schooling as a child. He was twenty-seven and might be compelled now to adapt to a wider world of which he knew very little. What was he to do? The irony was that he'd become captain of his own vessel, something that many on the canal could only dream of, yet he was not going to be able to enjoy the situation.

From this side of the valley he could now more clearly see the encroachment of industry into the countryside, and how the once isolated farmsteads and villages were gradually being surrounded by houses and factories. His sombre thoughts were not eased when the sight of Attercliffe's old windmill gave him a sad reminder of Dalton and the unfortunate duties which lay ahead.

After what seemed a remarkably short journey, one which would have taken most of the day by water, he stepped down onto the platform at Rotherham Station and started to walk the three miles still to be covered before getting home.

It seemed strange to be sitting before the comforting blaze in the blacksmith's large stone fireplace with the family around him. Compared to the confines of the keel's cabin the sitting-room seemed enormous, and Michael sprawled out in the worn old chair after enjoying a good hot meal. He was tired, tired of working, walking and talking. First one question and then another came to him about his father, the keel and the future, as though he hadn't had enough of it in the past three days. He closed his eyes as if wishing to sleep, so that the questions would stop. They meant no harm and things had to be faced up to, but surely they must know that he was nearly exhausted by the sequence of events which had overtaken him.

Some time later, however, he opened his eyes with a start to see why no-one was speaking and was puzzled to find the room dark, except for the glow of the fire. There was no-one there! He peered at the clock on the mantle-shelf and was amazed to find it almost midnight. He made to rise and found he'd been covered by a blanket which he presumed either his sister or his mother had placed there. This gave him a feeling of pleasure, as it had not been easy in these last few years on the keel to enjoy the softer moments of family life. Mostly his mother and sisters had stayed on land, and on the occasions when they had travelled with them the cabins were too cramped for comfort.

There had never been much to complain about though and, as a family, they were as happy if not happier than most of the waterfolk. Sometimes, however, especially in times of stress, he had of course longed for the comforts of a home of his own, where he wouldn't constantly be at the mercy of the weather for most of the year.

He rose slowly, realising that his leg felt easier even though his rest could only have been of short duration. Arranging some cushions on the sofa, he prepared to spend the night on it. He had no bed of his own in John's house, as they were short enough of space as it was and, like most canal folk, the whole family rarely left the vessel at the same time, for security reasons.

Having slept so deeply earlier, he was now quite awake and lay contemplating the coming day. The burial was to be at eleven, after which he would be compelled to return to the house where, after the reading of the will, plans had to be made regarding the future of the keel. The fact couldn't be hidden that he would now need help until he could find a buyer, or discover when an auction was to take place at the boat-yard. The cargo of ropes and canvas waiting in the warehouse had to be moved as soon as possible with or without permanent hired help—and Sheffield was not the place to find a good keelman. Once he reached Thorne, Keadby, or even Hull there would probably be a man available, but whether good or bad only time would tell.

It went without saying that his sister Maggy would have to accompany him for the time being, she could at least cook and work the locks, thus saving him constantly climbing on and off the keel. There was also no alternative but to pay for help loading up, and if John could be persuaded to let his eldest son come with them they should be able to complete the trip without too much difficulty.

One problem after another reared its head until finally he fell into a fitful sleep, only to be woken at daybreak by John shaking him gently by the shoulder. He was glad to rise and get on with things. He was stiff from lying awkwardly, and his head ached, but there was no time to linger as John needed his help to prepare the dray on which the coffin would be carried.

He stood at the kitchen sink, getting ready for the day ahead, and from the window saw the bell-turret of the church standing proudly on the far hill-top, surrounded by a cluster of old properties. Unfortunately, it would not be possible to save time by crossing the fields which divided the two hamlets, as the track was too rough. Instead they would have to traipse down the lane to the old road, go back towards Rotherham, then climb the steep hill on the other side of the valley in order to reach the church. At least it wasn't raining, which meant the lane would be less muddy than it might have been.

Being both blacksmith and wheelwright, John was very proud of his dray and wagon, and to draw these he kept a pair of well-groomed horses on which were placed harnesses gleaming with polished brasses. Today he'd taken greater care with the polishing; it was the least he could do for his late father-in-law. 'Jim would have appreciated going out in style,' he stated with some satisfaction when the two vehicles were cleaned and ready. The dray was draped with the black crepe which he often loaned out for funerals, as was the wagon which would carry the womenfolk following behind the coffin.

Observing the well-turned out wagons, Michael said, gratefully, 'I don't know what I'd have done without your help, John. I'm very grateful. You've been a good husband to our Mary, and when you took on Ma and Maggy so that we could give up the house in Doncaster, that relieved us of worry and responsibility'.

John smiled, his round affable face transformed for a moment from the seriousness of the occasion. 'They're no trouble to me, in fact between them I get looked after right well. Besides, your father's contribution from the sale of the house enabled me to get set up here.' He rubbed his sleeve vigorously on what he considered a not too well polished horse-brass on one of the harnesses. 'You've always paid your way,' he said, then added in a thoughtful tone, 'some men found your dad difficult to get on with, but I didn't! He was fair, honest, and wouldn't see anyone in trouble without offering a helping hand. What more could you ask?'

Michael was rather moved by this remark for he knew that beneath John's rugged, hardy exterior lay a decent and kindly man. He sighed, and with resignation in his voice, said, 'I've got a problem, John. Without Dad, and with this leg of mine, I'm not going to be able to work the keel much longer, not economically that is, and I can't afford to stand by and watch while other men are paid to load and unload the *Maggie Kelly*.'

'What will you do?' John asked, without any hint of being surprised or sign that he might have thought Michael weak in any way.

'God knows! I've racked my brains for three days now without finding a solution other than to sell the keel when the market's right. As for a job, it'll have to be one that's easier than canal work. But don't you worry, I'll still contribute to Ma's keep. Maggy can find a job surely?'

'Mrs Battersby down at The Grapes has a job going as a kitchen maid— if Maggy could start soon I think she'd take her.'

'She can't, John! I need her with me on the next trip, if only to cook, run errands and stand at the tiller while I do other things. Hopefully I'll get a keelman when I get to Thorne, or at least before leaving Hull again.'

'It's a pity for Maggy to miss the opportunity,' John replied, 'but I suppose we've no choice. Mrs Battersby will probably have found someone else before you get back.'

Michael nodded in agreement. 'It was fortunate that Maggy came along on this trip,' he said, 'or I really would have been stuck. It's usually too cold for her to be on the keel at this time of year, so I was lucky.'

John turned to face him with a question. 'You really had no idea, had you?'

'What about?' Michael asked, looking at him blankly. He was bewildered. 'What do you mean?'

'About your dad! He was a proud man as you know, but he'd not felt well lately.' Michael was taken aback but said nothing. 'I'm the only one who knew,' John went on. 'He made me promise not to say anything—I think he suspected there was something badly wrong and that's why he suggested Maggy went with you this time, to lighten your load.'

'The sly old devil,' Michael complained, hurt and puzzled by this unexpected news.

'I think he felt guilty because he knew you were in difficulty and, having shown you little sympathy in the past, he thought it unfair to complain and burden you with his problem. There wasn't much you could have done anyway, nor would he have wanted to sit at home for the rest of his life. That would have bothered him for sure.'

'I never guessed!' Michael said, trying to recall times when his father appeared off-colour. 'He always seemed well enough to me!'

There was a look of genuine understanding on John's face as he said, 'You're a lot like him, you know, sometimes a bit stubborn, although you're not as mulish as he was. But you never tell anyone what's going on inside you, either.'

Michael looked at John in amazement. In all the years he'd known his brother-in-law he'd never before had such a deep conversation with him. In fact, he had rarely unburdened himself to anyone, not even his own father with whom he'd lived and worked twenty-four hours a day. They'd often toiled for hours in silence, never really needing to talk. He was going to miss the old coot more than he'd imagined he would, and his throat tightened with a sudden surge of emotion at the thought. He suppressed his distress before it was noticed by John, but his eyes mirrored the depths of his feelings. He said nothing, but stared glumly at the dray, his eyes fixed on the hub of the large wooden wheel nearest him. Finally he turned to John who was waiting patiently, and said, simply, 'I shall miss him'.

'He was proud of you, you know,' John said, to comfort him. 'He may not have let on but you were his mainstay, especially since Ma stopped being her old self. I think he suspected that his life, on the keel at least, was coming to an end but he couldn't face the facts. He drove himself just as much as he did you.'

Michael was about to ask him what he thought of his plan to sell the keel, when a voice called to them from the house. 'Breakfast's ready! Hurry up before it gets cold.'

'She can be stubborn too, at times!' John smiled, eyeing his wife Mary fondly, before she disappeared back inside the house.

Michael chewed his lip, as he often did when he had things on his mind, and nodded in agreement. As they walked towards the door he said, 'I've a lot to talk about after the funeral. Do you mind if I come into the forge then, out of the way of the womenfolk?' He appreciated that it would be better if, in the long run, he took his brother-in-law fully into his confidence about everything.

They entered the house where the atmosphere was quiet and sombre, then sat down at the table where Mary had placed their breakfasts, having already fed and despatched her two sons on errands, telling them to be back well before ten o'clock.

Maggy and Ma toyed with their food but the two men, having risen early and accomplished a great deal, ate heartily as though nothing had happened. To everyone's surprise Ma suddenly asked, in a quite normal voice, 'Where's Jim?'

Thinking she'd forgotten that the coffin was in the outhouse, where it was cooler and also left them more space in the house, John replied gently, 'He's in the outhouse Ma. He's alright there.'

'Tell him to hurry up—his breakfast'll get cold,' she replied, and picked up her fork as if nothing was wrong. At this Maggy burst into tears. 'What's the matter, you silly girl?' Ma asked, agitated by her daughter's show of emotion, then she lapsed into silence, leaving them all to stare uncomfortably down at their plates.

Some days Ma was like her old self, on others she seemed to go into a twilight world from which they couldn't draw her out. This spell usually passed after a while and no-one made any reference to it; however it could be frustrating when she did silly things which only came to light later. That was why a couple of years ago, Jim had sold their own house and moved her and Maggy into John's home. It wouldn't have been so bad if she hadn't been such a beauty in her younger days. Michael remembered thinking as a young boy how pretty she looked, with her nicely formed and rounded face beneath a neatly-tied-back shock of auburn hair. In fact at Mary's wedding she was, in his opinion, far prettier than her thin-faced daughter, the bride. His father had been the envy of all the keelmen on the river when he'd married her, or so he'd told him. She'd had a temper in those days, of course, she wouldn't have been half Irish without one. Sadly, there was no longer any sign of that spirit and it was pitiful to see her when she had her bad days. Sometimes, however, there was a calmness about her that seemed to come from a quiet acceptance of old age. Stress did strange things to her mind though, as it had today. Every so often young Maggy reminded him of Ma and he just hoped she wouldn't end up the same way in later-life.

Before long the slight embarrassment passed and they ate in peace, each wrapped in thought, until finally Ma spoke again, and they all held their breath. 'I know he's gone,' she said, wistfully. 'I suppose it'll be my turn next.'

Together they tried to reassure her. Maggy quickly left the table, knelt down and put her arm round her mother's shoulders, 'All this will be over soon,' she whispered softly, 'then we can begin to look forward to summer and you can sit out in the sun again'.

Michael suddenly felt that he was seeing his family in a different light. Canal life was hard and although there were moments of fun to share, there never seemed to be sufficient room or privacy in which to express one's inner feelings. They were either all on top of one another, or living apart. This had never particularly bothered him before but today it did, although he recognised it was probably brought on by their present sad circumstances. Had things been different he would have enjoyed sitting round the table with them, but the knowledge that he would soon have to return alone to the keel quite disturbed him.

By ten o'clock the long trek for the funeral party began under weak but promising sunshine, although the accompanying cold, sharp wind reminded them all that winter was far from over. Eventually, on reaching the gates of the recently-built church, Michael was both pleased and heartened, particularly for his mother's sake, to find a small group of six or seven men and women waiting for them. Recognising these as belonging to several keel families he raised his cap in greeting. He was aware that they'd lost precious time by berthing their keels in order to pay their respects, yet it was no more than his father would have done for them.

When the final act of laying his father to rest was over, he stood by the gates of the churchyard thanking the mourners for coming and bidding them farewell. He then looked across the fields, and might have taken the shortest route back to the house alone, but felt it would appear churlish in the circumstances. Instead, he felt obliged to drive the dray back which carried some of the mourners and his nephews and, on reaching the bottom road, he stopped to allow several of them to alight before continuing. Now he was no longer crushed between John's two lively sons, Danny and Patrick, who had moved to the back, he realised that misery in the young was short-lived. Fortunately the horse was well behaved and seemed to know the way, which suited Michael's inexperienced hands on the reins. However, before long he was compelled to allow the leading wagon full of grieving women to draw ahead, and at sufficient distance so that the boisterous lads would not be heard.

He suffered their fooling about as long as possible, but knew that at their age he'd been just as incorrigible. 'Now, then you two!' he chided, not over-harshly. 'Don't forget your grandmother will hear you—this is supposed to be a funeral.'

Silence ensued immediately. However, it didn't last long and Michael shook his head, smiling inwardly. They were, by this time, a considerable distance behind the leading wagon and about to pass the gypsies camped in the lane. He had some sympathy for these nomadic people, for he thought himself to be of similar kind. He could recall his grandmother's anger when strangers had disparagingly shouted, 'Water-gypsies!' at them as the keel passed under a bridge, or when spotted by a group of cheeky village youths on the bankside. 'We're not the likes of them!' She'd hiss to herself, as she shook her fist in their direction.

The tousled head of Phoenix Boswell nodded respectfully as the dray passed by, whilst his wife Tetrania waved from the steps of their vardo. Michael smiled and raised his cap to her, just as he had done on his downward journey earlier.

'They're here a lot longer this year,' Patrick commented, once they'd passed the camp site. 'Some of the others moved on but Mrs Boswell had a baby a few weeks ago, I suppose that's why they've stayed.'

'They come up to the house sometimes to buy eggs,' Danny rejoined, sounding much older than his ten years.

As Michael listened to their lively banter he questioned the eldest, trying to establish whether or not the lad would be interested in joining him on the keel, if his father approved. 'Patrick, what do you do with yourself when you're not helping your father to shoe horses, or delivering the nails he makes?'

'I'm learning to shape iron, and work with wood,' came the enthusiastic reply, and his voice held a note of pride.

Danny interrupted. 'We muck out the stables and keep Dad supplied with fuel and water for the forge,' he said, not to be outdone.

They were likeable boys and a credit to their parents. 'Do you remember sailing with your granddad and me a couple of summers ago Patrick?' Michael asked casually, as though being merely curious, but he listened intently for the lad's reply. Patrick appeared not to hear him or chose not to answer immediately, as his attention was drawn to the activity going on in the quarry which they were passing. Michael followed his gaze. 'Aye, it's a hard job labouring there,' he said, still awaiting a reply to his question. 'What did you think of life on the keel?'

'He liked it,' Danny said brightly, speaking for his older brother. 'Will I be old enough to come with you soon?'

'We'll see.'

'You're too small,' Patrick scoffed, giving Danny a push. 'I liked travelling and seeing all those places, but I don't really think I'd like to live on the canal all the time.'

'No,' Michael agreed, concealing his amusement. 'I don't suppose you would, you'd soon get fed up. Perhaps you have to be born on the water to be able to enjoy it.' Letting the matter drop he urged the horse on up the steepening lane, until the animal turned off without need of his guidance into the small hamlet of farms and cottages half way between Dalton Brook and Wickersley.

There wasn't much of a wake for Jim Havercroft, after all he wasn't all that well-known in Dalton, being a Doncaster man. So, after a simple meal with only a few neighbours, life at the smithy quickly returned to normal, and for the rest of the day Michael endeavoured to comfort his mother, whilst gently sounding her out regarding the future of the keel. The will had revealed nothing unexpected, and the responsibility still remained Michael's whilst ever they ran the keel. Maggy accepted, rather too easily he thought, that she would not be able to go to The Grapes to work, and he suspected that she preferred going with him rather than working amongst strangers. Nevertheless, the time would soon come when she'd have to, as he wouldn't be able to provide for her indefinitely, especially as the future was so uncertain.

To feel solid ground beneath his feet for such a prolonged period of time seemed strange to him, and before long he felt the urge to escape from the house. When an opportunity arose, he left and wandered along the track towards the back fields where he could again view the church on the opposite hillside. It was now outlined against an almost indescribable background. Often at this time of day the setting sun displayed itself in the form of brilliant banks of orange clouds, floating in a turquoise sky. It rarely lasted longer than perhaps half an hour, yet the scene never failed to impress him, and remained in his memory long after the sun had set.

This was a poignant moment for Michael and he was sadder now than at any time since he'd discovered his father's lifeless body on the locker bed. He wasn't one for tears but, as he watched the light grow dim over the outlined bell-tower of the church, his eyes moistened. He reflected on the happenings of the past few days, and on his father whom he would miss more than he realised. Life would never be the same again, and the isolation which he faced was daunting. Darkness came swiftly once the sun had gone down and he slowly returned to the forge where his brother-in-law had been working hard for several hours since returning from the funeral.

John was ready for a break and, taking an upturned barrel, he seated himself thus allowing Michael to sit on a battered old stool before the glowing hearth.

'I'm restless,' Michael confessed, as he sat down. 'There's so much to sort out, and I'd rather get on with it than put it off.'

'Look,' John replied, 'I can deal with things out here—I told you yesterday. It's no good rushing decisions, only to regret them later. Don't you think that once you've got a good man as mate, you'll be able to carry on? There's better weather ahead so why rush things?' He let Michael ponder on his words, then quite unexpectedly said, 'You know, I've often envied you your freedom to move about so much'.

'Tch!' Michael said disparagingly. 'And I have often envied you your home here! But you're right, I'll not be hasty. With your good help I'll keep things going until the opportunity's right.'

'Well, you've always got a base here if you need it. We're not well off but we get by, and I know you'll not take advantage of that.'

Michael nodded slowly, contemplating what to say next. 'It's important to get back to the keel, stock up with food and water, then find a cargo to go with the ropes and canvas from Mudford's. Once I'm moving I'll be alright, at least 'till I get to Thorne where I might find permanent help. Do you think someone could take me to Rotherham in the morning so I can catch the first train to Sheffield at nine o'clock? It's no good me setting off any earlier and walking, it would take too long even if my leg could stand it.'

'Patrick can take you, he's a good lad with the horse. How long do you think it will take you to load and bring the keel back to Aldwarke, Mike? We can get you a stock of food together, but I doubt if you will be back before dark.'

'I agree, it may take all day just to fill the keel, and may stretch into two days if there's little available. You know what things are like, but I do need some supplies, and Maggy knows what we want. In fact I will be back by the following night at the latest, with or without a full load.' The two men sat quietly for a moment or two, then Michael said, hesitatingly, 'I was wondering, could you spare Patrick for about ten days? I'd pay him, of course. With him and Maggy I think we could manage up to Thorne well enough.'

John had picked up his pipe and lit it whilst listening, drawing on it several times before answering. He was not a man to make quick decisions, as Michael well knew. 'I can only spare him for a while,' he said eventually. 'He's a good worker, but he's young. Won't you have enough on without keeping an eye on him?'

Michael laughed out loud. 'I'm not that old that I can't deal with the antics of a lad—in any case it'll probably help take my mind off things. How old is he now?'

'Fourteen.'

'Is he really? But that's older than many of the lads who are already working on the keels!'

'Yes, but they're brought up to the life. He can't even swim!'

Chuckling, Michael rejoined, 'I'm not expecting him to! Not many people on the river can swim either, but he worked well for us last time and I think he'd enjoy it again. However, it's your decision.'

'If he wants to go then I've no objections, but I don't want him taking to the life. He's coming along nicely here and shows some skill with iron and wood-working. That's what I want him to do.' There was a certainty in John's voice which Michael respected, and accordingly they agreed to broach the matter with Patrick during the evening.

The following morning Michael was up early and anxious to be off but there was no point in leaving too soon, only to hang around the station. When it was time to go Patrick drove him down, questioning him about the unexpected adventure he was about to have, and agreeing to wait in The Grapes from three o'clock the following day, until Michael contacted him.

When Michael reached Sheffield later in the morning, the keel seemed almost to welcome him with a creak from her deck planks as he climbed aboard, and it wasn't long before he'd manoeuvred it to where her part-cargo of ropes and canvas would be loaded. Much of this was destined for the boatyards along the waterway to Hull and, by scouting round, he managed to obtain several other consignments including empty sacks, coils of wire and some bright steel. The *Maggie* was nowhere near full capacity but the afternoon was drawing to a close, leaving him no choice but to stay moored in the basin for the night. He felt better for having loaded Mudford's goods first as their foreman had been none too pleased at the delay of his shipment, but now at least all would appear normal to them. At the last minute he was able to load a consignment of agricultural implements, which although not large was better than nothing.

His cabin was cheerless after the comfort of John's home and, as there was little for him to do after dark, he decided nothing would be gained by moping around waiting for time to pass. The keel would be safe enough in the canal basin under the careful eye of the watchman, whose job it was to guard the vessels, warehouses and merchandise piled along the wharfs, ready for shipment. Michael's interest would be best served by being with his own kind, keeping his ears open for the hint of more business being available on the morrow. There were one or two ale houses nearby which he and his father had used occasionally, but as the hour was still early he was content to chat to the watchman and several of the other boatmen before leaving the basin.

After a while the men drifted away and he was left alone with the watchman who was about to patrol the yard. 'I suppose I'd better leave you to it then,' Michael sighed, reluctant to part company with the man.

'Come along if you like,' the man responded, being quite happy to have company for a change. 'I don't mind doing the rounds this early in the evening,' he said, 'it's later when everyone's asleep that I'm likely to find an intruder.'

'Right, I don't mind if I do!' Michael accepted readily.

It was never really dark in the canal basin due to the fiery glow in the sky from the blast furnace nearby on Blast Lane, so it was easy to talk as they walked along.

'Trade's not what it was,' the man said, raising his lantern and trying the handle of a door to make sure it was locked. 'And with the good harvest in England last year, we've only handled half the grain from the Continent that we usually do.'

'It's been a good time for our farmers though, but I know what you mean,' Michael replied. 'That's not such a worry, as one bad harvest here and imported grain will soon be in demand again. The main problem for us keelmen is that with the railway taking trade off the water we'll be left mainly with coal to take down to Hull. Some vessels have been unloading here, then having to go as far as the mines along the Dearne and Dove canal before they can get a cargo. Nobody can afford to travel light on return journeys.'

'Why do you think the Railway Company bought the canal in the first place? They're feathering their own nest by getting rid of the competition!' The watchman obviously felt strongly about the situation.

Finding the conversation interesting, Michael wanted to know more and asked, 'What will they do with the canals then?'

'Oh, they'll keep them as it's cheaper to put bulky, difficult loads onto the water and move the easier, lighter goods by train. There'll still be a market for you on the canal but mainly in coal, grain and ore. Now if I had any money at all I'd invest it in the railways, the canals are in for a rough time.'

'It would be nice if I'd got some spare money to do just that,' Michael replied, thinking himself lucky simply to own the keel.

They walked alongside a number of barrels and crates until they reached the end of the yard where a stack of timber had been off-loaded earlier in the day. Continuing the conversation, the man said, 'Thank goodness the Government was forced to relieve ship-building timbers of all taxes. That has helped the shipyards a bit.'

'It was a little late, don't you think?' Michael complained. 'With iron ships becoming more common and fewer cargoes for the keels it's a bit like closing the stable door after the horse has bolted.'

'That's why Tobley sold his timber yard last year, he reckoned the taxes on imported timbers were hitting the trade.' Having now retraced their steps they were almost at the tall Terminal Warehouse. 'Which is yours?' the man asked, looking towards the moored vessels.

'Over there, the *Maggie Kelly*,' Michael answered, pointing to the shadowy hull lying half concealed by another boat.

'Ah!' The watchman replied, knowingly. 'She's yours, is she? I heard the men talking last night about her losing her Captain. I'm sorry. Is she a family boat or are you hired?'

'Yes, she's mine now. My father and I worked well together on her for years, and goodness knows what I'm going to do without him. It'll not be the same working with a stranger on board.'

'At least you've got your own boat! I'm stuck here night after night working for a pittance, since I lost my job due to an accident.'

And that will be my lot, working for a pittance thought Michael, if I have to get rid of the keel. 'I don't suppose you know of anything coming in for shipment tomorrow do you?' he asked. His voice was casual but he was hoping and praying for better luck. 'I'm desperate to find something quickly to top up with.'

The watchman rubbed his chin and thought for a moment, then in a quiet voice said, 'Don't tell anyone how you found out but try Berry's; their dray arrives first thing in the morning. He usually brings something on a Friday'.

'Thanks,' Michael said, and pressed a coin in the man's hand. 'I'm finding things difficult at the moment until I get sorted out.'

'You go to Hull a lot, don't you?' the man went on, seeming reluctant to part company. 'I suppose you know about the march in Sheffield this week, when a hundred sailors from Hull came here on the train to ask for support and help to feed their families?'

'Yes,' Michael replied. 'I heard a lot of talk about it around the docks in Hull. This new Merchant Marine Act was passed when most of the nation's seamen were away at sea. They complain, rightly I think, that it is so full of fines and penalties that many men will return home in debt instead of having earned a wage. It allows the Captain to treat the men like slaves; no wonder they are parading their grievances up and down the country.'

'They behaved very commendably,' the night watchman assured him, 'and received a lot of sympathy from the folk here.'

'So they should,' Michael agreed. 'Their lives are spent in danger, carrying the imports and exports of the country whilst their families are poor, and never know if they will see them again.'

The man nodded. 'Their dignified march drew a considerable crowd and aroused plenty of support for their cause, not that it will do much good as far as this Government is concerned. Nevertheless, it was a treat to watch the sailors with their banners, and a lot carried models of various vessels.'

'That's all very well,' Michael said, 'but the ones who came are out of work seamen, they need more than words to feed their families.'

'Ah, but the shopkeepers of Sheffield were more than generous. Apparently they sent upwards of a ton of bread, ham and beef back with the sailors to Hull,' the man announced proudly.

'That's wonderful of them!' Michael exclaimed. 'Now let's hope the Government can be as generous as Sheffielders when re-examining the Act in Parliament.' He stayed talking a little while longer, then left the basin for the Bull and Oak in the Wicker, in search of other boatmen and a pint of ale. However, it seemed strange and somehow pointless walking along on his own, and now he had the information he needed he lost his appetite for ale altogether. Turning on his heels he headed back to the keel where he allowed himself one tot of brandy from the hidden bottle before settling down for the night.

Next morning he was up, dressed and standing with the other boatmen waiting for the Canal Company's office to open long before the rest of the town was awake. He was nervous, hoping to get the load which was due in and also because his father had usually been the one to stand. His job had been to fill the 30 gallon cask on deck with fresh water, and prepare breakfast. It had always amazed him that, no matter how early they rose, there was always someone ahead of his father in the queue! This morning, however, he was lucky to be first in line and quickly approached the counter when the door opened.

'Do you know when Berry's dray will be in?' he asked the clerk, with more confidence than he felt.

The clerk looked up. 'Not 'till about nine—are you waiting for it to arrive?'

'Yes,' Michael replied, feeling a little guilty, 'I was wondering if I could do some of the paper work now to save time later?' He didn't look at the other men for fear of giving himself away. Just as long as they thought things had been arranged beforehand there would be no trouble.

'Well, as long as you come back and get things signed before you leave, mind' the clerk said, sifting through the papers. 'It's not always the exact same quantity you know. Anyway, I'll make a start.'

He stood watching as the clerk inserted his keel's name on the Bill of Lading and with that done he calmly left the office, breathing a sigh of relief as he walked out onto the cobbles. Then, having estimated how long it would take to load up, he set off to find help and a marine to tow the keel back down the canal when he was ready to leave. This done he hovered impatiently around the entrance to the yard, waiting to catch Berry's dray on its way in.

Nine o'clock came and went, as did several wagons loaded with goods, and he began to wonder if he'd been foolish to risk causing resentment amongst the other men if things came to light. Had something gone wrong or were Berry's simply not shipping that day? He bit his lip wondering what to do next when a voice behind him called out. 'Hey, you!'

Michael turned round, his heart pounding for fear that he'd been caught out. To his great relief the remark wasn't addressed to him but to someone else across the yard. This distraction was almost his undoing, as in turning he nearly missed the dray he'd been looking for. There was no mistaking the large Berry's trade-board however, and he called up to the drayman, 'Your loads going on the *Maggie Kelly*, over there!'

'Right oh! I'll go and check in the details. Sorry I'm late!' the drayman replied, stepping down. He disappeared into the Company office, his large white apron flapping round his legs, and Michael waited tensely, knowing all would be lost if luck was against him.

The clerk was used to a constant stream of boatmen badgering for the slowly diminishing number of cargoes, and today was no exception. He looked up as the drayman entered, picked up his pen and Michael's Bill of Lading and said, 'Mornin' Sam'.

'Mornin' Bert,' came the reply, 'I'm loading on the *Maggie Kelly*. Is that right?'

'Yes, just give me the details, it won't take a minute.'

Several minutes later Michael could have cried with relief when the drayman re-appeared and said, 'Show me where to go!'

Leading the cask-laden dray to the keel where he'd already positioned wooden planks across to its deck, he then went quickly to fetch the man hired earlier to help him load the heavy barrels of ale into the hold.

The keel was still lighter than he would have liked, but there was at least sufficient weight on board to ensure she would pass under any low bridge without the need to take on water as ballast. With luck and no unforeseen incident his seven or eight hour homeward journey could be accomplished before nightfall, if he got a move on.

Fortunately, all went well and he was able to get through Aldwarke lock just before daylight started to fade, giving him time to reach The Grapes before Patrick gave up and went home. After despatching his nephew back to the farm he returned to the river where the marine was guarding the keel. He hated drawing attention to the fact that he was moored on the river, but to make it easier for John to find him in the dark he placed a couple of lanterns on poles on top of the bank. It would take Patrick at least twenty minutes to walk home and he hoped that John had not by now abandoned any thought of seeing him that day, and put his horse and supplies away.

Michael told the marine to stable the horse at The Grapes, then he set about securing the keel properly for the night. He was quite hungry by this time and eagerly awaited John's arrival, knowing that he would bring him something worthwhile to eat.

It was at least three quarters of an hour before he saw lights moving on the distant hillside in the direction of the house, and a further twenty minutes before they stopped by The Grapes. Now, of course, everything would need to be carried from the road rather than risk breaking an axle on the rough ground leading to the river, in the dark. When he heard voices approaching he climbed up the bank again and waited on the tow-path.

'We didn't expect you to arrive this late,' John called out, as he came nearer, 'we thought you wouldn't make it 'till tomorrow.' He and Maggy were carrying a large wicker basket between them.

'I'm sorry,' Michael replied, going forward to help. 'It took longer than I expected to get enough cargo. I hope it's not put you out too much.' He took the lantern from John and guided Maggy aboard, before passing the basket to her.

'We've had to leave Patrick with the wagon on the road,' Maggy said, 'and there are some more things need fetching.'

'Right, I'll go and get them if you watch the keel.' With this he quickly rejoined John and walked carefully back to where Patrick stood holding the horse, which he'd pulled into the inn yard.

'I've managed to get everything you asked for,' John told him. 'Mary's added a few bits, of course, but one more trip after this should do it.'

'Thanks, John,' Michael said, and after greeting Patrick he lifted down a wooden box from the back of the wagon.

John took a sack and they set off back along the uneven path, past the eerie shape of the windmill which was occasionally silhouetted by the fitful light of the moon. 'Can you get some sacks of potatoes on your way back from Hull?' he asked. 'We're getting a bit low. Anything else you can get cheap would be helpful while you're at it.'

'Of course, I'd be glad to help.'

On his final return to the wagon, John warned his son to watch his step on the river bank, wished him good luck and left him to carry the remaining supplies to Michael. With that he urged the horse on, and set off home.

When Patrick arrived at the keel he climbed aboard with less than nimble feet and, much to Michael's consternation, nearly dropped one of the bundles in the process. Admittedly the shadowy deck was unfamiliar to the lad, but as he helped him down into the cabin Michael couldn't help but wonder if instead of gaining help by bringing the boy, he had in fact saddled himself with even more responsibility.

With a journey of almost seventy miles to Hull ahead of them, which could only be done during daylight hours, and having little room for movement in the cabin, they chatted for a while then went to bed. Maggy stayed in the aft cabin whilst Michael and Patrick used the fore-cabin which would eventually be the home of the new keelman, or mate.

Patrick wasn't used to retiring early and it was some time before he settled down to sleep, only to start snoring so loud that Michael despaired of having a peaceful night himself.

At first light he woke them all and set them to work, Maggy to cooking breakfast whilst Patrick washed the decks. The marine, meanwhile, collected and attended to his horse while Michael prepared for their departure. Now, for the first time in days Michael felt optimistic, the weather was bright if cold, promising a pleasant run and, in spite of his apprehensions over the possible outcome of the journey, he was quite pleased to be on the move again. He knew Maggy was quite capable of handling the tiller whilst the marine led the horse on the towpath, and this would allow him to rest his leg ready for when he retrieved the mast and sail from the trap in Mexborough. On arrival there he was relieved to find Joe operating the lock and took the opportunity to inform him that he hoped to keep the keel, at least for the time being.

He paid off the marine, then with Joe and Patrick's help collected and re-fitted the mast and sail ready to continue the journey without being towed. Afterwards, Joe spotted Maggy coming out of the cabin, and made a point of sympathising with her on the recent death of her father. However, he couldn't hide from Michael the intentness of his gaze, nor the slight colouring of Maggy's cheeks.

Once under sail and no longer restricted by the slow pace of the marine and horse, his old sense of freedom returned and he felt in control again. He was pleased to find that his nephew learned quickly, even remembering things his grandfather had taught him two years before. Together they bow-hauled the keel in and out of the locks, making good progress as a result.

Dusk was falling as they left Sprotbrough locks and moored up in the river beyond for the night and Michael considered they'd done a fair day's work under the circumstances. Maggy had soon made both cabins spick and span again, and it wasn't long before she placed a good hot meal on the table for the three of them. It was too dark outside to wander once they'd eaten, as the steep wooded slope on the far bank intensified the gloom in the narrow valley through which the river ran.

Much to Michael's surprise, Patrick seemed to have a deep fear of the dark, murky river. After one quick look he shivered and hurried back down into the cabin. At first Michael chided him playfully, but he was not unkind and soon saw that the lad's disquiet was genuine. Fortunately, Patrick was tired from the unfamiliar bustle of life on the water and had no complaints about retiring early, nor, thank goodness, did he snore all night on this occasion.

Next day they were up and off early again. Maggy was quite capable of controlling the tiller, even under sail, although where the river twisted and turned and they had to tack to suit the wind, Michael kept a wary eye on her.

At last, with Doncaster and several deliveries behind them, they left the river at Bramwith and entered the Stainforth and Keadby Canal which led to the Trent. Once through the open swing-bridge at Stainforth, the canal banks were lined with houses and taverns, and Michael tied up alongside the Ship Inn which was near enough to the sail-maker's house for him to deliver a consignment of Mudford's canvas and rope. This done, they moved on and headed towards Thorne.

From this point the canal passed through flat fertile land where, on his return, Michael intended to collect some potatoes which were grown in the good peaty soil, to take back to John. The news of Jim Havercroft's death had travelled along the waterway, saving him the trouble of explaining to all and sundry, and as the passing canal-folk called out their sympathies he raised his hand in acknowledgement. It was obvious to them that he was still in business, and this he hoped would scotch speculation of any kind.

Gradually the breeze quickened and Michael thought it wiser to take the tiller himself whilst Maggy and Patrick adjusted the sails at his bidding. It was on days such as these, not sufficiently warm for him to remove his thick jersey, but pleasant enough to allow him to enjoy the wind on his face, that he felt alive within himself. He drew a deep breath and looked around at the sparsely wooded landscape with its isolated hamlets, and remembered the man at Parker's and his comments about the poor lives of the grinders in Sheffield. Then, however, a twinge of pain in his leg served to remind him that all was not well, but he pushed the thought to the back of his mind for the time being.

A keel in full sail, yet obviously light in the water, approached the *Maggie Kelly*. It was a magnificent sight to behold but he knew that an empty vessel meant an empty purse and that things were getting harder for his sort all the time.

They finally passed through the lock at Thorne, delivered some canvas, rope and twine to the boatyard then collected their keel-boards and twelve-foot cog boat which would be needed later in the journey. His enquiries at the boatyard regarding the possibility of selling the keel had so far met with little interest, nor did anyone know of a keelman looking for work. He was told, instead, to try at Keadby where he might be able to hire a man to accompany him to Hull. Michael had hoped for a better response than this and was quite worried, as, if he didn't find someone at Keadby, he'd be forced to take the keel onto the treacherous River Humber with an inadequate crew aboard. Hiding his concern, he returned to the keel and moved on to moor for the night near to West Street.

To Patrick, unaware of the seriousness of their predicament, it was merely an inconvenience, but to Maggy who knew the tidal estuary well, his news was worrying. She looked keenly at Michael, recognising the tell-tale signs, the absent look in his eyes and the way he chewed his lip, yet he said no more. She admired him with fond affection but knew that to him she still seemed a child. At eighteen she was hardly that, nor was she as slow as he often made out. He was thorough and meticulous to detail and, when not in pain, had the physical strength that all canal men needed, whilst she was a dreamer. If she forgot things it was because her mind was often elsewhere, she could read and write with some ability, and was proud to have been taught at the small school in Dalton which Ebenezer Elliot, the Corn Law poet, had attended as a young man. She was fortunate in this and, although Michael didn't know it, she spent much of her spare time scribbling on pieces of paper, thus emulating the poet, or making sketches, and these she locked in a cupboard out of sight at home. Whereas Michael enjoyed controlling the keel, she loved to observe wildlife along the banksides. The vole, moorhen and reed warbler were an inspiration to her, and it hurt when he took this absorption for some kind of mental slowness, but it was she who spotted the plate-size mushrooms growing wild, and she who kept the account books up to date.

Although there was still almost an hour of daylight left there had seemed little point in going further that day only to tie up in some isolated spot, when there was ample room here in Thorne. The journey from now on might be fraught with unexpected problems, and Michael considered they all deserved a break before that time came. He sent Maggy off into town to stock up with fresh bread and supplies in case their journey took longer than planned and, as usual, she was late coming back.

'Where've you been?' he demanded, when she eventually appeared on the bankside. 'I'm starving!'

'I've just been talking, that's all,' she explained, none too pleased by his tone, and made her way below to cook dinner. She did however feel a little guilty at her tardiness, especially considering the strain he was under, so resolved to make it up to him the following day.

When their evening meal was over it was still early, and Michael was aware that in the close confines of the cabin Patrick was like a caged animal, needing diversion. At least Maggy appeared to be trying to make amends for her earlier thoughtlessness and after washing up she sat contentedly reading a book. Michael envied her ability to read so well, but found difficulty in understanding her absorption, to the exclusion of practical things.

'Have you got any playing cards?' Patrick suddenly asked, obviously tired of small talk and needing to occupy himself.

Maggy looked up and smiled knowingly at Michael, who although sympathetic to the lad's frustration, said simply. 'You've got a lot to learn about river life, Patrick. It's considered bad luck to play cards on board a keel.'

With typical youthful directness, Patrick scoffed, 'What a lot of rubbish! What harm can it do?' At which Maggy gave a hearty laugh, much to Michael's surprise.

'It's thought to be unlucky, and that's that!' Michael explained. 'Besides, I haven't got a pack on board anyway so there's no point in arguing.' He was pleased to see Maggy still giggling, it was something she'd not done since their father's death.

Patrick gazed round, a look of sad resignation on his face. Then a couple of seconds later he dared to ask. 'Well, what do you do every night?'

Michael pondered for a moment; what indeed had he and his father actually done, apart from chat? He himself had often carved small ornaments from broken pieces of ivory that came his way, and of course they'd gone to local hostelries with other keelmen when at secure moorings. He shook his head, and explained, 'We get up early, work hard all day, then just relax! Sometimes we go to a tavern for a drink.' He saw Patrick's face light up at this, and the hopeful anticipation he saw there prompted Michael to take him for a stroll. He could do with a pint himself and it would do no harm for them to stretch their legs and mingle with the other canal men for a while. It would certainly open the lad's eyes a little. 'Would you mind if we went out?' he asked, turning to Maggy. 'The lad's been cooped up for two days now, what do you say to me taking him for a drink?' he winked at her slyly.

Smiling at them both, she replied, 'I'll walk with you as far as the swing bridge and then come back, there's some mending I've got to do.' Michael looked at her a little puzzled. She seemed much brighter now, perhaps this was the result of her shopping around the town earlier. He'd noticed her lightness of spirit when she returned to the keel but this disappeared the moment he'd grumbled at her.

As arranged, Maggy turned back when they reached the bridge, leaving the two of them to walk across to the Canal Tavern which they found was crowded with boatmen, all talking loudly in the warm, stuffy atmosphere. Patrick drew back, a little shy of the scene before him.

'Haven't you been in a tavern like this before?' Michael asked, nudging him towards a bench where there was just enough room for them to sit.

'Well, no!' came the slightly nervous reply, as the boy gazed from one weather-beaten face to another, not quite sure what to do, or say.

Michael chuckled to himself as he went to fetch them both a pint of beer, wondering at the same time what effect it would have on the lad. He waited as the landlord drew the beer, then, as he walked back he saw 'Swifty' of the *Mary Ann* engrossed in a lively discussion with another man. Michael's mind raced with unexpected pleasure and he gave a friendly nod to Swifty and his son, who sat with him.

Acknowledging his greeting, Swifty called out, 'I'm sorry to hear about Jim, Mike. Maggy told me earlier!'

As he sat down and handed the pint of dark frothy beer to Patrick, Michael wondered why Maggy hadn't mentioned that the *Mary Ann* was nearby. But then he realised she did not know of his particular interest in one member of its crew.

An old man sitting nearby leaned over and said, 'Sorry about Holy Jim, Mike, but it's the best way to go. I hope I go as quickly'. Strangely enough it was the first time anyone had referred to his father like that since his death, presumably out of respect for the dead.

'Why did he call granddad that?' Patrick asked, looking askance at the old man opposite.

'It's not an insult, Pat,' Michael explained. 'All the captains have nicknames. Your grandfather was a bit different to the others, he never swore or spoke dirty, not even about women. That should have set him apart, appearing weak for a canal man, but he didn't care what they thought and in sticking to his guns they learned to respect him.'

Patrick thought for a while, then said quietly, 'You don't swear as much as these men, I've noticed that. With them every other word's a swear word'.

'Nobody on the canal thinks anything about it, it's part of their way of life. I may do so in their company sometimes, but not often. Dad used to say when I did, 'Now then Michael, let's have none of that, it's not necessary'.

'Do you have a nickname?'

'Everyone knows me as Mike, Holy Jim's boy. What they'll call me now I don't know.'

The old man, hearing this last part of the conversation, piped up, 'I suppose you'll still be known as Jim's lad, or Mike. We've known you too long to change things now'.

Some time later, Michael gave Patrick a nudge, 'Come on, it's time to go, you're not used to drinking and we've got an early start in the morning. With what you've had you'll take no rocking to sleep tonight!'

Pulling a face, Patrick rose reluctantly from the seat and followed Michael to the door. 'I thought I'd feel funny,' he remarked, standing straight and steady, waiting to go out.

Michael said nothing, he just opened the door and stepped out into the cool night air, and paused. With an almost silly giggle Patrick clutched his arm and wavered about. 'It's the cold air that's hit you, boy. Just hold on to me, you'll be fine.' He walked the now garrulous lad slowly along the street to where the keel was moored, smiling to himself and remembering the first pint he'd downed, and how stupid he'd felt making his clumsy way back to the keel afterwards.

'Go on, lift your feet up,' he said as he helped Patrick aboard the keel. Then, hearing voices coming from the cabin below he slackened his grip in alarm, and Patrick almost fell from the deck into the dark, murky water he feared so much. Michael quickly caught him, sat him down on one of the adjacent hatches, and hurriedly lifted the cabin hatch to investigate. On looking down, two smiling faces greeted him, throwing him off guard. It was a second or two before it registered in his mind that Maggy had company in the shape of none other than Swifty's daughter, the girl on the *Mary Ann*. He felt his face flushing and mumbled, 'Hullo you two,' then a movement behind him brought him down to earth. He quickly grabbed Patrick, who was endeavouring to stand alone, and assisted him down the ladder, hoping that the lad's unsteadiness would conceal his own confusion from Maggy.

'Now then, what have you done to him?' Maggy reprimanded in a stern voice, as Patrick almost fell from the ladder.

'It's orl right, Maggy!' Patrick's slurred voice rang out. 'I'm 'appy!' Then he flopped down heavily onto the locker like a marionette without its strings.

'He's halfway to being a man, now!' Michael laughed. 'My dad did exactly the same to me. He's only had a pint—he's just not used to it. But he'll not know what's hit him in the morning.

'I'd better get going!' Maggy's visitor said with a smile, rising from her seat. 'It's late and Dad'll wonder where I am.'

Maggy turned, having half forgotten her. 'This is Lily from the *Mary Ann*,' she said, introducing the amused young girl. She was taller than Michael had expected, taller in fact than most of the women of his acquaintance, and her fine grey eyes were almost level with his. They seemed to challenge him with a merry twinkle.

'Hullo, I'm Mike,' he said a little nervously, not knowing quite how to respond to the teasing look on her face as she returned his greeting.

'You'll walk Lily back to the keel, won't you, Mike?' Maggy offered, giving him no opportunity to refuse. 'It's not far.'

He agreed, trying not to reveal the unease that he felt and climbed the ladder ahead of Lily. With the agility of all boat people she climbed the ladder after him and sprang nimbly from the deck onto the wharf side, in spite of the dimness of the lights, leaving Maggy to attend to her befuddled nephew.

Lily didn't appear to notice that Michael was reserved almost to the point of rudeness as she chatted on about Maggy and the loss of his father. He was both stunned and surprised to find himself accompanying the lively girl back to the *Mary Ann*, when only a little while before he'd wondered if he would ever do more than wave to her as she sailed by. He found himself asking her how they'd fared in carrying coal rather than the traditional cargoes of the past.

'It's mucky, and the dust gets everywhere!' she complained distastefully. 'And it takes forever to unload by basket from the hold. Do you know, we had to sweep out four times before washing everything down, as our present load is grain.'

Lily seemed reluctant to board the keel when they reached it, but he was ill-at-ease from striving to find a topic of conversation which was light enough to please without making him seem ridiculous. He just wasn't used to this kind of thing and could have kicked himself for his inadequacy, so instead of lingering uncomfortably beside her, he simply said, 'Well, I'd better be making my way back then.'

'I suppose we'll be off at the crack of dawn,' she replied, a little wistfully.

He nodded, 'You'll be gone before us. I'm afraid until I get a hired hand we'll make a slower start than we should.'

'See you some other time then,' she replied softly.

'Yes I expect so! Good night.' Michael said, as he turned and walked away.

'Good night!' she called after him, a note of disappointment plainly in her voice.

He didn't go down into the cabin straight away, but stood on deck looking at the friendly lights in the windows of houses nearby. What kind of fool was he to have let an opportunity such as that go by? It could be another ten days or more before the *Mary Ann* and the *Maggie Kelly* met again, and maybe even then only in passing. He was cross with himself now, as at the back of his mind he'd begun to look forward to doing more than just wave to the girl on the other keel.

'You look glum,' Maggy said, looking keenly at his face, when finally he re-entered the cabin. His eyes had an empty look and his face was grimmer than she'd ever seen before. 'Did you take Lily home?' she asked, not really knowing what to say.

'Yes!' he replied, but she knew he didn't want to talk about it, nor did she know the remedy for what ailed him.

She was more than a little perturbed by his behaviour, and as he sat dejectedly near the sleeping Patrick, she asked, 'Have you had too much to drink?'

He was hurt by her suggestion. 'I'm not drunk, Maggy, why do you need to ask?'

'Then what's the matter? Earlier today you seemed to be your old self again. Has Lily said something to upset you?' She joined him on the locker, waiting for him to reply.

'Oh, I don't know, it's many things, Dad's death, the keel, my leg, the future. Our future even, and the futility of it all.'

'Oh, Michael,' she said gently, placing her arm round his shoulder much as she'd done to her mother before the funeral. 'Things will improve, you wait and see! Once you've got a man to help you, it'll be so much easier on your leg. You'll be captain and the man will have to do what you say.'

'But will it be like that, Sis? Things are changing, Lily's family have had to take coal as cargo, and not out of choice. I can't stand by watching hired men unload baskets of coal, not sixty to eighty tons of it, Maggy, it wouldn't pay.' He stared gloomily down at his boots, knowing that she would like to help, but well aware that only he could resolve their problems.

Maggy withdrew her arm. 'Go to bed, Michael, things will seem better in the morning,' she said gently, patting him on the shoulder. 'Leave Patrick where he is, I'll cover him up. You'll never get him back to his own bed in his state.'

'Good night,' he mumbled, somewhat ashamed of himself for wallowing in self pity. When he'd gone she covered the boy and got into the sleeping compartment, pulling the curtain across for privacy.

On rising the following morning Michael saw, once the mist had cleared, that the *Mary Ann* had indeed left her mooring and he imagined was now already passing through Thorne lock, in the opposite direction to his intended route. Ahead of him lay Keadby and his last chance to find a suitable man before entering the treacherous waters of the Humber.

There was hardly a breath of wind and this meant that he and Patrick had to bow-haul the keel whilst Maggy held the tiller. Hopefully there would be a change in the weather soon, bringing a breeze to take them down the river. As it was now early April it probably would improve but with a vengeance, and just when he needed an easy run.

Progress was slow but uneventful, and at one point a rabbit sat undisturbed and unafraid as it watched them pass by, each with a harness and rope pulled taut over their shoulders. 'A rabbit's life might be short but it's easier than ours, don't you think?' Michael remarked to Patrick once they'd passed the animal. 'How's the head now?'

Patrick grimaced. Since joining Michael on the keel, his face had acquired a healthy, weathered colouring and he was beginning to show a confidence which comes only with independence and experience.

'You'll do, lad.' Michael spoke fondly. 'Your granddad would have been proud of you.' At this, the boy braced himself to the load again as if to prove Michael right.

The sun's heat intensified as the morning wore on, and this did not suit Michael at all as he hauled along the canal bank, his leg tiring and his thirst growing. Turning suddenly, he called out, 'Let's stop here and have a drink, Maggy'.

Once released from his harness, Patrick flopped to the ground, his face hot and sweaty. Michael looked at him, laughing. 'We've not done yet. Once we get to Keadby there's more work to do!' He saw dismay on the lad's face and was sorry for tormenting him, so added, 'Don't worry, there'll be time for a rest before we go on'.

At last, warm and very tired they reached Keadby where the canal joined the River Trent, their journey having taken them all of six hours. It wasn't a town like Thorne, merely a small row of buildings and houses which lay alongside the river. Here he would be able to off-load more of the cargo. To some degree he was relieved to have discharged so much en-route, even if it earned him less, as the lighter they were the less chance there was of capsizing if caught broadside in bad weather in the Humber. Often with a full heavy load they were so low in the water that waves lapped the deck, and one really heavy swell had the power to swamp them.

April was indeed an unpredictable month; this year it had started wet and cold, yet today was as warm and bright as one in mid-summer. However, he'd known snow fall in May, but it rarely lay on the ground for long. Today he hoped that the turn of the tide might bring a light wind which would enable him to use his sail beyond Keadby and into the lower reaches of the Trent before dark.

'I've got to go looking for help now,' Michael said, once the farming implements had been delivered. 'This might take some time, so have a rest, Patrick, but first just fill up the water barrel from that pump over there.' With that he gave Maggy some money and asked her to fetch a jug of ale from the tavern down the road to quench his thirst.

He had to find a man quickly if he was to move on without too much delay, otherwise another day would be added to their journey. Surely with trade falling off there must be a man somewhere who was desperate for work? However, Michael didn't want just anyone. It took skill and expertise to handle a keel and its cargo, and two men working together in all weathers had to get on with each other—their lives often depended on it. If only he could guarantee getting to Kingston-upon-Hull safely he would surely hear of someone there, either in the taverns or from one of the many Carrying Agents.

At last there was a gentle breeze and that was as much as he needed if he was to risk sailing the Humber alone, but, if this became too fresh, it could be dangerous. He tried several places where mariners might normally be found, but to no avail. Then, on chatting to the lock-keeper, he was told that the most likely place to find permanent help was in Hull, in fact he thought there was a man there who might still be seeking employment! Apparently the man had had a keel of his own but lost it for failing to meet payments due on it. This sounded promising, so, making a mental note of the man's name and where he might be found, Michael went back to the keel. Sadly this news did not solve his present difficulty; he needed to find someone with sufficient expertise to sail with him on the final part of this journey. He would have liked to take the *Maggie* further while it was still daylight, but he might now be delayed indefinitely. What if he were to remain in this small place for days and still not find anyone?

The queue of vessels waiting to enter the Trent was growing, making Michael anxious. The lock gates were about to be opened, Maggy had returned, and in a mood of exasperation he decided to hoist the mainsail and smaller topsail and follow the keels in front of them. He knew that once clear of the canal there would be sufficient time for him to sail down river to a good mooring where they could rest over night, ready to enter the Humber in the morning. If the weather then deteriorated badly, he would just have to stay there until it was safe enough to go on. At least tomorrow, if things worked out, he would be ahead of the morning traffic from Keadby and safely in the River Hull by early afternoon.

As they entered the Trent the keel was immediately affected by the surge of tidal flow, and Patrick's eyes widened with apprehension. 'Just hold tight on that taffrail,' Michael called out reassuringly from the tiller as Maggy altered the set of the sails to his directions, and the keel steadied to the following breeze. They made good time as a result of a fair wind until Michael decided to anchor in the river for the night just beyond the wooden pier at Burton Stather, where the river banks were steeper and gave them ample shelter. The water level had dropped gradually, leaving the keel imprisoned between the slimy, muddy shores, and from their position they could just see the tower of a church on the nearby hill.

Occasionally the solitude was broken by a gull swooping down across the deck seeking food, but finding none flew off back to the estuary. The twilight deepened and the wind increased, becoming colder as the sun went down. Michael stood watching the glowing orange sky but the sun sent a shaft of gold across the river, almost blinding him. He turned away, looking towards the wooden pier on the other bank, then to the distant church—the tower of which was illuminated by the sun's rays. Slowly, as the sun sank below the horizon, darkness closed around them, leaving only the lights of the houses on the hillside and those of the Ferry Inn visible. The smell of the sea was strong and he was tempted to take a lantern and scull the cog boat to the pier in front of the Inn, but thought better of it. He didn't want Maggy to get the impression that he needed a drink, nor did he want to give Patrick a taste for it.

Michael knew this stretch of water well but, from here on, the shifting sands and blustering winds of the Humber had caught many a seasoned boatman unawares, and he was taking no chances. He made sure all was safe for the night, and all three of them turned in early, hoping that tomorrow's rising tide would bring neither fog nor gale to hinder the final part of the journey.

At dawn he woke to find a fair wind and excellent visibility, so for once things seemed to be going his way. As they sailed from the shelter of the Trent into the unpredictable Humber, Patrick gasped at its broad expanse of water. 'It's wonderful,' he cried, 'I don't remember coming this far with Granddad Jim, last time.'

'Perhaps not,' Michael said, smiling at the enthusiasm in Patrick's voice, but he was more than relieved when eventually the town of Hull could be seen clearly ahead on the left bank. Although not a religious man, like all mariners he had a healthy respect for the Lord of the seas, and he said a silent prayer of thanks as they sailed the keel into the mouth of the River Hull and safety. However, finding a berth along the busy staithe proved to be more difficult than expected, as so many keels and vessels were already moored. They were, therefore, compelled to anchor in a less than convenient spot for several hours, during which time Michael made enquiries along the wharf, hoping to find a place to move to later. He also judged that he had sufficient time to find out where Mr Erikson, his prospective mate, lived, intending to pay him a visit later in the day. He knew only that the man frequented the Norwegian Tavern near the old dock, so that would be his first port of call.

Chapter 2

he house of Erik Erikson was like many others in the Adelaide Street area of Hull, set as it was between shops and public houses. Times were hard and money scarce, and under these conditions the atmosphere inside was often rife with irritable squabbling and accusation.

For a man of Erik's nature to be out of work was demoralising, and it was even more so to stand on the dockside waiting for each job to materialise. He didn't want to be forced to go to sea again but, if circumstances got much worse, he'd be compelled to take anything that was going. Having left the sea several years before, he had taken a job as mate on a keel and this suited him well, as it allowed him to escape from his growing family without the dangers of sailing the high seas.

He was fond and proud of his family, providing they didn't run around his feet for too long. Two years ago, to his great joy, he'd been given the opportunity to purchase the keel on which he worked from his captain, who was retiring to a small tavern beside the Trent.

So, the *Martha Jane* had become his, but he was not a business man, simply a good mariner, and things had gone badly wrong with the result that the keel had been repossessed. Now, with no money spare to spend in the taverns in an evening, he naturally stayed at home where he got in his wife's way, or in her bed, with the result that at the age of forty-three she was again with child. Miserable and fed up with struggling to make ends meet, Ellen Erikson's temper was short, and she was nearly at her wits end. The children had been particularly irritating that day, and she was almost at the point of throwing something at her dozing husband when a knock at the door saved him.

Michael knew immediately that the powerful, bearded figure framed in the front doorway was Erik Erikson. The man was older than he had expected and seemed to tower over him as he stood on the pavement, a little taken aback at what he saw. Meeting the man's clear blue and questioning eyes, Michael asked courteously, 'Mr Erikson?'

'Ya! that's me!' The strongly accented voice came from within the full reddish-coloured beard. 'What you want?'

'I hear you're used to working on a keel Mr Erikson, and might be looking for work?'

The man smiled, revealing several broken teeth. 'Come in, come in!' he said, catching Michael by the arm and drawing him into the house. 'How you know this?'

'The lock keeper at Keadby sent me to the Norwegian Tavern to enquire after you,' Michael replied, following the man inside where a strong aroma of coffee greeted him.

'So, everyone knows the downfall of Erik Erikson, maybe?' The big man asked seriously, though his blue eyes twinkled in a friendly manner.

'I know only that you had a keel for some time but don't have it now. The man who gave me this address spoke highly of you.'

'Good! Good!' Erik nodded approvingly. 'I'm not afraid of work! Sit down,' he said, pointing to an empty wooden chair. 'This is my wife, Ellen.'

Michael leaned over and shook her outstretched hand and noticed how rough and careworn her skin was. 'I hope I'm not disturbing you?' he asked, as he sat down and noted how clean and neat both she and the room were.

'Would you like a mug of coffee?' Mrs Erikson offered, indicating a pot on the fire hob.

'Thank you!' Michael accepted gratefully, watching as she poured out the dark, strong liquid and was grateful that neither of his hosts appeared to see him wince at the bitter taste. It was like sweet black treacle but, despite its strangeness, once swallowed it drew him back for a further sip.

'Good, no?' Erik asked, laughing. 'My wife, she makes the best coffee in Hull. But that's not what you come for, is it?'

Michael smiled at the frank, bushy-bearded man who had a charm all of his own, but charm wasn't what he was after. 'What I need is a well-experienced mate who is capable of heavy physical labour. I work my keel on the Hull to Sheffield waterways and I want someone who knows exactly how to load for balance, a man capable of judging winds and handling the sails efficiently. Are you from a keel family?'

'Twenty five years ago I came with the iron-ore boats and meet my Ellen. For many years I go to sea, then I work on keels. At last I buy my own keel—*Martha Jane*—you know her?'

Thinking hard, Michael could vaguely recall seeing a keel of that name. 'I think I may have seen it,' he replied.

'For two years she is mine, but I'm not a good businessman, I don't jump the queue for work, I am polite as you say, but it does not bring in money. I cannot pay for the keel, so here I sit, annoying my wife.'

'Could you work for someone else, though?' Michael asked. 'You've been Captain of your own vessel, so it won't be easy taking orders from someone else.'

Erik leaned forward intently in his chair, 'You give me the chance and I prove my worth. I pick up work where I can on the docks, heavy stuff too'.

'I'm not sure how long I shall keep the keel,' Michael replied, cautiously, so as not to deceive the man while at the same time not wanting to lose this opportunity of finding someone suitable. 'It depends on trade. I'll be honest with you, my father died only last week and we worked well together. I own the *Maggie Kelly* but trade is slowing down, as you have seen for yourself. Would you be available for a couple of trips say, until we see how things go?'

'I have nothing to lose,' Erik said. 'You pay me—I work hard!'

Michael, who stood to lose his keel, his livelihood and his home if he didn't find a man soon, liked what he saw in this genial foreigner. Without making it too obvious he let his eyes wander round the room, seeing its solid, homely furnishings, perhaps brought from the man's own country. Here, at least he could judge the man behind the beard better than if he were a stranger being interviewed on the dockside. They both had a lot to gain and a lot to lose, and Michael had a feeling that Mr Erikson could be a fierce ally, if the need arose.

All at once a loud clatter followed by excited squeals came from the back of the house. 'It's the children playing in the yard,' Mrs Erikson explained, 'I'll tell them to be quiet.'

'There's no need on my account,' Michael interrupted, 'besides, I have taken up too much of your time already.' He paused, then continued, 'Mr Erikson, I think we might be suited to working together, but I would like you to look the keel over first, then we can both make a final decision.'

'That will be good!' agreed Mr Erikson, nodding with approval.

This suited Michael who felt he could best make a final judgement by observing the man's reactions and behaviour on the keel. 'I have to discharge my cargo before I can seek another to take back with me,' he said. 'Would you mind if my sister came in the morning to let you know where we will be?'

'I shall wait here until she comes,' Erik agreed, 'and if we are suited I can maybe help you load up.'

Believing this arrangement to be a good one for both of them, Michael shook hands with the man and his wife and left, feeling much easier in his mind. Now he could concentrate on his work, and prepare for the immediate future.

Maggy looked at him expectantly on his return. 'Was he in?' She asked hopefully, as he climbed from the cog boat onto the keel.

'Yes,' he replied, his face reflecting the relief in his voice. 'I'm quite impressed. He's a big fellow, and sounds both experienced and sufficiently in need to work hard. He's older than I expected but as I don't know how long we shall need him, that isn't much of a problem. Don't let on about my leg though!' he added cautiously.

'Don't worry,' she assured him, 'but tell Patrick to watch what he says, not that he knows much anyway.'

The way was now clear enough for several keels to move, some round to the docks, some simply changing mooring positions whilst others headed away from Hull. Michael wasted no time in easing the *Maggie Kelly* into the first vacant spot before more vessels came into the river.

Once the keel was snug against the wooden staithe, he left Maggy and Patrick to look after it while he arranged for a dray to come later and take his cargo of beer casks to the warehouse. They then set about off-loading these onto the staithe and had time to spare before the dray arrived to relieve him of a commodity much sought after by thieves. Hull had been notorious for smuggling liquor of all sorts, indeed rumour had it that some tunnels built for that purpose still remained, running from certain ale houses down to the staithes.

There were several small consignments to deliver, and when this was done Michael was able to hand in his bills of lading at the Town Docks' Office and seek more work. He set off, leaving Patrick to scrub the decks whilst Maggy fettled both cabins in anticipation of Mr Erikson's visit the following day.

Michael was quite light-hearted now. They had been lucky to get into the river and unload their cargo all on the same day, but Michael knew it would be a miracle if he managed to get new work as well. Sometimes it took days to find a free berth, let alone enough freight to make sailing back worth while. Several large ships had arrived with the afternoon tide, but by the time he joined the queue of captains also seeking cargoes, all the consignments had been allocated to other vessels. He knew that if he was to succeed then he must be up early next morning in order to get something from one of the next vessels to arrive. So, giving Maggy instructions where to find Mr Erikson's house, he retired for the night.

When Maggy woke at six the next morning she wasn't surprised to find that Michael had already left for the offices, and on leaving the keel herself at nine o'clock she found both the dockland and town a hive of activity. It was a noisy yet lively place, one where she always felt a surge of excitement as she mingled with the crowds. The cries of the workmen, and the bustle of the people around her added to her distractions, so that she was almost run over by a horse and dray when once she stepped off the walkway. Now and then there were voices in strange languages mixed up in the babble around her, and she wondered where these foreigners came from.

She had to travel a considerable distance beyond the Town Docks, and needed to make several enquiries in an effort to follow Michael's instructions. Eventually, however, she located Adelaide Street and the two-storey house of the Erikson family, where Mr Erikson sat waiting impatiently for her visit. She knocked on the door and was as surprised as her brother had been to find a tall bearded man looking down at her with clear penetrating eyes.

'Mr Erikson?' she asked, just as Michael had done.

'That is me!' he replied. 'And you, I think, are Miss Havercroft?'

Maggie smiled, her face relaxing. 'Yes. Michael sent me to tell you where to find us.'

'Come in, come in!' He opened the door wider. 'Come and meet my wife and family.'

It had not occurred to her that he might be alone in the house and as such, a possible danger to her. She had taken an instant liking to him and hoped that he might prove to be the answer to all their problems.

Taking her through to the back room, he said, 'This is my wife, Ellen,' and placed his arm proudly around the shoulders of the small but not unattractive woman, as she stood holding a posser at the wash tub.

'Hello,' Maggy replied pleasantly, sensing the other woman's fluster at being caught dishevelled and warm from her exertions, 'I'm Maggy Havercroft.'

Brushing a strand of hair from her forehead, Ellen Erikson smiled back. 'I'm please to meet you,' she replied. There were three children sitting at a table, two preparing vegetables whilst the eldest appeared to be mending some garment or other, and all were observing their visitor with interest. 'Say ''Good morning'' children,' Mrs Erikson told them as she dried her reddened hands and arms with a cloth.

With one voice the children replied, brightly, 'Good morning, Miss Havercroft'.

'Hello, children,' Maggie responded, delighted to be treated so formally. 'What are your names?' she asked, trying to make friends with them.

Before they could reply, their proud father spoke for them. 'This is Lucy,' he said, pointing to a girl of about twelve years, 'Johann is my youngest son, and the baby is Kristen.' This latter child Maggy judged to be about six, and her brother no more than eight.

She smiled at the trio and gave a playful nod. 'Hello,' she repeated, then turned her attention back to Mr Erikson. 'We're tied up in the river by the end of Scale Lane staithe. My brother went to the carrying agents very early, before it was fully light I believe, to seek a suitable cargo for Sheffield. He asked if you would come to the keel straight away and wait there until he returns. If this isn't possible would you meet him at the Anchor in High Street at one o'clock, as he may have been forced to move to another berth in the meantime.'

'I come now!' Mr Erikson responded enthusiastically. 'He can't afford to lose time, and I have plenty of that on my hands.' He seized his coat and a small bundle, then waited until she'd said good-bye to his family before ushering her out into the street. He knew all the short cuts back to the river and although Maggy was tall for a girl it was still hard for her to keep up with Mr Erikson's long strides. 'You must come and see my family whenever you are in Hull,' he said to her as they went, 'even if I don't work for your brother. Ellen will be pleased to have company.'

'That's kind of you,' she replied breathlessly due to the pace at which they were going, and then pointing said, 'there's the *Maggie Kelly*, and Michael's waiting for us already, I can see him on the bow.'

Several keels were already busy discharging coal brought down from the mines along the Sheffield and Barnsley canals. It was a dirty, tiring job to unload sixty to seventy tons or more of it by hand, basket after basket onto the staithe, and she could quite understand Michael's fear that it might eventually become too difficult for him to manage.

As they approached, Michael looked up and saw them. 'Ah, Mr Erikson,' he cried, 'I'm glad you could come now, I have to move the keel and work her round to the Town Docks before the tide goes out. Would you like to come aboard, then you can see how she handles. I'll be tying up to a ship that's just arrived from India, and Maggy will take you to the wharf side in the cog boat when you're ready to return home.'

'I'll do that,' Erik Erikson replied, as he looked around him. 'She looks a trim vessel.'

'She is,' Michael stated proudly. 'My father took good care of her.'

'What will you be carrying this time?'

'Hemp,' Michael said. 'It was sheer luck that this ship missed the tide last night and came in this morning whilst most of the other keels were still off-loading.' He then turned to Maggy and asked, 'Did you get some fish from the market?'

Maggy gasped, pressing her finger to her lips. 'Oh, no! I forgot!' She exclaimed, realising that in fact she hadn't done any of their shopping. 'I need to fetch everything else, as well.'

'Maggy!' he remonstrated. 'You'd better go now, and come to us at the dock when you've finished. I'll have to collect you in the cog boat.' He was more than a little irritated by this added complication. 'You'll have to get one of the sailors on the *Bengal* to give me a shout or we'll never hear you from the other side of it when we're loading.'

'I'm sorry,' Maggy said, knowing that he had enough problems without this, and so she dutifully hurried off down the cobbled street towards the market.

Michael then led Mr Erikson down onto the deck of the keel. 'I've got to move her now,' he said, lifting the hatch of the fore cabin which the mate usually occupied. 'You're a big man, Mr Erikson, you might find the sleeping compartment a bit short, but do go and see for yourself, by all means.' He watched him disappear into the cabin, noting how nimbly he moved. Leaving him there to look around, Michael signalled to Patrick and by the time Mr Erikson re-appeared at the hatchway, they had the keel ready to move. With Maggy away shopping, he had no choice but to tell Patrick what to do, but the lad was hesitant and clumsy.

Sensing this Erik said, 'I'll help if you like?'

'Thanks!' Michael replied, gratefully. 'Maggy knows what to do but Patrick's a bit inexperienced. Will you take the tiller while I push her off. You know the water round here as well, if not better than I do.' Together they manoeuvred the keel out of the river and entered the first of the three town docks where the water was deeper for the larger sea-going ships. 'There's the *Bengal*,' Michael said, pointing ahead, 'We're to go alongside her straight away.'

Once the keel was made fast to the *Bengal*, they had to wait a while before loading and Michael took this opportunity to quiz the big Norwegian. He'd certainly handled the tiller with expertise, so Michael asked him how he would load the keel for balance and safety. After an exchange of ideas and opinions he was quite impressed at what he heard, and realised too that the man had actually expected such an inquisition. His presence on board gave Michael a boost in confidence, leaving him with no desire to seek the services of anyone else. He had to acknowledge, however, that life on board the keel would now be a very different one to that which he had known before.

The *Bengal's* mate signalled that he was ready to off-load, and Michael realised that he could not delay his decision any longer. 'Do you feel we could work together, for at least a couple of trips?' he asked, hoping that his offer would be accepted. 'Wages would be the same as on any other keel, and there'll be extra if we haul ourselves when we can.' He waited anxiously whilst the man ran his fingers through his beard and appeared to be reflecting on the offer. Then a broad grin crossed Mr Erikson's face and he held a hand out to Michael.

'I start work now, I think' he said, shaking Michael's hand with such a firm grip that it almost crushed his fingers. 'I like what I see, and tonight I pack my things. You'll not be sailing today, I don't think.'

Michael stretched his fingers tentatively, admiring the strength of Erik's grasp, an admiration which grew as the pair worked together throughout the afternoon.

When Maggy returned from the town she took over from Patrick who had been adjusting the lines which held the keel to the ship's side, for as the keel became heavier it sank deeper into the water, so tightening them. Patrick joined the two men in their work and, to give him his due, he made no complaint even though the unfamiliar heavy lifting tested him to the limit of his strength. After six hours of strenuous effort Michael was suffering considerable pain in his leg, a reminder that problems still lay ahead, but at least there would be several days in which to rest before unloading again in Sheffield.

'We sail tomorrow,' Erik stated, rather than asked, as he helped put the last hatch cover in place. 'I look forward to that.' He had correctly judged how long it would take to load the hemp and this pleased Michael. They worked on for several minutes tidying up, then Erik added, 'First we move the keel and moor her safely for the night, then I go home'.

By this time, with the keel fully laden and low in the water it probably would not be safe to move out of the dock as there might be insufficient depth of water in the Humber. Also, it was too late in the day to sail far anyway. Michael looked forward to a relaxing evening in Hull. 'Come at seven tomorrow,' he said. 'Ready to sail about eight.'

Erik looked at Michael enquiringly, 'We work hard today, are you satisfied with what I do?'

Without hesitation Michael quickly replied, 'Yes! I'm more than pleased. I think we shall get on well together.' He put his hand in his pocket and paid Erik there and then for the day's work. 'Here, Mr Erikson,' he said, 'you deserve being paid. Tomorrow we can start as we mean to go on.'

'My wife will appreciate this,' Erik said, taking the money, 'and now you call me Erik, eh? Or Big Erik as sometimes they call me.'

'And I'm Mike, though what they'll call me now I'm captain remains to be seen.'

Together, they edged the keel away from the ship towards the quayside where other vessels were moored three abreast. The smell of fish frying hung in the air as Maggy prepared dinner in the cabin below. 'I think my Ellen will have something tasty ready for me also,' Erik said, preparing to leave, 'and don't bother with the cog boat, I can climb over the other keels to the quayside.' He smiled, 'I see you early tomorrow'. Before Michael could stop him he jumped onto the adjacent vessel as nimbly as a mountain goat, then passed on to the next until he reached the dockside where he waved before vanishing down an alleyway.

'Will Mr Erikson be suitable?' Maggie asked Michael as he came below for his dinner.

'He's certainly not afraid of work,' Michael conceded, 'and he can handle the keel as well as I can. If he's as good on the Humber then I'd say we were lucky to have found him.'

A feeling of calm settled over the keel as the three occupants ate the meal which Maggy put before them, and it wasn't long before Patrick's eyes began to close involuntarily after the heavy day's work. 'You've done well, Patrick,' Michael praised him with genuine warmth. 'If all goes well you'll be home again in four or five days.' Patrick's smile was a wry, half-hearted one which Michael found hard to interpret, but being tired himself he let the matter ride.

Relaxing for the first time in nearly a fortnight, Michael decided to take a stroll before retiring for the night. The docks were sparsely lit by lanterns both on board the numerous vessels and by those hanging from the warehouses on the dockside. There was much to see that wasn't already familiar to him, but he felt better for being able to stretch his legs freely as he walked. He passed the time of day with one or two of the men whom he knew from previous meetings, yet there was an eerie sense of isolation in the surrounding gloom and with the jet blackness of the water, now far below.

During the hectic activity of the past two days there had been little time to think about his father and their life together, but he missed him and wondered if there wasn't more to life than back-breaking work. Strangely, in the past, he'd been one of a pair in his father's company and had never considered creating a separate family life for himself. Existence on board the keel had been sufficient in itself, and the intimacy of family life kept firmly within the cabin, to the exclusion of others who were thought of as mere passers-by.

Now, with his future still uncertain, the thought of battling on alone once Maggy and Patrick went home offered little comfort to him. His unexpected encounter with Lily had left him disappointed with himself, so that he was a little afraid to face her again. What he'd admired from a distance had been something of a shock when it was placed before him! She was a 'looker', that was plain to see; however, she had the power to make him tongue-tied and clumsy, like a fool. Instead of looking forward to seeing the *Mary Ann* again he now quite dreaded doing so.

Pushing these thoughts to one side he re-boarded the keel and sat for a while on the hatch cover, listening to the sounds of the town and dockland around him. Finally, with a slight shiver he rose and joined the others below in the cabin.

As arranged, Erik arrived on the dock-side next morning promptly at seven, in time to sail when the lock opened at eight. He was accompanied by his wife and family, and was pushing a wheel-barrow which held a small well-worn trunk containing everything he felt he would need for what was a comparatively short inland journey. Crossing the decks of the two keels which separated them, Michael joined the party and spoke to Mrs Erikson before saying 'Hello' to her excited children.

A shy-looking young woman stood near them, and Michael took her to be one of the many curious bystanders who were always drawn to the water's edge. Taking no heed of her he was quite surprised when Erik turned suddenly and drew her forward, saying, 'This is my daughter Anna,' to which the quiet figure nodded and smiled demurely. However, before Michael could say or do anything her father said, laughingly, 'She'd make you a very good wife, no?' At this the young woman's face flushed crimson with embarrassment and she lowered her eyes to avoid his gaze.

Michael was somewhat disconcerted and embarrassed himself at this remark but he managed to smile sympathetically and nodded amicably to her, even though she was probably oblivious to the fact. He fervently hoped that Erik wouldn't make a habit of being so outspoken, and it was perhaps fortunate at this point that the big man spotted Maggy on the deck of the keel and called out to her.

'Ah, Miss Havercroft—come and meet my Anna!' he cried out, beckoning to her. Pleased to be included in the gathering, Maggy did as he asked and when she reached them was amused when he said, mockingly, 'They have all come to make sure I am leaving, I think!'

In spite of his frankness, it was impossible not to like the man who obviously meant no harm, but he had inadvertently caused distress without meaning to do so. Michael thought it best to ease Miss Erikson's feelings by paying her no special attention at all, and this was a pity for she believed he was deliberately shunning her because of what her father had said.

Taking hold of one end of the trunk, Michael helped Erik carry it across to the *Maggie Kelly*, becoming aware as he did of the pungent odour of spices which surrounded it. This caused him to ponder on how far the trunk had travelled, and to what far countries? The smell tickled his nose, making him want to sneeze, but he daren't for fear of dropping the trunk onto the deck, or into the water, and he secretly wondered what Erik's reaction would have been, had such a disaster taken place!

Leaving the trunk in the fore cabin, they both returned to say farewell to the watching group on the dockside. Anna Erikson, however, having spoken briefly but cordially with Maggy, had then slipped quietly away leaving her a little disappointed and, of course, unaware of Mr Erikson's remark before her arrival.

It didn't take long for Erik to miss his daughter and he looked enquiringly at his wife, asking, 'Where is Anna?'

Turning and finding her daughter gone, Mrs Erikson was equally disturbed for Anna was a sensitive girl, sometimes a little too much for her own good. She knew that it had been wrong of her husband to tease his daughter in that way especially in front of strangers, but she said, concealing her disquiet, 'She must have gone to work'. Then, addressing Maggy particularly, she added, 'She really ought to have said good-bye but I expect we were all too busy to notice her going'. When Maggy then occupied herself with the children, Mrs Erikson stepped forward so that only her husband could hear her and said, quietly, 'Anna has gone, and you were wrong to embarrass her by talking of marriage. You embarrassed Mr Havercroft too, if I'm not mistaken'.

He looked startled. 'I wouldn't hurt my Anna!' he protested. 'I make a joke, that is all.' Beneath his breezy bluster she knew he was a soft and caring man, but occasionally he needed reminding that not everyone understood him as she did. 'You find her for me and tell her I'm sorry,' he said with a tremor in his voice, and he placed an arm around her waist. Looking keenly into his wife's eyes, he said, 'You take care now, whilst I am away'. For a moment he was almost childlike; then drawing himself up tall and straight he added, 'Now I must work! You take the children home'. He opened his arms wide to embrace all of them and was nearly knocked over as they all clamoured for a kiss. Ellen watched, her heart full, and she was pleased that he had found regular work and grateful that he wouldn't be forced to go to sea again. She felt little anxiety at this particular parting, only relief that life would be easier for a while.

At a distance, peering from behind the corner of a warehouse Anna watched her father, wishing she could hug him now as she had done as a child, but today he had hurt her more than he knew. She turned away and walked despondently along the cobbled streets to the tavern where, for little reward, she cleaned and scrubbed until her back ached.

From the deck of the keel Maggy watched the little family depart homewards, Johann pushing the wheel-barrow, the other two scampering ahead, their mother following behind at a more leisurely pace. She quite envied the children's youthful exuberance and wondered why Anna had disappeared so quickly after such a short meeting. In greeting Maggy she had betrayed a timidness which was puzzling, for she had a comely face beneath her straw bonnet and hair of almost flaxen colour which was quite attractive. Given time Maggy felt she could befriend her, but much would depend on Michael's health and his approval of Mr Erikson's capabilities as mate.

With everyone now back on board, the two men and Patrick prepared to move the keel into position for the opening of the lock gates, and Erik looked intently at the sky. The day had dawned tolerably bright and a fair wind blew, so with luck he estimated they might reach the River Trent by lunchtime. However, as time went on a frown appeared on his face. 'That's a worried sky,' he said to Michael as they waited to leave with other vessels.

'You know the conditions here better than I,' Michael replied, knowing that the weather was unpredictable and fickle with its blessing, 'Do you think it'll hold Erik?'

His new mate shrugged his shoulders. 'Often when the tides change the weather changes, sometimes for the better, sometimes for the worse—we'll see!'

'Do you think we will understand each others sailing methods sufficiently well to cope with any trouble that may occur?' Michael asked, not doubting the man's skill with the keel but anticipating the possibility of a mishap, or something which might lead to a tragedy in the Humber.

'Whatever you say, I do,' Erik replied, meaningfully. 'We can't hang around hoping for perfect weather. Trust me!'

Michael felt foolish, for he'd sailed these waters all his life albeit under his father's direction. He smiled nervously at the big, capable Norwegian. 'My father's death has shaken me,' he said, trying to explain away his doubts. 'Previously I've respected the Humber, not feared it.'

A look of understanding crossed Erik's face. 'It'll take a while, Mike,' he spoke kindly and reassuringly. 'I was also young when my father died in an accident. I grow up fast then, but for some time I am unable to trust my own judgement too. You do well to be cautious, many a loaded keel has sunk in a storm or broken her back after foundering on the shifting sandbanks. It is nerves, that is all.'

If being outspoken was Erik's only fault then Michael felt he could live with it, the strength of the man before him was comforting. For several minutes he stood staring down into the water, a lump in his throat; his father hadn't been a sentimental man but he had been the rock upon which Michael had perhaps relied too much. However, things were different now, nothing could change that.

The congestion of water traffic in the town docks was now the worst Michael had ever known, with every type of vessel from sloop to keel and sea-going ships, waiting impatiently for the lock-gates to open. 'This is going to take some time,' he grumbled to Erik as they waited in the middle of Junction Dock, powerless to do anything about it.

'It gets worse,' Erik replied with considerable irritation. 'We were hoping things would improve when the new dock across the river opened.'

'It was long overdue,' Michael commented, looking angrily at another vessel as it bumped against their protective fenders. 'This is going to cost us valuable sailing time, I'm afraid.'

After a long delay they eventually passed through the locks, and, once beyond the outer basin, the heavily laden keel heaved on the choppy water of the Humber, salty sea-spray wetting its decks. With all the hatches secure, and the sail set, the strength of the wind took them swiftly upstream. Although the estuary was very wide with the tide in, the deepest channel was quite narrow in places, and passed between various sand bars which had to be navigated with care.

Michael wasn't one to dislike a challenge, but the responsibility of having Patrick and Maggy on board concerned him greatly. In spite of this, the combination of wind and waves gave him a sense of freedom that nothing else could.

The ominous clouds which had troubled Erik earlier had soon blown away but now, unexpectedly, the sky became overcast again and a squall arose, so Erik relieved Michael at the tiller in order that he could help Patrick. The boy was as white as a sheet, his stomach heaving with every movement of the keel, so Michael tied him to the taffrail where he could vomit when he needed without being washed overboard. 'You'll be better up here in the fresh air rather than down below in the cabin,' he told the trembling lad, refraining from telling him the true state of affairs, that these conditions could continue all day, nor did he want him below in case the keel capsized.

With the tide now ebbing fast it was important that they should keep to the deeper channel, but this was becoming extremely difficult. It was too late even to find shelter, so there was nothing else to do but lower the sail and ride out the squall where they were. After dropping the bow anchor, Michael and Maggy fought the cold westerly wind and lashed the sail to the boom in a not too tidy fashion. This done, Michael took stock of the situation and realised that they had already drifted further than he would have liked due to the fierce buffeting they had received.

Unfortunately they were now in the narrow channel off Whitton Sands, a bank of mud and sand, the most dangerous part of the Humber. Although anchored, the keel still had to be steered in case she was hit broadside by turbulence and waves which could easily sink her. While Michael and Maggy constantly checked that the hatches and rigging were secure, Erik stood firmly at the tiller. For about an hour the wind roared about them and the waves sprayed the deck, whilst poor Patrick, secured by ropes, feared for his life, yet wanting only to die. 'Can I go below?' he begged when Michael came to see how he was faring.

'I'm sorry, lad,' Michael shouted, 'but if I open the cabin hatch now water might wash over the deck and get into the cabin.'

The fully laden keel was low in the water, with little more than eighteen inches of freeboard at its centre, and if the cabin or hull took in water then the extra weight could spell disaster. Wondering just how long the squall would continue, Michael decided to relieve Erik at the tiller for a while.

'I don't like it,' Erik commented as he passed the tiller over. 'We've been here too long, the tide is getting very low. I think we need to move further over to where the channel is deeper.'

Estimating their position between the sandbank and the distant shore, Michael agreed. 'I had hoped that the wind would have dropped by now, I don't think we've any choice but to try and move her. I'll tell Maggy, so take over again, give me a minute or two and I'll signal when I'm ready.' He walked cautiously for'ard to where Maggy was clinging to the rigging, taking care on the wet deck. Thinking he heard a strange sound he paused and looked aft to where Erik was standing, and was suddenly struck by the irony of the situation. Centuries earlier the Vikings had sailed these same waters, raiding and pillaging all before them from longboats with sails just like those of the keels. Today, there at the tiller of his keel stood yet another Nordic sailor, tall and proud as if invading yet again.

Seeing Michael hesitate, Maggy set off to meet him, wondering if something was wrong. Then the wind suddenly and unexpectedly changed direction, taking them by surprise and snatching violently at the keel, as Erik fought to hang on to the tiller and control it. It had been some time since he had faced such wild conditions and the strain on his arm muscles was making him tired. However, he was a strong man and knew that to let go would lead to a catastrophe.

The quick lurch of the keel took Maggy off guard, and she screamed and fell sideways, slipping on the wet decking. Realising that she was about to tumble overboard, she lashed out, clutching for something to hold onto but just missed the bow rail. Instead her hand seized a fender rope as she fell, taking the fender with her. She clung desperately to it, praying that she could hold on long enough for someone to help her.

As her piercing scream rent the air, Michael turned and saw her go over the rail into the turbulent water. Leaving Erik to struggle with the tiller he hurried along the side of the hull as fast as he could knowing that every second counted; there wasn't a moment to spare. If he couldn't pull her out before the current drew her away from them it would be too late! There was no time to fetch the boat hook so he knelt, anchoring himself with one hand on the rail and the other reaching out in an attempt to grab at Maggy's arm, but she was too far below. 'Hold on!' he yelled, desperately trying to reach her before the next gust of wind whipped against the keel.

Fear seized Maggy even more, and her fingers locked tight as she clung frantically onto the rope which secured the fender to the keel. Her clothes were heavy with water, dragging her body down and away with the current, while the waves splashed menacingly over her face, taking her breath away. She swallowed a mouthful of salty water, gulping, gasping, all sense of reality beginning to fade.

To extend his reach Michael threw himself full length along the narrow deck, hoping and praying that his awkward purchase between the gunwale and the hatch upstand would prevent him from falling into the water too. He managed from this position to just clutch Maggy's arm. 'Let go!' he shouted at her, 'let go!' But Maggy's fingers were rigidly clamped round the rope, in fear. He knew that if she stayed in the water much longer she would lose consciousness and could slip away from him. His body was now twisted awkwardly with a leg pressed tightly against the hatch, forming a wedge, thus giving him greater freedom of movement with his arms.

From this cramped position he stretched further down and seized her roughly with both hands. 'Let go, damn you!' he shouted harshly, as she still clung to the rope while he tried to pull her upwards. His grip bit so savagely into her flesh that her white, numbed fingers suddenly gave way. The unexpected weight of her body almost yanked Michael overboard as well but his leg held firm, giving him the leverage he needed. He was conscious of his own pain but there was nothing he could do to ease it. In desperation he pulled hard, seeming to draw on a hidden source of strength, and slowly Maggy's limp, sodden form came up out of the water and slumped onto the deck.

They lay exhausted for a while like this, unable to move, but at least he knew that she was alive. He could now feel the drag of the out-going tide pulling the keel against its anchor, and prayed that they were still in the deeper part of the channel.

Maggy moaned softly.

'Are you hurt?' Michael cried anxiously as he gathered his remaining strength in an effort to get closer to her. Then, shaking her gently with one hand he repeated the question.

'No!' she moaned, shivering from shock and clinging fiercely to him. 'I'm just so cold.'

'Thank God!' he sighed, and struggled to his feet, helping her up as he did so, but when his legs took the weight of both their bodies he winced and stumbled.

'What's the matter?' she cried in alarm, her eyes filling with tears as she looked at his worried face.

'I'm alright,' he lied, still aware of the pain in his leg but relieved that they were alive, and still afloat. He too was badly shaken by what had happened, but now he was becoming concerned for the safety of the keel, and turned to see if Erik was still at the tiller. He need not have worried on that score however; Erik was still there, outlined against the sky which appeared to show signs of lightening.

'Can you manage, Mike?' Erik called, anxiously craning his neck to see what had happened to Maggy. He had watched Michael's frantic actions, but from his position at the tiller had been powerless to help him. To have left his post could have resulted in a capsize and the death of them all.

Knowing that his answer would be snatched away by the wind Michael raised his hand, his thumb indicating success, and merely shouted back, 'YES!' Gritting his teeth he helped Maggy to sit on the hatch, thus releasing the pressure on his leg which he rubbed to ease the pain. His sleeves were wet and his arms cold, and he knew that Maggy in her sodden, clinging clothes must be suffering too. If she stayed on deck in such a state she would be vulnerable to the biting wind which was buffeting her numbed limbs, and could become ill from exposure. Obviously they might all be in danger now unless he could help Erik move the keel immediately, and this left him with two options, whether to leave Maggy on deck to suffer and perhaps become a liability, or send her below to change so that she could help. As she was now shivering violently he chose the latter. 'Get changed as quickly as you can, then come back up again,' he ordered, helping her towards their cabin, and loosening the hatch in readiness. 'NOW!' he yelled suddenly, after judging the force of the wind. 'Knock hard when you're ready to come out,' he said, lifting the hatch firmly with one hand and thrusting her roughly onto the ladder with the other. Once she was low enough he wasted no time in closing the hatch again, leaving Maggy to descend the ladder as best she could, her movements hampered by her wet, clinging skirt.

Moving to where Erik stood at the tiller, and limping badly with pain he could only gasp, 'Phew, that was close!' There was a catch in his voice and he was too shaken to conceal his discomfort.

'I cannot come to help, or we would have capsized,' Erik said, 'I am standing here helpless. And you, you have hurt yourself, no?'

Michael grimaced, it was no good trying to hide the fact that he was in difficulty. 'An old injury, I'm afraid,' he replied, playing it down and then grasped the tiller as Erik shifted his position. 'Are you alright?'

'Tired, but I'll live,' Erik answered, grinning. He'd been at the tiller for part of the journey up river and then had stood a further hour and a half in gruelling weather. However, it was no good complaining, that's how things were. 'The wind, she's slackening now, but I'm still worried in case we're out of the channel.'

Michael nodded. 'As soon as Maggy comes up I'll raise the sail if the wind continues to ease. I've told her to hurry.' He looked around at the swirling current which was still tugging them against the anchor. 'If I'd known we were going to be here this long I would have thought twice about dropping anchor at all,' he told Erik, who was flexing his wrists. 'What do you think?'

Suddenly there was a low sound that was just discernible, 'Is that Maggy knocking?' he asked.

'I don't think so,' Erik said nervously, 'I think we scrape the bottom!'

'Here! Quickly Erik, take the tiller again,' Michael cried, 'I'll untie Patrick and get Maggy out! They can raise the anchor as I try to pole her off.' The wind was dropping now, and this was just when they could have done with the sail to move them the few yards which would make all the difference. He breathed a sigh of relief as Maggy knocked hard and he immediately lifted the hatch to let her out. 'I'll untie Patrick', he cried. 'Take him and lift the anchor while I use the stower.'

Michael limped to where Patrick sat at the stern, his head down, utterly miserable and fortunately unaware of the tragedy which had nearly overtaken them. 'The wind's dropping,' he said, encouragingly, 'I want you to go and help Maggy with the anchor, it's not as rough now.' He felt sorry for his ashen-faced nephew who would probably never forgive him for tying him up. 'You've been very brave,' he said, as he released him. 'Here, Maggy, help him.' It had been conditions such as these which he'd imagined and dreaded encountering when on their way to Hull, situations which would have been beyond his physical powers to cope with on his own.

He seized the pole whilst Maggy and Patrick went to the for'ard windlass, then used all his strength to try and push the keel away from the treacherous sandbank.

There was a low, ominous dragging sound now and the keel shuddered. 'She's catching!' Michael shouted loudly, as he struggled against the odds. For several more minutes he strained hard but to no avail, as slowly the keel's motion ceased and her flat bottom stuck firmly on the bottom. They were grounded! It was a miracle that the keel was still fairly level, but they could do nothing now but wait in the hope that the next in-coming tide would lift them free. He watched helplessly as other vessels passed them by, unable to assist, knowing that they all ran the same risk of being grounded if they tried.

'It's no good!' Erik called out. 'We're stuck!' There was a note of resignation in his voice.

Michael nodded. 'We've a long wait for the next tide to refloat us!' he admitted, ruefully.

'We make the most of it until she floats again. Let's hope she's not sitting on mud.'

'God forbid!' Michael cried out, 'then we would have a problem.' If that were the case, and they were stuck hard on mud, when the tide did return it could immerse them completely. He'd heard of such incidents before. 'We'd better prepare the cog boat in case we have to abandon her, even though it will be dark.' There was a note of desperation in his voice.

'We prepare, yes?' Erik butted in, 'But it is unlikely in this spot. Just be ready that is all.' There was no nervousness in his voice or eyes and Michael relaxed a little.

'Thanks, Erik,' he said, acknowledging that without him they could have been lost. 'Dad and I never had trouble before, and I suppose it's just unfortunate that things went wrong today. I'm glad of your help.'

Maggy and Patrick had been unable to raise the anchor and stood pale-faced and anxious, looking first at Michael then at Erik, wondering what to do next. Fortunately there was no immediate danger from the out-going tide, and the heavy keel seemed not to be in a position even to roll or rock. 'Go below you two,' Michael called to them, 'get warm and dry, and get us all something hot to eat.'

'I'm sorry, Michael,' Maggy murmured tearfully, before she went below. 'Is it all my fault?'

'Of course not! It's nobody's fault, Maggy,' Michael reassured her. 'It was an unexpected twist of the wind that could have thrown the best of us. That's why we can't afford to take any risks at all, there are enough problems without that.' He looked at her carefully. 'Were you hurt when you fell?' he asked anxiously.

She shook her head, 'My arms ache where you grabbed me and my fingers are sore where the skin has gone, but I'm alright now.'

'Good girl!' He turned then to Patrick. 'I'm sorry you've had a rough time, lad, but I daren't risk you falling in or drowning if the keel sank when you were in the cabin. Both of you go below, you're safe enough now.' He watched the somewhat bedraggled pair until they were out of earshot, then turned to Erik. 'I don't understand it, Maggy's used to bad weather so I just hope she wasn't day-dreaming.' He caught Erik's sharp look and felt guilty, for he realised that it was he who had, in fact, been the one day-dreaming, not Maggy! Conditions had hardly allowed her to do so, and until that moment she'd done exactly what she'd been told. 'That was unfair of me,' he conceded, his face drawn and weary. 'It's no good blaming anyone is it!'

Erik leaned against the winch, his tall figure outlined against the sky. 'You were lucky this time,' he said, nodding, 'you go easy on the young ones, they are frightened.'

Michael considered his remark for a moment. 'You're right,' he sighed. 'Let's check everything over and then go below for a break. I think we deserve it, don't you?'

Despite the nagging ache in his leg, Michael knew that with barely three hours of daylight left they had much to do to ensure their safety, whatever happened. The sail took some sorting out and where it was strengthened at its edge by rope he found it needed some repair. Fortunately, the hatch covers had remained intact but the violent movement of the keel had caused crockery to fall to the floor in the cabin, which Maggy cleared up whilst the kettle was boiling. When she'd finished she took a mug of steaming hot tea to both Michael and Erik who were in earnest discussion on deck. She still felt a little shaky but showed a brave face to the men.

'Thanks, Maggy,' Michael said, looking to see if Patrick was out of earshot. 'Are you feeling better now?'

She nodded. 'It was horrible!' She shivered as she spoke. 'I hope that never happens again. I don't know how, after all these years, I could have been so clumsy.'

'We were very lucky,' he admitted, 'but now we've got another problem to worry about.'

'I know,' Maggy said. 'We're grounded. What are you going to do?' She'd realised what had happened immediately she felt and heard the grating on the hull but had said nothing to Patrick, behaving as if all was well. Of course he knew that she'd fallen into the water, but not just how close she'd been to drowning, and he certainly had no idea that they were in danger now.

'I don't want to frighten Patrick,' he said, in a low voice. 'We're hoping to re-float on the incoming tide, but we have to prepare in case the keel won't lift off. It's going to be dark in a couple of hours or so, and everything possible has to be done by then. After that we've no choice but to sit and wait it out with the cog boat ready, as the tide comes in.'

Erik then commented hopefully, 'If she's on sand, and we can pole her, we might be able to get into deeper water where we can anchor again until dawn, Mike. How many stowers have you?'

'Two,' Michael replied. 'But I think she might lift once the water's deep enough anyway, without poling. Let's hope so!'

'Ach, No!' Erik said, politely but firmly, shaking his head. 'We'd better think the worst. If she is on mud then we've no chance, but if it is sand we must try to push her off, maybe.'

Pondering this for only a moment, Michael agreed. 'The best thing then, is for Maggy and Patrick to sit in the cog with a couple of lanterns. If at the last minute the keel doesn't rise, we'll join them and sit it out until daylight. It could be a long, cold and uncomfortable night, so let's just pray that the weather isn't too rough. At dawn we'd get picked up by a passing boat, but we must leave a marker attached to the keel or else someone could come a cropper on her during high tide.'

'What shall I tell Patrick?' Maggy asked anxiously.

'Just don't tell him how bad things are. At least the wind is dropping now, what we don't want is for the tide to bring fog with it, that could be nasty. If the *Maggie* does float quickly we must control her straight away, so we'll put a stern anchor out as well.'

'I think it will be about nine o'clock that we might have to abandon her,' Erik cautioned, looking at his pocket watch. 'The lights of Whitton village, they give us a bearing.' He looked across the broad stretch of water towards the bank where a cluster of houses lay behind a swathe of marshy foreshore.

'Right! Now we know what we're up against, Erik and I will repair the sail. Maggy, you've got time to cook us a good hot meal, and that should keep us going through the night. Erik and I will see to everything else on deck. Just let Patrick be for a while, he can come up and help if he likes but don't say anything, he's had a bad enough fright as it is.' Then, softening his voice, he added, 'That was a close thing earlier, Maggy. I'm sorry if I hurt your arms'.

She smiled weakly, 'I thought you'd never get me out!'

'I thought that way too,' he acknowledged, his face very grim, 'I really did!' Then, cheering up a little he said, 'Be a good lass, and bring us a bite to eat while we're waiting for dinner.'

After Maggy had gone below, Erik remarked to Michael, 'She's a brave one, your sister. If she's frightened she doesn't show it.'

Michael laughed. 'I almost forget she's now a grown woman,' he said, as he attached a longer line between the keel and the cog boat which, when paid out, would allow it to float above the keel yet remain tethered to it should she be submerged. 'This way we'll stay moored in one place rather than be taken along by the current in the dark.'

'I'll fasten something to the mast to mark her position anyway,' Erik added. 'Then I do anything else you need.'

'I must mend the sail first in the hope that we can move on tomorrow. Will you top up all the lanterns and then come and help me sort things out?'

'I do this, then if you do not mind I get a few precious things in a bundle.' Erik paused and looked around him. 'At least the wind has dropped now,' there was a note of relief in his voice. 'We make it or I am very disappointed! I have survived worse things than this in my life, I'm not going to be beaten now.'

As twilight deepened, Michael made one final check on everything they had prepared and settled down to wait for the remaining time to pass. He rested his leg which he rubbed with liniment hoping to ease the toothache-like pain. Every so often the keel creaked as it settled, and at every sound Michael and Erik exchanged worried glances. Under these conditions it was impossible to relax, so as time went by the atmosphere in the cabin became strained and Patrick began to realise that there was something wrong. Michael had already explained to him exactly what to do with the cog boat in an emergency, though he hadn't added that one might occur that very evening. He had more to think about than having a terrified lad on his hands whilst they waited.

Patrick suddenly spoke up. 'I'll be glad when it's daylight and we can get away from here. It will float, won't it, Mike?' His voice faltered and he went on, 'I know what's going on, you know, I'm a bit frightened. I don't like dark water at night.' His eyes were wide with fear, seeking reassurance.

Accepting that he couldn't protect the boy any longer, and knowing he owed it to Patrick's intelligence to give him a straight answer, Michael decided to be honest. 'You'd best know the truth, Patrick,' he said, not unkindly. 'If the *Maggie Kelly* won't lift with the tide, and there's no reason why she shouldn't do,' his confidence hardly matched his words, 'then we can't sit down here because she'll fill up with water. Instead, we would simply sit in the cog until someone picks us up in the morning. That's all!'

Patrick listened, watching Michael's face for signs of doubt there. 'Don't worry,' Michael added cheerily, trying to calm him. 'We'll be alright. It's losing the keel and cargo that would be a disaster. Just think, once you're home you'll see this as a great adventure to tell your friends about.'

Patrick's face suddenly came to life, his voice filled with indignation as he exclaimed vehemently, 'I won't! I'll never come on another boat as long as I live! And how Granddad stuck it all his life I don't know!' His voice suddenly broke, 'I want to go home!' His head dropped with misery as he sat there.

'Calm down, calm down,' Erik broke in quietly, understanding that fear could drive Patrick towards hysteria. 'I have sailed the seas and oceans of the world all my life, I never came to harm, and look at me!' He had a broad beaming smile on his face, 'Now would I sit here like this if I was worried? I have been on big ships and small ships, I catch whales, and have sailed through dangerous seas full with islands of ice bigger than the ship I am on.' He paused, looking directly at Patrick who had now managed to control his emotions. 'I tell you a story,' he said, and, turning to Michael he winked knowingly and asked, 'That alright, Mike?'

'Of course!' Michael replied, relieved that the older man understood the workings of a young mind better than he did.

Scratching his beard with his index finger, Erik began. 'When I am eighteen I go to sea to make money and leave my beautiful Norway with her high mountains and deep fjords full of salmon. Of course, there are some things I don't miss, in the winter it is only daylight for a few hours, and in summer midges are everywhere. On the ship I know nothing and the sailors tease me, but I laugh and take good part. I catch whales as big as houses.' He paused, then chuckled, 'Well, perhaps a little smaller. Then I go to China, where the men have slanting eyes and the women have feet so small that they would fit in your pocket.'

Maggy interrupted, 'Why? Why have they got such small feet?'

'Ah,' Erik explained. 'They bind the little girl's feet with bandages so that they stay small.'

'But why?' Maggy persisted, a look of disbelief on her face.

Erik grinned mischievously. 'So they don't run away from their husbands! You, I think, have big feet and run too fast!'

Maggy returned his grin, well aware that he was teasing her. 'Go on,' she said with a wry smile.

'I have seen red-skinned Indians in America with men's scalps hanging from their belts, and other places where men live in houses made of snow.' Patrick's eyes were watching him now, and Erik knew he had to go on, even if it was necessary to stretch the truth a little here and there, as a distraction. 'I have been places where it is too hot for things to grow, and others where it rains at the same time every day. Places where men eat each other, and Ireland where there are little folk only as big as my hand.' Maggy giggled, having heard of leprechauns from her grandmother, and wondered just how far Erik had really travelled.

He carried on, 'Then I come to Hull where the rats were as big as cats, and they nibbled your toes at night.' He saw a smile on Patrick's face, and was pleased with his success as a story teller. 'I came first with the iron-ore ships and meet a beautiful mermaid; my Ellen. I go to sea and come back many times, but always to my Ellen and so we have seven children and one more to come.'

'Where are the other children?' Maggy asked, intrigued to learn more of Erik's family, 'I have only seen four of them.'

'You meet Anna, Kristen, Johann and Lucy.' His face suddenly became grim. 'My darling Sonja died two years past, of the cholera. She would have been fifteen.' He sighed. 'She is safe now, in Heaven.' He looked older now, and the merry twinkle had gone from his eyes.

'I'm sorry,' Maggy whispered sadly, feeling for him.

'Thank you!' he responded. Then, remembering his task was to provide distraction, not sadness, he continued. 'I have two grown sons. Harold is away on a whaling ship and Olaf, my Ollie, is a sailor too but now he is in California to find gold.'

Patrick's attention was now well and truly captured. 'Is there really gold in California?' he asked enthusiastically, then, as an afterthought asked, 'Where is California?'

Not wanting Patrick to get fanciful ideas, Michael butted in at this point. 'On the far side of America. Can you imagine sailing for several weeks just to get to the East Coast and then travelling many more weeks overland as well?' Patrick's face fell at this remark.

'Especially if you not find gold either,' Erik agreed with an impish smile. 'I would tell Ollie all this but he goes straight from Australia across the Pacific Ocean to get there. Besides, it is too late to save my *Martha Jane*, she belongs to someone else now. If I had changed her name, perhaps my luck it would have changed too!'

'Perhaps your son will find gold!' Maggy replied hopefully. 'What would you do then, buy another keel?'

Erik shrugged his shoulders. 'That I don't know. My Ollie is very like me, tall and fair, with the need to be a big man too. I think perhaps I get in his way. Perhaps he never comes back.'

For a minute or so there was silence in the cabin as the four reflected on different things. It was broken when Erik took out his pocketwatch, and held it towards a lantern. 'I think soon we must prepare. The tide she is lapping stronger now, yes, Mike?'

Realising that Erik's stories had distracted them all, Michael said, 'I'll go up and see.' He lifted down one of the lanterns and as he climbed the ladder, added, 'It might also be best if we have a hot drink beforehand, Maggy, then secure everything down here. Will you collect anything valuable and our spare clothing into a bundle ready to put into the cog. If the worst comes to the worst we might be able to salvage some other stuff later.'

Once on deck he studied the speed at which the incoming tide was running, its wavelets shimmering in the moonlight. He was grateful for the comforting light given by the moon and stars, and their brilliance and beauty humbled him. Water held no fear for Michael, no matter how dark or turbulent it was, he'd known nothing else all his life. Tonight, in the silvery light, the keel was merely a long dark silhouette and with a sigh he realised that if she refused to refloat then all would be lost; his home, the cargo, and worst of all she would probably be beyond recovery. Whereas only a short while ago his future was bleak, without the keel there would be nothing at all!

The tide was no longer rippling gently against the vessel's side but slapping it strongly. His hand shook nervously as he shortened the cog line a little, keeping the smaller boat closer as the tide rose higher. 'Please God, let her float,' he begged, in a silent prayer. All around was shadowy, unreal, the silence broken only by the sound of the water. How many times had he stood like this, with his father, taking a final breath of air before retiring for the night? It had been an enjoyable habit of theirs, but Michael had to remind himself that he was now alone, on the brink of ruin, if not worse. The responsibility for everyone aboard, to their families at home in Dalton and Hull, weighed heavily on his mind.

In his preoccupation with these terrible thoughts he failed to hear the movement behind him, and it was only when Erik spoke that Michael realised he was there.

'The night is beautiful, is she not?' Erik said, wistfully. 'I watch you for several minutes now, seeing your troubles lying heavy on you.'

'Yes,' Michael admitted, glumly. 'Shortly, no matter how calm the sea is now, we may be forced to put our lives at risk and there is nothing that you or I can do to prevent it.'

'I think of my Ellen and the unborn child,' Erik confessed, handing Michael the tea which Maggy had made. 'To have her here beside me now would be a pleasant thing, if it were not for the danger.' He fell silent for a moment, then asked, 'You have no wife, no children, I think?'

Michael stared out across the water, 'No, nobody but my mother,' he answered sadly.

'But there is Maggy and Patrick also,' Erik reprimanded him quietly. 'They look to you with trust and affection.'

To this Michael could give no reply, and merely said, 'Before long they will go their own way and I shall carry on alone.'

'I think,' Erik continued gently, 'your father is heavy on your mind tonight. He would want you to be strong. Come, it is nearly time, we will beat this thing together, you and me. Me for my family and you for your people, no?'

Michael turned and smiled at him. 'Yes, you're right, we must do our best for them all.' He paused, then with a tightness in his throat, said, 'If we do survive this, I really do believe we could work together, don't you?'

Erik chuckled good naturedly. 'You may live to regret those words, Mike, I am a strange man sometimes.'

Supping the last of his tea Michael went below to where two young people waited anxiously for him to say something. He found it hard to appear cheerful and difficult to lie, even more so to brush aside his own fears.

'How much longer, Mike?' Patrick's now steadier voice interrupted his thoughts.

Taking care to conceal his doubts, he replied, 'About an hour, it being a clear, moonlit night will make it easier but we still can't take any risks. If the keel doesn't move before the deck is awash we'll get into the cog with you two. Keep sculling her clear Maggy, until I tell you to pass the boat-hook out to me, and even then don't stand up, we'll do the rest. Remember to hold on tight as she lifts, as the cog will be jerked about but she won't sink.'

Maggy rose and took the mug from him. He hardly recognised her, clad as she was in a pair of his corduroy trousers pulled tight at the waist with string to keep them up. With her hair concealed beneath a knitted scarf and his Guernsey jumper on, she could easily have been mistaken for a youth. 'You don't look much of a catch like that, Sis,' he commented with a grin. 'But at least you'll be warm, and safer than in a skirt.'

She touched the scarf instantly, as if by adjusting it her appearance improved. 'I realised earlier that if I went into the water again in a skirt it would drag me down. You don't mind me borrowing these do you?'

'It's a bit late to ask,' he chuckled, then added cynically, 'at least if the keel goes under I've got another pair of trousers left.' He saw Patrick's eyes widen at this remark, and gave him a quick knowing wink.

'Hello, there!' came Erik's voice from above. 'I've lashed the tiller, and put the stern anchor over. I think it is time to stand by now.'

'Thanks, Erik, we're coming up,' Michael called back, before speaking directly to Maggy. 'Now, Maggy, I've explained what you're to do. If the keel does move, stay in the cog until I relieve you; don't get confident and try anything else. I'll decide if and when to abandon her.' Maggy nodded, understanding perfectly well what he wanted of her, and why. He turned to Patrick, 'We might be some time at the ready, Patrick, so don't panic, just do as Maggy tells you and wait. The tide won't obey us, and you two are our only hope of safety if the worst happens. I know you can do it, just stay there with the line payed out, as I said, to allow the cog to lift with the rising water, but close enough for me to reach the boat-hook.' He couldn't help but feel sorry for the lad but he daren't show it for fear of unnerving him further. 'Another foot of tide and it should be at the level when we grounded; after that Erik and I will push and pray like mad. Right, up on deck you go.'

Maggy climbed purposefully up the ladder, while Michael had to assist Patrick who seemed to freeze on the top rung. 'Go on,' he said, calmly, although he knew time was precious now. Once on deck, he took the lad's arm and helped him down into the cog which floated about three feet below them. 'I'll keep hold of you, but mind the oar,' he warned. 'Now sit there while Maggy gets in, and I'll pass the lantern and boat-hook. Don't do anything from now on, except keep your position and see to the line.'

Together, Michael and Erik stood poised near the stern, each with a long pole, waiting tensely for the moment when the water reached the level it had been when they first settled on the bank. Neither man spoke. Michael could almost hear his heart beating and he knew that his breathing was erratic. Every nerve in his body was taut, and seemed to scream, 'Come on! Come on!' Sweat began to run freely down his face yet he felt cold as his hands clutched the long pole. With each fresh swirl of the tide Michael expected to feel the keel lift and float, but she didn't. 'Patience! Have patience,' he kept repeating over and over in his head. He was also unaware that he was chewing his lip until a strange taste appeared on his tongue. It was then that he realised that his teeth had punctured the tender skin of his mouth. 'Damn!' he exclaimed, trying to swallow the blood.

'It's not too late,' Erik called out from nearby, thinking Michael had given up.

Michael could hear the keel creaking with the strain and he listened hard, knowing that the water must be exerting enormous pressure on it. His nerves were jangling with fear, a fear which had the power to paralyse him. Taking a deep breath to calm himself, he looked towards Erik to make sure he was ready. The creaking became more frequent and louder. 'Oh, God, don't let her break apart,' he gasped, as the waves slapped harder on the stern, and spray came over the taffrail. 'Now! Erik!' he shouted. 'She must move soon!'

In unison both men slid their poles down into the water until they touched the bottom, then, heaving with every possible ounce of their strength, they endeavoured to push the *Maggie Kelly's* stern sideways into the channel. Nothing moved, and the tide lapped further and further up the hull.

'Next time there's a swell,' Michael shouted out almost angrily, and rested for a moment. He waited until he saw another surge of water approaching them. 'NOW!' he yelled, and once again the two men heaved against the poles with all their might. Had the tremendous weight of the keel sunk it too deeply into the bank for it ever to come free?

Michael felt his strength ebbing away, and knew he had little reserve of energy left with which to push.

'She's going, I think!' Erik's breathless voice called out suddenly. 'Keep pushing, Mike!'

Michael summoned up what was left of his strength and with one desperate thrust he felt a slight tremor and the keel suddenly shot upwards like a sounding whale. Both men staggered, clutching the taffrail for support. The keel jerked and swayed between its two anchors for a few moments, then its motion settled to a gentle sway and pitch. A wave of nausea welled up in Michael's stomach and he felt as weak as a kitten. He was now conscious of the pain in his leg and he sat down heavily on the hatch, knowing that he mustn't give in until Maggy and Patrick were safe from harm, but he felt quite unable to stand up and pull them alongside. Nevertheless, he tried to rise but couldn't.

Sensing Michael's difficulties, Erik called out to Maggy, 'Are you alright, Maggy?' Hearing they were both safe, he turned to Michael and said, 'I take over now, you rest that leg of yours.'

'Thanks Erik,' Michael replied. 'I couldn't have managed without your help.' Although his voice was full of gratitude his face was racked with pain. 'Can you help Maggy and Patrick back on board?' he gasped.

'You're injured!' Erik stated, 'Is it your leg?'

'Yes, I'm afraid it won't take any weight. Get those two aboard first, I'll stay here.' If it wasn't one problem it was another, he thought, watching Erik pull on the cog rope and take hold of the boat-hook which Maggy held out.

'Come on boy,' Erik said encouragingly, stretching a hand out to Patrick. 'We make it without much trouble. Now, hold tight and climb up slowly.' When at last Patrick was safely on deck he was trembling. 'You've done a good job, boy, you be fine now.'

'I've got a drop of brandy, Erik, Maggy will give him some of that, he'll be alright,' Michael said, as Erik helped Maggy aboard with their belongings. 'Now, let's get down into the cabin to warm up.' Michael could barely stand and had to be helped down into the cabin, and for once in his life he drank sufficient brandy to kill the pain. The relief this gave made him realise how exhausted he really was, and he started to doze.

'Let him be,' Erik advised Maggy. 'Tomorrow he will be better off for it. You, me and the boy, we can move the keel by ourselves before the tide turns again.'

'Thank you, she replied. 'We owe a lot to you.'

'It's nothing, he said quietly. 'But Captain Mike, he is a good sailor, no?'

The sleeping crew of the *Maggie Kelly* woke at daylight to find a cold drizzle falling, but such was their relief at not having spent the night exposed in the small boat that this seemed of little importance. Even the muddy grey river and the prospect of a dismal day did not quell their optimism. All that remained now was to wait for the wind to pick up and they could continue their journey.

Michael knew they had been extremely lucky to have come through the night's ordeal without serious mishap. What he needed now was a relatively straightforward day, one in which they could move into the safety of the Trent, and then into the canal.

Even Patrick was somewhat cheerful as he said in his youthful way, when assisting Michael to prepare for the journey, 'I'd not thought much about the weather before. Only a few days ago I was roasted when we hauled the keel in the hot sun, and now look at it!'

'That's where people make a mistake, Patrick. You'll learn never to trust the weather. Within ten minutes the change can be so violent as to be dangerous. Now then, am I forgiven for tying you up yesterday?'

Patrick mumbled something beneath his breath, to which Michael responded with a chuckle, 'So you'll not be wanting to come again?'

'No fear!' came the emphatic reply.

'Do you know something?' Michael said seriously. 'You've been a great help, and there's not many lads new to the water who would have been so courageous.'

At these words, Patrick looked directly into Michael's face and said, 'I'm going to visit Granddad's grave when I get back. I've only just realised how hard he worked and how brave he must have been!' It was a simple statement, and one which took Michael by surprise. He accepted then that if nothing else had come out of the trip it had made quite a man of Patrick.

With little or no wind they were temporarily becalmed, and as everything was as ready as could be for moving on at the first opportunity, there was little point in standing around on deck getting wet. 'Join us below and have a mug of tea,' he said to Erik, who was heading for his own cabin.

'That will be good,' the mate replied, happy to enjoy their company.

As they sat on the lockers they were in far better spirits than on the previous evening, even Patrick seemed more forthcoming than usual, and asked Erik, 'Have you really seen all those things you were telling us about last night?'

Erik grinned at him. 'You think I lie?' he asked.

Patrick's face flushed. 'N,n,no, I didn't mean that,' he stuttered, clearly embarrassed at his own question.

'No matter,' Erik laughed. 'Some I see, some I hear about from other sailors.' He touched his trouser pocket. 'Here, my Ollie writes telling me about America.' He drew out a letter. 'Anna read it to me, I can only just write my own name.'

'Maggy can read real well,' Patrick announced proudly. 'She could read it for you.'

'No, she couldn't,' Michael broke in. 'That's Mr Erikson's private business, Patrick.'

Waving the well-creased letter, Erik ignored this comment and continued, 'I would much like her to, if she doesn't mind.'

Maggy felt quite honoured to be asked to do such an important task. Besides, it would be the first proper letter she had ever read! 'Of course I don't mind, I would like to help you,' she offered, holding out a hand.

With a tingle of excitement she took the letter and carefully unfolded its pages, marvelling at its length and the clear bold handwriting. There was a smell of tobacco from the paper and she tried to imagine if the writer, Ollie Erikson, was like his father.

As if reading her thoughts Erik apologised. 'You forgive the smell but I keep my pipe in that pocket.'

Maggie felt a little disappointed at this disclosure, for with it he had destroyed the tantalising image she had momentarily created. Slowly and with only slight hesitation, as she was not used to reading out loud, she spoke the first few lines. Then, becoming absorbed in the contents and forgetting herself completely, she became more fluent.

Her voice was quiet but clear, and it dawned on Michael that Maggy was worthy of a brighter future than the one she appeared destined to attain.

Erik listened, wondering again if his eldest son would ever return, now that he had apparently found gold.

California
December 5th, 1850.

Dear Father, Mother, brothers and sisters,
*   At last you are to hear from me. I finally arrive in the Port of San Francisco per the Barque Indiana, after a very long and tedious journey from Sydney. I worked my passage on various vessels, much of the happenings I will tell you about when I eventually come home. I did fall in with a man on board who taught me to be more cautious with my friendship in future. My lesson, once learned, was not to be so trusting, and now I feel I am more prepared for whatever lies ahead. I keep my money about my person and tell no one about it. This should protect me from clever rogues and carpetbaggers.*

We disembarked here in early September and pitched a tent on the beach where stood hundreds of others. After roaming about for several days I took a situation for a while before sailing for the mines, arriving in Sacramento City in five days, quite safely, and in good health. Several of us engaged a wagon and proceeded at once to the mines known as Dry Creek where we arrived after four days journey and pitched our tents. We amused ourselves on the first day watching the operations of others, the day after we commence working for ourselves in right good earnest.

I soon left the party and dug on my own account, which suited me better. I dug near to a very ladylike female digging, the wife of an old doctor who together came across the plains from the State of Missouri. I spent a pleasant evening with them before moving next day further into the hills to dig. For several weeks I did well taking care not to let anyone know that I had found anything at all. Many others found little, not enough to pay their way or they spent what they got shortly after finding it.

Patrick sat enthralled, visualising what he heard, his mind no longer in the cabin but in some distant place. Maggy read on:

I had thought to go on to Oregon but haven't yet decided what to do. The conditions here are both dangerous and hard. Two years ago a party of emigrants crossed the plains late in the season and were caught in a fall of snow before they crossed the Sierra Nevada mountains. They numbered about twenty-five, and decided to pitch their tents for the night, unfortunately during the night seven foot of snow fell and they had to dig themselves out. Their oxen were buried without trace in the snow. They remained cut-off in this dreadful situation until their provisions ran out, then came starvation. They even considered eating each other and by the time an expedition found them only two poor creatures, girls of about seventeen years, survived, quite insane and had been living on human flesh.

Here Maggy stopped abruptly, deeply shocked by what she had read, as were Michael and Patrick. After a little while, she continued.

The girls recovered their senses and are well apparently.
In crossing the land there is great hardship and privation. There are tribes of Indians who have men's scalps tied to their waists and wild animals attack them and there is no food for

many miles for their cattle. I was told recently by a traveller just arrived that on crossing the plain he had seen nineteen hundred graves, many with two or three bodies in them, and thousands of animal carcasses. Supplies of every kind had been abandoned by bands of emigrants along the tracks. I should return the long way round, if I came, past the Horn. It is safer and that way I can work my passage to save money.

I do not recommend anyone to come to California, it is such a lottery. The climate is not over good and the price of everything fluctuates dramatically from day to day, week to week. A fortune can be made or lost overnight, without being careless. I don't believe I shall stay away very long as the life doesn't suit me, but I do not intend to return penniless.

There are men of every nation here, I favour the Chinese best, being the most honest and punctual. The French are industrious, the Spanish lazy and there are many Irish, but not many English. I suppose that will change.

I often think about you all, especially Father and Hal on the keel, water has more attraction for me than dry wild land. I understand a post wagon is leaving tomorrow for the East and so this may be my last chance to write for some time.

My kindest love to you all, especially Mother.

Your son Ollie.

'I think he makes a lot of money and stays there,' Erik sighed wistfully, taking the letter back from Maggy and returning it gently to his pocket. 'Thank you for reading it to me' he said with a smile, 'you are a bright girl.'

The spirit of elation which she'd felt in reading the letter subsided, leaving Maggy with a strange feeling of emptiness. 'Who is Hal?' she asked casually.

'He is my other son, Harold. He worked on the *Martha Jane* with me, but when I sell her he goes with the whaling ships, but that is a dying trade too. Where will it all end?' he queried, not really expecting an answer as none of them were in a position to recognise or even understand the rate of progress that was overtaking their world. 'Everything is getting faster; travel, machines, and I can see steam taking over completely from sail in the end.'

'Don't say that,' Michael complained, although he could see some truth in Erik's words.

'But imagine not having to rely on the wind or the currents, and never to be becalmed.' Erik seemed almost to welcome such changes. 'We do not haul or use the horse again for pulling.'

'They'll always need horses,' Patrick piped up, full of confidence.

'In that I think maybe you are right.' Erik agreed with a smile.

At this Michael rose and, followed by Erik, went up on deck where he concluded there was now enough wind for them to set sail. 'It's time we went,' he informed Erik. 'The topsail will provide a boost. Let's go.'

It wasn't long before the keel left the Humber and started moving up the Trent to Keadby where the canal started. This was a great relief to Michael who was looking forward to the easier sailing conditions in the still waters of the canal. Whilst the drizzle had now stopped, it was still very damp with a grey overcast sky through which only an occasional glimpse of the sunlight could be seen. Remarkably, from this point their journey went without mishap, and to Erik the venture into new territory was a small but interesting change. He and Maggy worked well together, allowing Michael to rest his leg, and by late afternoon they reached Thorne. They soon settled down for the evening but Michael was disappointed at seeing no sign of the *Mary Ann* amongst the other keels along the bank side. Although he made no mention of this, he continued watching out for her and could not help wondering if and when she would pass by. He was anticipating this moment with mixed feelings. Prior to his recent meeting with Lily, his attitude had been one of indifference to women, but since then he had begun to allow himself the luxury of speculation. Circumstances had changed, leaving his emotions a combination of bewilderment and anxiety. He couldn't simply nod at her when they saw each other again, nor just admire her from a distance when she waved from the deck of her father's keel, as she had previously done. Somehow though, he hadn't felt entirely comfortable in her company, due no doubt to his own shortcomings, she on the other hand had been friendly enough! In spite of these confused thoughts and misgivings, it was impossible for him to suppress a warm surge of anticipation at the thought of seeing her once more.

His preoccupation must have been obvious to Maggy for she asked if anything was amiss, to which the answer was a short uncommunicative 'No!' Understanding him so well, she knew exactly when he wanted to be left alone with his thoughts, so went below to cook dinner for them all.

As darkness fell, Michael's disappointment at not seeing the *Mary Ann* made him quiet and withdrawn. Seeing this, Erik thought it best to retire to his own cabin where he stayed for a while before emerging to ask if anyone minded him going off for a drink at the nearby inn. Realising that whatever his feelings were about the *Mary Ann* there was no point in spoiling the evening for everyone else, Michael offered to accompany Erik and introduce him to some of the other boatmen.

Before too long, the atmosphere of the Ship Inn mellowed Michael's thoughts and he found Erik's company a good distraction. Much later, however, as he settled down for the night, he reflected that Erik had quite a way with him and concluded that people either liked him instantly at first meeting, or they did not. He was certainly a man of strong character, and one who knew his job and got on with it, without the need of persuasion.

The following day, without realising it, Michael watched the approach of every keel in the hope that he would see Lily again. When they reached Stainforth they left the cog boat and lee boards in storage once more, and soon entered the River Don. He'd been busy in the cabin below for several minutes when Maggy suddenly called out, 'The *Mary Ann's* ahead, do you want a word?'

In his haste to climb on deck he nearly slipped, and to Lily on the other keel he must have appeared like a jack-in-the-box from the hatchway. As usual she waved enthusiastically in their direction, full of life, her hair blowing in the wind as the two vessels passed each other. She traversed the length of the *Mary Ann* breathlessly chatting all the while to Maggy, her eyes glancing frequently towards Michael as he stood near Erik at the tiller.

'Hello, Mike,' Lily called with a bright smile as she drew level with him. 'Here, catch this!' She laughed, tossing him the object she had been holding ready.

Surprised, and not knowing what it might be, Michael raised his hand and deftly caught it.

'Mornin', Swifty called out as he too drew level with Michael as he examined his catch.

'Oh, morning,' Michael hailed back, somewhat distracted by Lily's action. He then saw her waving happily to him as the distance between them quickly lengthened. Raising his hand in a friendly manner he waved back, and laughed.

Maggy had watched all this with some amusement, and remarked with a knowing look, 'So! That's how it is!'

'Get on with you,' he replied, glancing at her. 'You've got too much imagination for your own good.' He was not a little embarrassed by the turn of events, and had difficulty in marshalling his thoughts.

'Well, what did she throw you?' Maggy asked impatiently, watching his flushed face.

Looking at the lump of coal clenched in his hand, he grinned, 'It's only a piece of coal, what did you expect it to be?' Disappointment was written clearly on Maggy's face now and he laughed. 'She's young and likes teasing, that's all, so don't go reading something into it that's not there. Now, can we get on with things?'

Maggy let the matter drop and returned to hanging the washing from a line attached to the mast, while Michael mused on Lily's strange action. Now he would probably have to wait another ten days before their paths crossed again.

As if to compensate for their misfortunes during the previous few days, the weather was now mild, bright and good for sailing, and the *Maggie* made good progress towards home. The nearer they approached, the more an air of relaxed anticipation came over them, and this did not pass unnoticed by Erik. 'Is good to have a happy ship,' he commented to Michael in a quiet moment. 'I can tell, the young ones are joyful again.'

'Yes,' Michael replied thoughtfully. 'But it's been a difficult trip, and one I would not like to repeat.'

'The lightning, it never strikes twice' Erik said, trying to reassure him. They were leaving Mexborough now and under tow once again, but this time by a different marine and his horse. 'I never come this far inland before. How far is it to Sheffield, Mike?'

'About thirteen miles. When we get to Aldwarke I would like to see my mother for a couple of hours. Would you mind staying with the keel?'

'I wait as long as you like, you are boss!' Erik agreed.

'After Rotherham the last stretch is a bit tedious I'm afraid. There's a long ladder of locks to climb and they seem never ending.'

'Rotherham!' Erik exclaimed, shaking his head. 'I hear of that place before and it sticks in my mind. Very sad I think. All along the water we hear it, it was years ago but I remember.' Michael looked at him rather puzzled and there was a note of real sadness in Erik's voice when he continued. 'The children drown, so many, it makes me teach mine to swim!'

'Oh, yes!' Michael said quietly, as he too recalled the incident. 'You mean at the launching of the new barge. Why, it must be nearly ten years ago; a terrible thing.' He pondered for a moment, 'I was away at the time but the horror of it hung over the town for a long time afterwards. I was told that over forty children were on the barge when it sank, due to them all lining one side and this caused it to overturn. Fancy you knowing about it!' Michael said, looking at Erik in amazement.

'I never forget those children. I have a soft spot for them, I think.' There was a catch in Erik's voice and Michael wasn't sure if he also saw signs of moisture in the big man's eyes.

'Yes,' he agreed. 'It must have been devastating to the families involved. I remember my father watching Maggy for weeks after, fussing like a mother hen whenever we were moving on the keel. Now, of course, I can appreciate why.'

'Very sad, very sad,' Erik muttered to himself.

There were things about Erik which sometimes seemed odd to Michael. Here was this large, affable man, often too powerful for his own good, yet there were times when he was so unlike the hard, rough men of the waterways. Perhaps that had been the reason his business had collapsed, sentiment had little place in a dog eat dog world.

'So, your father he teach you to swim, then?' Erik asked after a few moments.

'Gracious me, no!' Michael laughed. 'My father couldn't swim, and there's not many canal people who can.'

'It is a mistake. Water is very dangerous even for children playing. Mine can swim.' There was a touch of pride in his voice, which he made no effort to conceal.

Michael laughed again. 'If you try swimming in the waters hereabouts you'd die from disease as quick as drown. The water's filthy—best thing is to make sure you don't fall in.'

'How's the leg?' Erik asked, changing the subject. 'It's not well, I can see, but better than it was?'

Michael nodded. 'Given a chance to rest for a while the pain goes away, especially in summer, but this year I've had a bad start.' He paused, wondering how much to tell Erik at this point; however he decided to let things ride for a while longer. 'Let's hope I can have a run of luck with no more mishaps,' he added finally.

'An old injury, you say?' Erik probed further, whether out of curiosity or some other motive Michael wasn't sure.

'Yes, as a child my grandmother dropped me down the stairs. My right leg gives me trouble every so often. It must have been the muscle that was damaged rather than the bone. Sometimes standing for any length of time doesn't help, and an unexpected movement sometimes starts it off again.'

'Mm,' Erik responded, 'you have a problem there.' Then he changed the subject again, much to Michael's relief.

Michael said nothing to Erik about his main reason for calling home, other than he wanted to make sure his mother was well. It was, of course, the future of the *Maggie Kelly* which he needed to discuss.

Patrick's face was a picture of relief when the keel rounded a bend in the river and finally drew up alongside the steep bank, just short of Aldwarke lock. He was keen to be home, away from the water and ready to describe his adventures to anyone who would listen. 'You go ahead, Patrick, and ask your dad to let you bring the dray down to collect the potatoes and things I've brought him. You can go faster than I can. Pick up the stuff from the other side of the lock when you get back.' He could see the boy was impatient to go and, smiling, added, 'Go on then, off you go, you've done well.'

'Thanks, Mike,' Patrick shouted as he grabbed his small bag and scampered up the bank, nearly losing his footing on the grass as he did so.

'Poor lad,' Erik laughed, watching him. 'I can still see his face when he was tied up back on the Humber.'

After Patrick had gone, Michael and Maggy brought all the items for the farm up on deck, ready for his return and then left for the farm, leaving Erik and the marine to work the keel through the lock.

Ma seemed bright enough, and on seeing Michael she hugged him, something she'd not been in the habit of doing in the past. 'Patrick's told me about your business on the Humber,' she said later, in a quiet voice, as if by speaking softly this would somehow reduce the horrors that might have been. 'It's the first time the *Maggie's* been in such trouble,' she went on. 'It's a sign your father's not here.' There was a hint of criticism in her voice, which hurt Michael.

'It was a number of things, Ma!' he said defensively, yet he knew he should be making allowances for her state of mind.

Realising how he felt, Maggy butted in, 'It wasn't Michael's fault, Ma, everything happened so quickly, and you know what the Humber's like. If he hadn't acted so promptly there would have been a tragedy. It was my fault.'

'Jim should be here to look after us,' Ma muttered sadly, and Michael wished he'd told Patrick not to say anything in front of her. It was fear more than anything which had disturbed her, but her words still hurt, as he did feel that in some way he'd let them down.

'Come on, Ma,' he coaxed gently, 'we're all safe now and we've got a mate to help—you'll like him, he's a big bearded Norwegian.'

'No, I won't,' she said petulantly, before her thoughts wandered off into a comfortable twilight world again.

John came into the house just then, his face red from the heat of the forge. 'What's this I hear about...?' Michael raised his hand to silence him and nodded cautiously towards Ma.

'You've a grand lad in Patrick,' Michael said quickly. 'I'd have been hard pressed to manage without his help. You can rightly be very proud of him.'

John acknowledged this, but with some reservation. He then asked, 'So how do things look for the future? I hear you've got help?'

'Yes, I'm going to do a couple of trips to see how things go, and to find out if I can afford to pay for any extra help I might need. As I've only got an hour to spare now while Erik and the Marine take the keel through the lock, I'll try to make a longer visit next time to give you more details. I've brought the items you wanted and a few extra, but there's no need to pay for them, they'll cover the stuff you gave us on the way out.'

'Fine! Is this Erik any good?' John asked.

'Couldn't ask for better! However, I've had a lot of trouble with my leg and that could be the decider in the end.' Michael sat down while John leaned back against the dresser, his arms folded over his leather apron. 'I'd like to take Maggy on this next trip too,' he continued. 'After that I'm afraid she'll have to find other work as I won't be able to afford the cost of hiring extra help, and support her as well. That's if we keep the keel, of course.'

Maggy looked glum. The thought of skivvying for a wealthy family hardly suited her idea of a happy future, yet she acknowledged she would somehow have to pull her weight within the family, as John couldn't keep them all. 'Shall I get a change of clothes now?' she asked, resigned to the news. 'Or will you pick me up on the way back?'

'No, hurry up and get anything you need, I won't want to lose time on the return trip. As it is we'll need to stock up with more provisions in Sheffield for the next run.'

Without hesitation Maggy went to collect her belongings, wishing she could have had a little more time at home with her mother and Mary.

'Well, that seems to be that for the moment,' Michael said, when she'd gone upstairs. 'I know she's disappointed but there's not much I can do about it. Anyway, are things alright here?'

'Trade's fine,' John replied, 'in fact I'm glad Patrick's back to help me. I just hope he's not hankering on travelling about.' There was a serious tone in his voice as he asked, 'He's not got the wanderlust, I hope?'

Michael laughed, 'Far from it, but I suppose he'll tell you all about it in detail when he gets a chance. I'll say this, he's a good worker. I had no trouble from him, and the experience won't have harmed him, it's just a pity there were a few bad moments on the Humber.' He took the sandwich which Mary had brought him, along with a mug of tea. 'Thanks Mary, that's very kind,' he said gratefully.

As he ate they discussed a few local matters, then he rose and went to the foot of the stairs to call out, 'Come on, Maggy, we haven't all day.'

She came hurrying down and warmly embraced Mary and her mother. The pair then said good-bye and set off down the lane back to the keel where Erik stood chatting to the Marine, waiting for their return.

Chapter 3

As the miles slipped by, Ollie Erikson looked through the window of the railway carriage at the passing landscape. Springtime in England was a glorious experience after the dry, parched land of California. The sea journey had been long but good compared with the overland trek to the East coast which many had to endure if their funds were low. He was a sailor after all and it had been no hardship to work his passage back, thus convincing everyone aboard that he had not found gold. This way he felt protected from prying eyes and theft. It had suited him to work rather than sit idly by staring at the waves as a passenger.

He was tanned, his hair bleached blond by the Californian sun and his short trim beard gave him a Viking warrior look, much like that of his ancestors before him. He was pleased with himself, his clothes were of good quality and there was an air of self-confidence about him which attracted occasional glances from passers by.

With money in his pocket he was now in a position to determine his own future and possibly that of his father as well. The old man had struggled to give the family a better way of life, and he intended to make sure his father reaped his reward. He knew the repayments on the keel were a burden but now he was bringing the means of easing that situation. Ollie felt proudly at the bundle of notes and letters of credit secreted beneath his shirt. Therein lay their salvation.

When he arrived in Plymouth he'd wasted no time in travelling immediately to London, where he'd acquired the clothing he wore and a few extras before catching a train north. He was not a feckless man, however, and had wasted none of his money on inferior or useless items. He now felt capable of conducting himself well in good company, and hoped that in Hull he would eventually be able to build himself a respectable business.

It was pleasantly warm as he left the railway station to walk across Anlaby Road towards home. Nothing seemed to have changed very much during the comparatively short time he'd been away, but he knew he had. The rows of shabby, but familiar, back to back houses seemed to close in on him, and he knew that for all he was glad to be back he would not be content to remain here for ever.

Adelaide Street was a little wider and less shabby than most of those surrounding it, brightened as it was by its many shop fronts and public houses. As he approached his parents' house, he adjusted his clothing a little, then knocked on the door. A tremor of excitement ran through him as he waited to see the look of surprise on his mother's face when she saw him. Would she recognise him immediately he wondered, after two years? The door knob turned slowly, seeming to take forever. Then there she was before him, the most precious thing in his life. Her eyes opened wider as the truth dawned on her.

'Ollie,' she cried, staring at him in amazement, and powerless to move after the shock of finding him there.

'Mother!' he said, laughing and hugging her. She seemed rounder than he remembered, and he pushed her gently from him to look down. 'Mother!' he cried mockingly, 'What's this?'

Ellen blushed furiously. 'Come in,' she rebuked, 'the neighbours are looking.' They probably weren't, of course but he understood, and followed her inside, placing his bags near the door.

Little was, or could be said during the following minutes, for he was immediately met by the clamour and chatter of excited children. He found himself almost swamped by their enthusiastic welcome, and was grateful at last to be allowed to sit and enjoy a mug of coffee.

'Go outside and play,' Ellen ordered gently but firmly, pushing Johann, Kristen and Lucy from the room. 'Ollie is tired from travelling and I want to talk to him quietly for a while.' Protesting loudly, the children left the room, and peaceful contentment reigned after the wild hubbub of their welcome. 'Oh, it is good to have you home,' she said happily, when they'd gone. 'You're so handsome too!' Only a mother could pay compliments such as that, he thought. 'I feared never to see you again; that you would stay away once you'd found your dream. And you have, haven't you?' She smiled, her eyes full of admiration, 'You are too well-dressed to be penniless'.

Ollie laughed and exclaimed, 'I didn't travel from America like this! I wore what all disillusioned immigrants wear, to conceal my luck. That way I was less likely to lose it.' He paused, took another sip from his mug, and went on, 'I have learned a lot since I left you and Father, much of which I hope to use in order to do well here. So, with luck, we shall all prosper, but I may have to return to America for a while, first.'

Ellen's face fell a little, her joy temporarily dulled. 'Things have not been so good here,' she confessed in a low voice, and Ollie's eyes darkened with apprehension. 'Your father lost the keel last August,' she stated simply.

Ollie gasped at this news. 'How so? I knew things were bad in the town before I left, that's why I decided to go. Couldn't he and Hal manage to hold on?' There was disappointment and a little anger in his voice.

'He couldn't wait for you to return, and trade fell off when the railways started taking the best work from the canals. He's not afraid of hard work but he never managed to get the best cargoes or prices.' Ellen was on the defensive now.

This explanation failed to placate Ollie's mounting indignation and he muttered something to himself which Ellen failed to hear. 'So where's Father now then?' he demanded.

'He's working for the captain of a keel on the Hull to Sheffield waterways, and he's been gone for nearly a week. It's good for him to have regular work again. He was so miserable hanging round the docks waiting to be hired as a labourer. He was even thinking of going to sea again.'

'He's been busy enough round here!' Ollie snapped sarcastically, looking knowingly at his mother's swollen waistline. 'He's found something else to do.'

'Oh, Ollie,' Ellen cried in anguish. 'Don't be coarse, don't say such things. He's a good man and he's had such a hard time since you went.'

Tears were running down her face now, making Ollie regret his outburst. This wasn't the homecoming he'd planned. 'I'm sorry, Mother,' he cried, rising from his chair to kneel and place his arm around her. She tried to push him away. 'I had such dreams of coming home to find everything as it was,' he said lamely, 'and I could have helped.'

'No!' Ellen responded fiercely, 'Your father's a proud man, he wouldn't have taken your money.'

'That's ridiculous,' Ollie retorted, but the harshness had gone from his voice. 'We're a family. Anyway, where's Hal and Anna if the keel's gone?'

Calming down a little, Ellen wiped away her tears. 'Hal had to find work, and went to sea on a whaling ship. He's been gone for month's now.' She paused. 'And Anna's out.' She said this last statement with such reluctance that he felt there was more behind it than was spoken.

'Where is Anna, then?' he asked, watching her.

Lowering her eyes she said simply, 'At work.'

'Work! What work? She should be here looking after you by the looks of it.' There was more anger in his voice now, and he stood up, disappointed that his homecoming was being spoilt by the unwelcome revelations.

'Oh, Ollie,' she cried. 'You've come back as an angry young man, what's happened to you?'

'I'm not the only thing that's altered,' he declared. 'Every time I ask about something or someone there's been a change, and not for the better either. What is Anna doing?'

With a sigh Ellen brought herself to confess the truth. 'She's cleaning at the Old Black Boy, in High Street.'

'Good God, Mother, I know where it is!' he shouted. 'And Father let her go there? Just wait until I catch up with him.'

By now Ellen had begun to recover from the shock of Ollie's unexpected return and the change in him, and as usual rallied her strength of mind to try and ease the situation. 'It's no good, Ollie, we were getting desperate for money—you're young, you were able to go off and seek your fortune. We had no choice. It's bad for other people too!'

'I want to try and help us all!' he cried out. 'Perhaps it would have been better had I stayed.'

'Perhaps so, son,' Ellen conceded. 'Perhaps so.'

Realising that shouting was getting him nowhere, and conscious that his mother might have a point, he calmed down. 'I'm sorry Mother, I'm just upset to see the predicament you're all in. But one thing's for sure, Anna's not staying at The Black Boy any longer than I can help.'

Earlier in the day when Anna arrived at The Black Boy Inn, she entered the small narrow white-washed passage, and shivered. To her the place had little to commend it, being merely an old run-down building which had been used for various purposes. Now it was just a pub, frequented by sailors and watermen who wanted nothing more than a convenient place to meet for a drink. Only a stone's throw from the river, it attracted a motley assortment of characters into the small front bar, or its larger back room. In the evenings, bodies spilled out from these rooms into the passageway, bumping boisterously against each other, and Anna was glad that most of this occurred after she had finished her work.

The hard wooden floors which she scrubbed, quickly became filthy again from spilt ale and dirty boots, and she dreaded returning each day to clean the place once more. It was not the love of the work which brought her here but the pittance the landlord paid her, which was so much needed at home.

Now that her father was in work again she would, perhaps, be able to leave and find more suitable employment, but she knew that she would always have to work, or marry. This latter thought filled her with dread, and her flesh crawled as she watched the early drinkers arrive, their faces greedy for grog and anything which might bring some titillation to their senses. They were, in her opinion, a loud bawdy lot, unlike her father who was, in her eyes, a good honest seaman. Yet, if the truth be known, Erik Erikson was quite fond of The Black Boy when he had a few pence to spare. It had been his acquaintance with the landlord that had provided Anna with the very job which she hated so much.

Every day was the same, a drudgery, and a far cry from the happy times before the keel had been repossessed leaving her father with nothing. Inevitably, one day, she would have been forced out into the world, but her father had mistakenly equipped her for nothing more than domestic work, whereas Ollie and Hal had been given sufficient schooling to enable them to make something of themselves. Even their education had been patchy, possible only when sufficient funds had been available, and it was Ollie who'd taught her what she knew, in his spare time.

She worked on for hours, washing and scrubbing, fetching and carrying. The day seemed unending and weariness prevented her from looking forward to anything more than a meal and bed. Slowly she began to sense that she was being watched, something which she disliked especially in this place, for it was usually by leering, greedy eyes. She carried on working, hoping the person would tire and lose interest. The figure in the corner of her eye remained motionless for some time until, in the end, Anna felt drawn to glance very quickly in his direction. In spite of herself she could not deny that the man was handsome; he was fair and bearded, but she deliberately avoided looking into his eyes. As he neither moved nor tried to intimidate her, it wasn't long before curiosity persuaded her to look again. She was taken aback by the familiarity displayed on his smiling face, and when finally she looked at his over-friendly eyes, it was with a strong sense of recognition.

As if taking a liberty the man spoke, 'Hello!' Then it was the movement of his mouth which struck her forcibly, causing her to stare hard at him. 'Don't you recognise me, Anna?' he teased, his eyes twinkling merrily.

Stunned and for a moment unable to move, it suddenly dawned on her that the bearded figure was her brother, and with a cry of, 'Ollie! Oh, Ollie!' she rushed towards him.

'Steady on,' he laughed, catching her in his arms and hugging her tightly. 'I thought you'd never turn and look my way.' He then held her away from him and examined her face. 'You've been working too hard, you've got crows feet from scowling,' he said, with a playful tweak of her nose. A look of sad resignation filled her eyes. 'There, that makes it worse!' he chided, thinking how worn and pale she looked. She'd never been a robust child, but delicate in frame and manner, and certainly unsuited to the drudgery which she suffered now.

'Get your shawl, Anna—you're not working like this any longer. I've had a word with the proprietor and he understands that you're needed at home.'

At this statement Anna gasped; all manner of fears passing through her mind. 'Not Mother! There's nothing wrong is there, she's alright isn't she?'

'Of course!' Ollie quickly reassured her. 'Don't worry. But you're needed at home to help her.'

Without waiting for further explanation she sought out her employer, thanked him for his kindness at letting her go and collected what monies were due to her. Then she obeyed Ollie and left The Black Boy forever.

'Oh, Ollie, it is good to see you again, especially with your beard. I didn't recognise you at first,' she said happily, as they made their way home.

'I knew you wouldn't,' he chuckled, 'but you couldn't resist a second glance, could you?' A touch of colour appeared on her cheeks. She didn't reply but poked him instead with her elbow.

With the return of Ollie, an air of excitement hung over the small house in Adelaide Street, giving Ellen a much-needed lift of her spirits. The joy of her husband finding work again had palled a little after he'd been gone a few days, for she was lonely without him. After having complained constantly that he got under her feet she now realised that she missed his warm, affectionate nature. For a while, however, she basked in the pleasure of having her eldest son home again.

To say that Ollie was disappointed at his father's loss of the keel was an understatement. He had no intention of throwing his money about, but he realised that, because his father was a proud man, it would be difficult to help him financially now that the keel had gone.

By eight o'clock that evening they were all tired after the events of the day, but the children were allowed to stay up a little longer than usual, playing with the small gifts which Ollie had brought them. In the end Ellen could stand the noise no longer and they were sent to bed, leaving herself, Ollie and Anna to savour the peace that followed. After a while Ellen asked, 'What plans have you, son? Do you think you'll be able to find work? Now that the keel has gone you may have to go to sea like Hal.'

'I have some half-formed ideas, Mother,' he replied, 'and these will need a lot of thought and planning if they are to work, but until then I shall take no risks with my savings.' He thought it best not to disclose exactly what his financial position was, so gave only the impression that he had done well enough, but needed to be extremely careful lest his funds soon ran out.

'What a shame father couldn't have kept the *Martha Jane* a little longer,' Anna broke in. 'Now you're home we could have kept it. Might you buy another keel, Ollie?'

'No,' he replied, shaking his head. 'If father couldn't compete then, he's not likely to be able to do so now.' He saw his mother's eyes widen at this. 'Now I'm not being disloyal, Mother, but we have to be realistic. I wouldn't want to work on board a keel indefinitely, and a keel must pay it's way or end up like the *Martha Jane*.'

'But won't you help Father at all?' Anna asked, looking at him in some dismay.

'Try to be patient, both of you!' Ollie cautioned, realising that such reactions were only to be expected from them. 'Father is a proud man. He needs to work and I will see that he doesn't go short, but I don't want him to know how successful I've been until I can ensure I remain so. Then things will be different. As I said, I will need to return to California again, sooner or later, at least for a short while.'

Ellen watched her son carefully; she knew him well. 'Ollie's right,' she said, 'your father is happiest working for his keep, and if he and Mr Havercroft get on well things might not be too bad.'

'Thank you, Mother,' Ollie replied, giving her a grateful look. 'Just trust me for a while, that's all I ask. I'll not be splashing money about unnecessarily and you might find some of my actions puzzling, but bear with me. Until Father returns I have many enquiries to make in the town. Meanwhile, I shall pay for my food and lodgings, and that will enable Anna to stay at home and help you.'

Ellen could now see that he was very tired and needed to rest. After the long uncomfortable train journey, he had troubled himself on Anna's behalf and then had patiently answered all the younger children's eager questions. 'You are your father's son, more than you know,' she told him. 'With a good schooling your father could have achieved much. It is given now for you to do what he could not. However, it's late and time you rested, my lad. The bed is made, so off you go, and I'll send Anna up with a hot drink.'

Leaning over, Ollie kissed her on the cheek, saying. 'Thank you, Mother, I won't let you down.'

When he'd left the room Anna turned to her mother. 'Things will be better now, won't they?'

Looking at Anna's pale face, Ellen smiled. 'I think so. You have a lot to be grateful to Ollie for, it must have been hard for you at The Black Boy. In return, try to help him when you can.'

Nearing Hull at the completion of their first trip together, Michael reflected on his journey with Erik. Twelve days had passed since the near disaster in the Humber, ordinary days which had almost blanked the incident from his mind. That was, of course, until they passed the same spot off Whitton Sands. However, he did no more than thank God for their safe deliverance and then got on with his work.

There had been a period of warm, sunny weather since leaving Sheffield and this provided the opportunity to get to know Erik quite well. The daylight hours were lengthening, and as they sat on deck each evening, Erik smoking his pipe, Michael listening to his tales of Christiania,[1] his home town in Norway, their companionship began to grow. Erik was an interesting man to talk to, as Maggy had also discovered.

The keel was deeply laden with heavy chains and hoisting gear for the docks, a cargo which needed no attention during the journey, thus giving Michael time to rest his leg. Only one thing marred the trip for him, they had not seen the *Mary Ann*, and he could only suppose she was moored in one of the canal side basins out of sight, or had gone for coal again up the Dearne and Dove canal. Although he was disappointed by this, he was in good heart, something which was not missed by Erik.

1. Now known as Oslo.

'You're feeling better now!' Erik remarked one evening as they relaxed.

'I am,' Michael replied, acknowledging that for some time the pain in his leg had been easing, so that the future now appeared less bleak than it had. 'Yes, I must admit I am.'

'That is good!' Erik said, 'and soon we get to Hull. I wonder how my Ellen will be when we get there?'

'How long has she to go before the child comes?' Maggy asked, her interest in the conversation now aroused.

Erik thought for a moment. 'Two months it will be,' then with resignation he added, 'and another mouth to feed.' As if trying to shake off this thought he chuckled and said, 'But another to look after me in my old age.' He seemed incapable of letting life get him down for long, always making the best of any situation.

'I quite envy you,' Michael said thoughtfully. 'I might end up on my own!'

'It serves you right,' Maggy chipped in. 'You should get married. What about Lily? She fancies you!'

He chose to ignore this remark, but caught the twinkle in Erik's eyes. He held his breath, hoping the man would keep his own counsel about his daughter and to his surprise he did, but the look said it all. Michael decided that once in Hull he would keep well away from Erik's family in case similar thoughts might be expressed regarding their Anna!

The docks in Hull were crowded with shipping of all sorts, and it would obviously be some time before the keel could be relieved of her cargo, so Michael was compelled to moor in the river. In view of this he decided to send Erik off home to see how his wife was faring, and to tell her he would be home that night.

They had been fortunate to get such a good shipment after only two days at the basin in Sheffield, as this enabled him to return to Hull in time to pick up Parker's monthly supply of ivory and horn. As usual, of course, he would need to top up this cargo, then they would be off again.

Now that Michael was more like his old self, Maggy risked asking if she too could leave the keel and look round the town whilst they waited. She had very little to spend, it was simply a matter of being able to mix with other people after being cooped up on the keel for so long. When he agreed she changed her cotton blouse for a clean one, tidied her hair and endeavoured to make her plain, workaday attire look more presentable. Her woollen skirt had seen better days but amongst other seafarers and market people this would not be unusual. It occurred to her that this might be her last visit to the town, at least for some time, and this saddened her for she liked the place. She'd never known it to be a quiet town, how could it be when sailors of every nation thronged the streets and crowded the public houses and inns? She liked the shops, filled as they were with items she couldn't afford, and it didn't cost money just to look. There was Parliament Street with its elegant porticoed buildings, and the Land of Green Ginger tucked away in a corner, which fired her imagination. The old town was full of alleys and cobbled streets, and was a far cry from the wet, lonely, meandering canals and river thoroughfares of her life.

Even if Michael kept the keel it would no longer be a part of her future as it seemed she was destined to fetch and carry in some big house, and be a mere nobody, a servant, and a slave. With these gloomy thoughts in mind, Maggy found herself tempted to buy something, anything to cheer herself up. Counting her few coins she boldly entered a small haberdashers through whose window she had often peered. It was a flippant gesture, an act of defiance against her circumstances in life, yet she did not intend to waste what little money she had. With so many fine things before her, most of which were beyond her means, she eventually left the premises empty handed, more despondent than when she'd entered.

She wandered aimlessly, hardly noticing the passing of time, the town had this effect on her. All around, people worked or walked with a purpose, girls obviously shopping for their mistresses, urchin children getting under everyone's feet. She noticed it was getting late and, although Michael didn't particularly need her, she felt she had wasted far too much time in idleness. Making her way back through the narrow streets and alleys towards the keel, she was surprised to find Erik engaged in heated conversation with a stranger on the wooden staithe. Maggy was quite taken aback by this as she could not remember him raising his voice at any time since they'd met.

Hesitating, she moved into a doorway so as not to embarrass him. From here she noted the angry face and gestures of the younger man. Under normal circumstances she might have admired his appearance, but she didn't like the way he was shouting at Erik. His eyes were cross, his face irate and, strangely, Erik seemed flustered and disturbed rather than angry in return.

Fearing that he was going to be attacked by some madman, Maggy darted quickly to the staithe ladder and climbed down onto the keel. Michael was nowhere to be seen, but the cabin's hatch was open so she bent over it and called quietly to him. 'Michael, come quickly, someone is rowing with Erik.' Then more urgently cried, 'Are you there?'

'Yes, Maggy, but it's alright,' he replied. 'Come down here a minute.' Puzzled by his apparent indifference she did as he asked. 'It's Erik's son,' Michael explained. 'I came down here to leave them to it.'

Her face fell. 'He's not very nice,' she said, still rather alarmed by what she had seen. 'Which son is it, and what does he want?'

'I think it's Ollie, because when Erik came back he said his son had returned home from America unexpectedly, and was looking for him. The next thing I knew, this chap came walking along the staithe. Everything seemed fine at first, he and Erik embraced then chatted for a few minutes, but then suddenly they began to argue and his son became angry. I thought it best to get out of the way, for Erik's sake.'

'He sounds a very disagreeable man—Erik shouldn't put up with it,' Maggy said firmly, having decided to take Erik's side although she had no idea what the row was about. She couldn't understand a word that was being said, but certainly the argument was fierce. This went on for several more minutes, obviously in Erik's own language, but was gradually becoming inaudible to Maggy and Michael due to increasing activity and noise on the staithe.

Although her curiosity was aroused, she assumed this was only one of the occasional spats which occurred in most canal families, a normal part of water folks' lives. Sometimes arguments between Captains became heated, but rarely turned violent unless it was over queue jumping for cargo or at locks.

On hearing the sound of someone stepping onto the deck, Maggy made to climb out of the cabin but Michael held her arm and warned her to stay where she was. After a few moments he rightly decided to waste no more time hiding discreetly below deck, and climbed up to see Erik, flushed and gloomy, sitting on the taffrail. 'Erik! I'm going to the Docks Office again to find out when a berth with a crane will be free, and also if Parker's shipment has arrived from Africa. As soon as we can get a convenient spot I want to off-load this lot straight away.'

'Alright,' Erik replied, his voice quiet and lacking its usual brightness. 'That was Ollie!' he stated simply.

'Ah!' Michael responded, 'I thought it might be.' Then he let the matter drop, but Erik seemed inclined to explain further.

'He thinks everything is my fault, and can't understand why I lose the keel.' Erik made sure Maggy wasn't nearby before quietly adding, 'He's furious that I give my wife a child, too.'

Michael didn't know what to say, or if indeed he was expected to say anything at all. He merely replied, 'Did he do well in America?'

Shaking his head, Erik thought for a minute. 'He never really said. I suppose he didn't, or he would not be here worrying about everything. Young people are usually keen to show off their good fortune.'

'Well, at least he's home. I don't suppose many come back if they don't do well; there's no point in returning empty-handed and with no job to go to.'

Erik thought about this. 'I try to think how I behave as a young man,' he said. 'I was fiery too but my father was dead, so I have no one to rebel against. Yes, it is good to have my son back—I talk to him later when he calms down.'

Michael left him to ponder on these words and set off through the town towards the Docks Office. When Maggy appeared from below, Erik was cheerful again and whistling a tune which she'd often heard whilst working with him during the past two weeks.

She liked him, he wasn't without fault, of course, but he'd brought life back to the keel and stability into Michael's life. With luck, and if he stayed, they would be able to keep the keel for a while at least. 'How is Mrs Erikson?' she asked, after a while.

'Fine, very fine,' he replied, without looking up. 'Why not go and see her for yourself? We will be here for several days more, I think.'

Maggy liked this suggestion. 'Do you think she would be pleased if I went?' she asked hopefully, for she had few real friends and didn't like to push herself forward.

He looked up. 'My Ellen likes everyone,' he said proudly. 'You go, you have a lonely time here on the keel. I tell her tonight that you go tomorrow, yes?' Seeing the delight on Maggy's face he added, 'There, you look happier already,' and resumed his whistling.

He was right, it might be days before they left Hull and she couldn't spend her time wandering the streets feeling sorry for herself. The cramped confines of the cabin didn't bother her as much when they were on the move, but when they were hemmed in by boats on the foul-smelling waters of the docks, it was dreary.

When Michael returned he brought the gloomy news that there was no chance of unloading that day, and worse still the vessel bringing in the ivory and horn hadn't yet been sighted in the estuary.

'Have you tried the new Victoria Dock across the river?' Erik asked. 'There's often timber there that's needed for the mines.'

'That's a good idea,' Michael conceded. 'It's no good hanging around, the boat from Africa might be anything up to a week late. Thanks.' He glanced at the sky. 'It'll be dark soon, Erik,' he said, 'you go home now, there's nothing more to do here.'

'You sure?' Erik asked. 'I don't mind staying longer,' he added, waiting politely but hoping Michael would dismiss him.

'No, off you go,' Michael insisted, thinking that it would give Erik extra time at home to talk to his son and see more of his wife and family. He smiled at the speed with which Erik took him at his word, collected his belongings and marched off along the staithe.

Once he'd gone, Michael and Maggy had the keel to themselves for the first time since they'd taken their father home to be buried. It had seemed strange enough after Patrick left, but now without Erik's lively ways and cheerful whistle a stillness settled over the *Maggie Kelly*. Later, as they ate their evening meal together, Michael paused and looked around the cabin.

'It's queer how things have worked out, Maggy,' he said. 'What do you think Dad would make of it all, if he could see us now?'

Contemplating this, she replied fondly. 'I think he would be pleased at how you have coped.' He grimaced with embarrassment and shrugged his shoulders as if to deny the praise. 'He would, you know!' she insisted. 'And I'm proud of you too.' She reached over and squeezed his arm in a sisterly fashion and wondered what he was thinking about, deep down.

He sighed, 'I'm trying, Maggy, I really am. Sometimes I feel a bit hollow and empty inside without him, and wonder if it's all worth while.'

'Of course it is,' she reassured him firmly. 'Besides, what choice do you have?'

'I suppose you're right. But it's not going to be easy in the future for you either.'

'You and Dad have kept me long enough,' she replied, 'and one day I would have had to do something more than just help Mary with Mother. I'll not be a burden to you Michael, and whilst John lets me live with them it will be easier. I can repay him a little.'

'Oh, you'll find a husband to take care of you, I don't doubt that, it's just that I think you're cut out for better things before then.'

'Such as?' Maggy scoffed, her voice ringing with doubt. But he could see something like hope in her eyes as she waited, half expecting him to describe how best she might shape her future.

'You're a looker, Maggy, and better educated than most canal folk, but who am I to say? I'm just like the rest, that's why Dad struggled to let you get some schooling, but as to where it might lead to I don't think he ever really though about it.'

'Perhaps it would have been better to remain in ignorance,' she lamented, 'than see an open door and not be able to go through it.'

'That's what I mean, Maggy, you've a better idea how to put things. You'd be wasted skivvying for some toff.'

Averting her eyes she said, softly, 'But you need looking after as well, Michael. Why don't you find a nice wife to share your life?'

'Don't start that!' he laughed. 'Erik tried matching me up with his daughter and you're after tying me to Lily. I'll find someone when I'm good and ready. Besides, what about you setting your cap at Ollie, he's come back from the gold fields, so he's probably rich as well as good-looking!'

'Alright, I'll shut up,' she cried, tossing a spoon at him, 'but only if you do! Anyway I don't like the look of Ollie, he wasn't very nice to his father.'

Michael retrieved the spoon and wagged it at her. 'That's more like you,' he chuckled. 'I wouldn't wish you on him anyway.'

Deliberately ignoring this remark, she asked, 'Do you really think he has come back rich? Because if so he might buy his father another ship! Then we'd lose Erik as mate!'

Michael was leaning on his elbow, his chin resting in the palm of his hand. At this he lifted his head and looked hard at his sister. 'I got the impression that Erik didn't think he had?' He sat for moment, his finger pressed against his lips, then he sighed. 'Good God, Maggy, you do come up with some stunners, and here was me thinking that I was getting somewhere at last.'

'I'm sorry,' she said, 'but it does change things doesn't it?' Then, with a flippant toss of her head she said, 'Look, you marry Anna and I'll marry Ollie, then we'll both be rich!'

'And what if he hasn't got a penny to his name?' Michael asked, pretending to be serious. Maggy laughed out loud, but Michael's face was suddenly still, and he raised his head cautiously. 'Shush!' he hissed, 'I can hear footsteps on the deck.'

'Do you think someone may have heard us?'

Keeping his voice low, Michael replied, 'I doubt it, but I'll go and see who it is. You stay here and lock yourself in if there's any hint of trouble.'

Peering cautiously out of the hatchway, Michael looked around. There was enough light from the wall lanterns on the staithe for him to see immediately that there was someone standing on the deck. The man was making no effort to conceal himself, quite the opposite in fact, as the moment he saw Michael climbing out of the hatch he called, 'Good evening!' Then stepped forward to ask, 'You're Mike Havercroft, I hope?'

'Yes, I am.' Michael admitted, recognising the figure. 'And you're Erik's son, Ollie, aren't you?' He shook the man's outstretched hand.

'Pleased to meet you,' Ollie replied, 'I was wondering if we could have a word in private?'

His voice was that of a man with some education, but there was no arrogance or condescension in it, as Michael had thought likely from his earlier judgement of the man. 'By all means,' he replied, 'but why now at this hour? Is Erik not with you?' He was puzzled by the visit and hoped it didn't mean bad news.

'Father is at home, and doesn't know I'm here. In fact I'd rather he didn't know of this visit, if you don't mind.'

'We could go below, although my sister's there at the moment,' Michael told him, a little unsure at what to do.

'I'd rather we were alone if possible,' Ollie said. 'How about a drink, and we can talk as we go?'

Agreeing to this, Michael explained to Maggy who their visitor was, and that he would be away for an hour or so, adding that she should not open the hatch until he returned. His mind raced with questions, mainly as a result of Maggy's earlier warning regarding Ollie's intentions.

Once on the staithe, the two men were able to talk easily as they walked towards the town. 'There's nothing wrong with Erik, is there?' Michael asked.

'No, no!' Ollie answered. 'But first I'd like to apologise for the confrontation this afternoon. I really should have kept my temper, and once I'd lost it, I'm afraid I was in no mood to meet strangers.' To this Michael said nothing, knowing that by keeping quiet he would learn the reason for the visit that much quicker. 'I suppose my surprise return caught the family on the hop. But never mind! You can't be interested in our tales of woe.'

'Your father's a good worker, Mr Erikson,' Michael replied, not knowing whether to call him Ollie or not. 'I've a lot of respect for him even though I've only known him two weeks. You soon get to know people when you work closely with them. I've also learned a little about your family, as you can't help chatting about all sorts of things when work's done.'

'I'd like you to understand my motives for leaving in the first place,' Ollie went on. 'My sister had just died of cholera, and father had decided to invest in the keel taking Hal, my brother, as mate. I'd been at sea for a couple of years, sailing from here to Norway and Sweden, when an opportunity to go to Australia came up. While I was there I heard about the American gold fields, and decided to work my passage there and thus lose nothing by trying my luck. Finding a ship was no problem for a sailor, nor was returning to England later, as men were deserting the sea in droves just to take their chances in California. The worst that could happen would be for me to work my way back as a sailor if I was unsuccessful. Some poor devils are stuck out there now, penniless and with little hope of ever returning.'

To Michael the story was interesting, but he was desperate to learn where he and Erik fitted into this man's plans. 'Perhaps I shouldn't ask,' he said, 'but I fancy you didn't find any gold, otherwise you would not have returned?'

To this Ollie simply replied, 'I found enough to make life bearable. What I have left now I consider should not be wasted.'

Ah, thought Michael, here it comes. All he said was, 'I'm still not sure why you're telling me all this. I can't afford to take on another man, if that's what you want.'

'Oh! No!' Ollie broke in quickly. 'I'm not looking for a job, but I've been hearing about you from my father, enough to believe that you're not the sort of man to take advantage of anyone.'

The conversation seemed to be getting nowhere, and Michael's patience was being stretched. 'I really don't see what you're getting at,' he said, his tone reflecting this.

'I'm sorry, I'm taking up a lot of your time, aren't I? The thing is that I have a few plans which involve going back to America. Before I do so I want to be sure the family are alright, and it would help to know that Father is settled in work. I also need to go to Sheffield to investigate business possibilities, and maybe bring a few bulky items back, but I don't want to build up Father's expectations of me.'

'You want a lift on the keel, then?'

'Not exactly. I could afford to go by train, but I'd really like Father to see me working my passage to Sheffield. I'd like to spend some time there with the keel as a base, before working my way back again.'

'I can't afford to pay you,' Michael stated bluntly, thinking Ollie to be very full of bright ideas and fancies. 'I'm having a tough time myself, and I can't hang around in Sheffield any longer than necessary.'

'That's the point I'm making. I'm prepared to work, and the longer you rest your leg…' He saw Michael start with annoyance at this remark. 'Father's no fool,' he said hastily. 'He knows that you've got a problem. Anyway, with an extra unpaid hand you could take it easier, couldn't you? I'll fund any delay in Sheffield caused by me. There's no need to tell Father that I'm not being paid. Just offer me the job. Now then, what do you say, Mr Havercroft?'

This stumped Michael for a moment or two, and although he could see no reason to object, felt bound to ask, 'I had wondered if you were considering helping your father get another keel?'

'No,' Ollie shook his head. 'That would involve a lot of money, and a risk I'm not prepared to take. He wouldn't like it either, he's a proud man who wouldn't take charity, even from me. Besides, he's not a good businessman.'

'But even I can't guarantee keeping the *Maggie Kelly* beyond the end of summer,' Michael informed him bluntly. 'It might be physically impossible for me to carry on; you obviously know I've got leg trouble and if it should come to moving coal I'm finished.'

'I've considered all that,' Ollie replied, 'and I know you'll try to manage. What do you think?'

The pair had now been standing in earnest conversation for some time in High Street, where the light was stronger. Michael was relieved to see no guile in Ollie's face; there seemed no reason to doubt his sincerity, but every word had been carefully thought out, that much was obvious. What was there to lose, he thought, yet nobody worked for nothing.

Michael's quandary must have been reflected on his face, because Ollie suddenly spoke again. 'Let's have a drink,' he said, 'you can consider the matter…'

He got no further, a window above them was flung open and an irate voice called down. 'How much longer are you two going to stand there jawing? Bugger off!'

Feeling like ne'er-do-wells Michael and Ollie quickly moved on without saying another word, and entered the nearest ale house where further conversation was almost impossible. Ollie was just able to say. 'If you accept my proposal, let Father think it was your idea to hire me for a while.'

Michael knew that if he accepted Ollie's plan it would certainly make life easier, but might sometimes make conversation with Erik less than frank. Between drinks the two men chatted as best they could on a variety of subjects, but Michael's mind was never very far from Ollie's proposition. 'I don't know,' he said finally, during a quieter period, 'what if Erik finds out? What happens then?' Such deception did not rest easy on his conscience, he respected Erik too much to feel happy about it.

'Only you, my mother and I will know, and she loves him too much to hurt his pride by telling him. All she knows is...' but then he fell silent, and Michael was left to wonder exactly what Mrs Erikson knew that Ollie didn't want to share with him.

As the two men separated, Michael did at least promise to think about Ollie's proposal. When he arrived back at the keel he found that Maggy had gone to bed and presumed she was asleep, as the dividing curtain which closed off her recessed bunk from the rest of the cabin was drawn across. He soon realised his mistake when she gave a cough, then eased back the curtain so that she could see him.

'What did he want?' she asked, curious to know what had occurred. 'And at such a late hour?'

Knowing he must be discreet, Michael thought quickly. 'He came to apologise for his behaviour this afternoon, and says he wants a job,' he explained, as he untied his boots. He looked up quickly and added, 'Now look, don't make a lot of this but he'd like a lift to Sheffield and wants to earn his way.'

Maggy's face dropped. 'Oh,' she said, in a disappointed voice, 'so he's not rich after all?'

Michael chuckled. 'It would appear not, if he wants to work for me.'

'But we can't afford to pay him, Michael!' she broke in, knowing their circumstances. 'Anyway, what's he like?'

'Not as bad as we thought. I think having been away and then returning to find so much had changed upset him a bit; anyhow he seems to have made it up with Erik.'

'But what did you say about him working for us?' she persisted.

'I didn't promise anything. I told him to come down tomorrow and I'd consider it.'

'Well, I think he's got a cheek, nor can we afford it, Michael.' She was a little annoyed at this idea, for her brother worked hard for his money and there could be difficult times ahead. 'He shouldn't have gone off looking for gold in the first place, then Erik might not have lost his keel.' Maggy was quite indignant by now, and although Michael could see her point, he daren't tell her the truth.

'I know,' he agreed, 'but it wouldn't cost anything to give him a lift, he could bow-haul us when we need and save us the Marine's money. He can also help unload which will rest my leg nicely.' He waited a moment before going on, anticipating her reaction to his next words. 'He wants it to look as though the suggestion was my idea, so don't let on.'

Maggy's face was now a picture of astonishment. 'Well!' she said, 'Well! I don't think much of him at all, causing trouble the minute he gets back, and now he's begging for a job but is too proud to let his father know about it!' She was preparing to go on, but Michael interrupted her.

'That's enough, Maggy!' he told her firmly. 'I'm not a fool, and I'll make my own decisions if you don't mind.'

She was taken aback by his reaction and looked at him keenly, none too pleased. 'Well, if things go wrong it's your own fault, Michael Havercroft!' At which point she closed the curtain with an angry jerk, and lay back in the gloom, her opinion of Ollie Erikson getting lower by the minute, as her displeasure at Michael's attitude increased.

Michael, on the other hand, was amused at Maggy's strength of feeling. Recent events had changed all of them, she perhaps the most, and gone was the placid and compliant sister of the past. He had seen little of her during the winter months, indeed her first journey had been this spring at her father's request, sadly the one which turned out to be his last.

Getting into bed he found that sleep evaded him, his mind grappling with Ollie's conversation earlier. He could quite clearly see what the man wanted, but now he began to question his motives. Had Ollie actually made a fortune, or was Maggy right to think him proud and devious? At least with his father on board, Ollie, if dishonest at all, could do them little harm. But what was he going to do in Sheffield of all places?

His mind was too active for sleep, so he rose quietly, turned up the lantern and took a small piece of ivory and his knife from a drawer and began to carve. It had been weeks since he'd done such a thing, mainly due to the over-riding problems that had beset him, and lack of time, but before long his absorption in the task soothed him. He worked for half an hour until his eyes began to feel the strain, and, fearing he might make a mistake, he gave up and climbed back into bed again. He fell asleep almost immediately this time, but not before deciding to go along with Ollie's request.

Next morning Maggy rose to face two problems. She'd already promised Erik that she would visit Ellen, but she no longer wished to in case she met Ollie; yet if she stayed on the keel he could easily turn up again seeking an answer from Michael. Perhaps, with luck, Erik might forget to tell Ellen, thus giving her the reason she needed not to go.

Unfortunately this wasn't the case as the first thing Erik said when he arrived was, 'I tell Ellen to expect you and she is happy at this'.

Not wanting to hurt his feelings, and unable to find a plausible excuse, she answered, 'Thank you, but I'm afraid I won't be able to stay long'.

'No matter,' he replied. 'If you go this afternoon she should be resting then, you understand I think? It will make her sit down for a while.'

Maggy smiled. He was a thoughtful man and Ellen was certainly lucky to have such a husband. Her previous observations of keelmen's behaviour towards their wives had not impressed her, but Erik was different. In his son's case however, she saw an attitude similar to that of some men which she didn't much like. For the time being, however, there was nothing to do but wait for Michael to return from his search for somewhere to unload the keel. She knew this sometimes could take hours, even days, with the result that the staithes and wharfsides were often cluttered with bored, noisy and mischievous children who constantly got in the way. Wives too would stand chatting, although perhaps gossiping best described what they did. Maggy was still considered too young for this distraction, so the hours sometimes hung heavy on her hands. She exchanged a few words with Erik who always seemed to be busy, finished her tasks, then fell to daydreaming, a pastime she enjoyed.

Eventually Michael returned. 'I've found a berth which should become empty in about an hour!' he called for'ard to Erik, 'and there's just time for us to work her round to the Town Docks.' Turning to Maggy he whispered, 'Has Ollie been round?'

'No,' she replied, shaking her head. 'Perhaps he's changed his mind?'

'I doubt it, Maggy. He was quite serious.'

'Well, once we've moved he won't know where to find us, will he!' The note of triumph in her voice did not go unnoticed by Michael.

He disliked the shrewish attitude displayed by some of the keelmen's wives, and hoped that Maggy was not being influenced by them. 'You sound like Rose of the *Bessy May*,' he said, giving her a meaningful look.

Stung by this Maggy scowled, for Rose was known along the canals for her sharp, waspish tongue. Colouring, she turned and went below feeling a little ashamed, and could not ignore the feeling that she'd let herself down.

There was no reason for Ollie to return to the *Maggie Kelly* early that morning, as he well knew just how long it could take to unload and then reload such a vessel, even if work had begun at first light. Besides, he was quite confident that Michael Havercroft could not afford to turn down his offer, considering all he'd heard of his plight and difficulties.

He was determined, after his many enquiries in Hull, to press quickly on with his plans, and the less he discussed these with others the better, in case of failure. However, he had no intention of failing, and knew that success would speak for itself. He was full of confidence in his ability to succeed, and his optimism to do so knew no bounds, yet he had enough common sense to change direction if things looked like going wrong. These strong characteristics had taken him to sea, to the gold fields, and made survival possible in dangerous circumstances. It was his air of self-assurance which sometimes caused men to be wary of him, thinking him foolhardy, whilst others envied him.

Now, at twenty-four, he felt driven to make his mark in the world as soon as possible, before it was too late. His strength of mind came from the influence of his mother whilst his father was at sea. He was the eldest child and she had always looked to him for support and companionship. His ability to speak Norwegian fluently permitted him to discuss things with his father which were well in advance of his years; as a result he had grown to be an independent and self-reliant young man determined to escape his lowly station in life.

By drawing a mantle of privacy around himself he appeared to some as being stand-offish, and while this kept the curious and unwanted at bay, he found it difficult to make friends. For a young man used to travelling this had its merits, but the roots of genuine friendship are harder to put down as the years go by.

Scale Lane and Church Lane both led off High street towards Market Place, and as Maggy went along one of these on her way to the Erikson household, Ollie Erikson was making his way down the other in the opposite direction, to the keel. Had Maggy known this her steps would have been lighter and quicker, and her mind at ease. Instead, she'd waited several minutes on the staithe until Michael was well down the river, before plucking up courage to leave and visit Ellen.

When Ollie arrived at the riverside, he was not surprised to find the *Maggie Kelly* gone, and rightly assumed that Michael had been able to locate a suitable berth elsewhere. His father had warned him of this possibility, and that a message would be left for him at the chandler's shop on High Street, to advise him where they were.

With this information it didn't take long to locate the keel where the two men were already hard at work, unloading her cargo. 'Hello there!' he called, raising his voice above the general hubbub.

Looking up, Michael glanced towards Erik, quickly remembering that as far as his Mate knew he and Ollie hadn't actually met. 'Hello,' he shouted back, 'can I help you?'

'It's my son,' Erik broke in. 'Can he come aboard?'

'Of course,' Michael replied, and shouted, 'come on down!'

'Thanks,' Ollie responded, and joined his father on the keel as Michael climbed out of the hold.

'Pleased to meet you, Mr Havercroft, I'm Olaf Erikson,' Ollie said, shaking hands. 'I've heard a lot about you from my father.'

'Nothing bad, I hope,' Michael replied with a smile, though his eyes widened in speculation.

Ollie laughed. 'On the contrary, Sir, and I hope he's pulling his weight, and not trying to bully you as he does us at home?'

'He might try,' Michael said, good naturedly, then added, 'but I'm quite capable of sorting him out.'

'I wish I could,' came Ollie's hearty reply. 'I wondered, Mr Havercroft, do you need help with unloading? I'm free for the rest of the day.'

Michael looked first at Ollie and then at Erik, wondering what to say and indeed what to do. In the end he just said, in a quiet voice, 'I can't pay much'.

'That's alright—I wasn't expecting to be paid, but it will give me a chance to keep an eye on the old man here, and I could do with some exercise.' He looked towards his father, as if expecting some comment, but when none came he asked, 'Where do you want me?'

'If you can help me pass these chains to your father it will make things easier.'

'Come on, then,' Erik chipped in, 'we've not got all day to stand around.'

Smiling, Michael agreed, but added, 'Call me Mike, everyone else does.'

'Thanks! And I'm Ollie. I can't stand Olaf, I'm afraid.'

There was little chance to talk as the three men worked on, raising the heavy links of chain and sections of hoisting equipment, and whether he would have to pay for the extra help or not, Michael was grateful for it.

Maggy by this time had just crossed over the bridge between the Town and Junction Docks, having dawdled to gaze in shop windows. She was now familiar with the journey to the cobbled street where Erik lived, and it wasn't long before she reached his home. Several women were huddled in a whispering group outside the red-bricked house, while one peered quite openly through the window. What they were doing appeared slightly ominous to Maggy who approached cautiously, trying to overhear some of the conversation, but to no avail for when they saw her interest they stopped talking immediately.

Anna opened the door to her knock, and on recognising Maggy pulled her quickly inside, closing the door as soon as she could. 'Thank goodness you've come,' she said, her voice strained and low-pitched. 'Mother tripped on a flagstone as she came back from the midden and she's bleeding!'

'Has she hurt herself very badly?' Maggy asked, seeing the distress on Anna's face and looking round for Ellen.

Anna shook her head, 'It's not that, it's the baby. Can you fetch Father, please!' She was near to tears, and from the redness of her eyes it was obvious that she had already been crying before Maggy arrived.

Shocked, Maggy tried to think what to say. 'Of course I will,' she assured her, 'but have you fetched the doctor to her?'

'He's upstairs with her now, and there's a neighbour there too. Apparently Mother is to stay in bed, and only time and rest will tell. But she's not young any more and I'm afraid something might happen to her. Please go now,' she urged, 'I must stay with her. I didn't know where to find the keel and Ollie is out too.' By now her voice was near to breaking with panic and Maggy realised the urgency of the situation. 'Please hurry,' Anna urged once more.

'What shall I say has happened?' Maggy begged, afraid to take the bad news to Erik.

'You'll think of something. Just go!' Anna said, opening the door and pushing her out.

'How is she?' A woman called out, but the door closed before Anna could hear her. 'How's Mrs Erikson?' The woman asked Maggy.

'I don't know,' Maggy cried, and ran off down the street towards the docks, her boots clattering as she hurried along, the enormity of the news she carried worrying her. What could she say that wouldn't cause great alarm and anxiety, yet if she didn't tell the truth Erik might delay his return home. Maggy had known similar incidents where women had lost the child they were carrying and, worse still, sometimes their lives. As she hastened breathlessly on she felt sorry for the Eriksons, mainly because Erik had spoken of them so often that it was as if they were her friends. Their distress over this present mishap would be her distress too. She broke into a run again; it wasn't a warm day but her nervous haste made Maggy hot and flustered by the time she reached the wharf where she knew Michael would be off-loading. Poor Michael, was this going to be yet another setback for him, if Erik was compelled to stay at home with Ellen?

She was fighting for breath as she approached the keel. 'Michael!' she cried out, as she ran alongside. 'Here, quickly!'

Seeing her in such a state he knew immediately that something was badly wrong. Maggy never rushed anywhere; she wasn't slothful, her steady determined gait usually took her where she was heading in plenty of time. 'Hold on, you two!' he shouted to Erik and Ollie. Then, making sure nothing could slip, he climbed quickly onto the wharf side. 'What is it? What on earth's the matter?' he asked, trying to make out if she was hurt in some way.

'It's Ellen,' she gasped, 'she's fallen.'

'Ellen?' He exclaimed loudly, without thinking, and quickly turned to look at Erik who was peering up at him from the hold. The alarm on

Michael's face was sufficient to bring Erik stumbling over the mass of iron links of chain and quickly up onto the deck.

Looking up at Maggy's stricken face he asked anxiously, 'Something's happened, no?' His eyes were wide with anxiety.

Numbly Maggy nodded. 'Ellen's slipped in the yard. She's in bed. The doctor's there but Anna says you're to go home straight away.'

'Oh, God!' Erik cried. 'Oh, God!' He sprang up the ladder on the dock wall like a man possessed, and ran to where Michael stood with Maggy. 'We have to go, you understand?' He looked back at the hold, knowing that when they left Michael would have to carry on alone, yet they couldn't delay. 'We come back as soon as possible,' he apologised with a helpless gesture.

'Of course you must go,' Michael urged him. 'Go on, hurry up.'

By this time Ollie had joined them to see what had caused such a commotion.

'Your mother has had a fall,' Maggy quickly informed him, her tone gentle, forgetting her earlier unkind thoughts.

'Is she hurt?' He demanded anxiously, glancing at his father, and back to Maggy, his face showing signs of distress.

'She has to rest. Anna sent for a doctor, and there is a neighbour with her as well. I didn't see your mother, instead I came as quickly as I could.'

'That was very good of you,' Ollie replied, looking gravely at her.

Erik was anxious to be off. 'If Ellen is alright I send Ollie back to help, then I come as soon as I can.'

There was nothing Michael could do under the circumstances, he was as concerned about what had happened as everyone else. 'The best thing is for Maggy to go with you,' he offered. 'Then she can come back and tell me how things are. I'll wait until then and if necessary I'll have to make arrangements to hire some help. You two get off!'

'Thanks, Mike!' Erik said, and hurried along the wharf, his face pale and drawn, leaving Maggy to accompany Ollie at a slightly slower pace.

Ollie's steps were long and brisk though, and Maggy found it hard to keep up, she knew she was holding him back. 'You go ahead,' she panted, 'I'm afraid I can't go as fast as you.'

'I'm sorry,' he said, slowing down a little. 'Would you mind if I did? You know the way, don't you?'

This suited Maggy. 'Yes—I'll follow, you hurry,' she urged. As he almost ran ahead Maggy wondered what he would find when he got to the house. Her thoughts reeled with all sorts of dire possibilities, so much so that when she arrived at their door she knocked on it timidly, not knowing what to expect. The women were no longer gathered outside, they'd quickly dispersed when they saw Erik approaching and disappeared into their own homes for fear of upsetting him. Anna came to let her in. She was calmer now and Maggy stood shyly in the doorway afraid that she might be intruding.

'How is your mother?' she asked anxiously.

Anna smiled at her. 'She's very pale and uncomfortable, but the bleeding's stopped. All we can do now is wait and hope she'll be alright.' Seeing that Maggy was hot and tired she offered her a chair to sit on and said, 'Thank you for going back, even if I'd known where Father was I daren't have left the house because the children were very frightened.'

Taking the drink which Anna brought her, and remembering that Michael was waiting on the keel unaware of what was happening, she dared to ask, 'Are your father and Ollie with her now?'

'Yes they are. Would you like to go and see her?' Anna asked.

Hesitating a little Maggy replied, 'Will she mind, doesn't she have to rest?'

'I told her that you had gone back to fetch Father and she was very grateful. Come, she wants to say thank you. She can rest soon, when Ollie and Father go back to help your brother.' She led Maggy up the stairs and then paused before knocking gently on the bedroom door, waiting to be invited in. Her father called for her to enter, but Maggy stood in the doorway, shy of intruding on the group now gathered around the bed.

Seeing her hesitate, Erik smiled and said again, 'Come in'. He was sitting beside Ellen holding her hand tenderly in his. Maggy was embarrassed by this open display of affection, and averted her eyes. Unfortunately, in doing so she found herself meeting Ollie's direct gaze, and this served only to increase her discomfort. In dismay she lowered her head and wondered where to look next.

Observing this, Ellen smiled gently and spoke up. 'Thank you Miss Havercroft, for your help.' Ellen's face was pale against the white pillow, and Maggy could see she was very tired and in need of rest and quiet. 'I'm sorry to have caused so much trouble for your brother, but I'm sure that while I take a rest these two can safely leave me and return to work.'

With these encouraging words, Maggy went closer, saying, 'Please call me Maggy; Miss Havercroft sounds so strange'. Ellen smiled back in acceptance. 'I do hope you'll feel better soon,' Maggy concluded, pleased to have Ellen's friendship.

'It's not so bad now,' Ellen replied, although her voice was low and strained, 'but I think perhaps that I'd better sleep for a while.' Looking fondly at her husband, she urged. 'You go, my dear, Anna will sit with me. Tell her where to find you if I need you back here. I'll be alright.'

'Are you sure?' Erik's voice was husky as his throat tightened with concern.

'Of course, and perhaps Maggy can sit and talk to Anna while I sleep, if she can spare the time. The children are playing next door.'

'But perhaps Maggy has more important things to do,' Anna suggested, not too convincingly, and Maggy realised from her manner that she wanted her company.

Smiling at her, she agreed to stay, at which point Erik rose from his chair, kissed his wife lovingly, and offered his chair to her. 'Here,' he said, 'sit down, you've been rushing about all afternoon for us, and we're very grateful.' Maggy wasn't used to such open praise and flushed. 'You are much prettier when you blush,' he said, with a twinkle in his eye.

'Erik Erikson!' Ellen cried, 'leave the poor girl alone and go, now!'

Like a lamb he left the room, taking Ollie with him, much to Maggy's relief.

Maggy and Anna sat talking quietly and amicably as Ellen slept. Meanwhile, Michael struggled on alone, aware that he was taking up valuable space on the wharf side. His cargo was divided between the keel and the wharf, and the hired crane was idle more than it was in use. He had no idea when either of the men would return, even if at all that day, and he waited impatiently for Maggy to come back with some news of them, and Ellen. What he wouldn't have given to be sailing along the canal with the wind in his face, instead of straining to lift heavy chains into position for the crane! He was in pain now as well as despair, near to acknowledging defeat, and his movements were getting slower as time went on. As he paused to ease his muscles before trying to move a larger piece of machinery, he became aware of someone calling to him.

'Hello Michael, where's Maggy?'

Startled, he looked up to find Lily perched on a bollard. He'd no idea how long she'd been watching him but from her relaxed manner it was obvious she hadn't just sat down. He waved to her from the hold and called, 'What are you doing here?' At the same time he tried not to let her see how happy he was to see her.

'We didn't have to hang around on our last trip, and the winds were good. Where's Maggy?' she asked again.

'Gone to a friend's house,' he replied, avoiding enlightening her about his situation in case her father should smell an opportunity to get one up on him.

'That's a pity,' she answered, although he wasn't sure she meant it. She stood up and looked down on him. 'I had wondered if she'd come round town with me. Never mind!' She shrugged her shoulders as if about to leave, but instead climbed down onto the deckway of the keel, and stood looking keenly at him. 'You look tired, Michael,' she said sympathetically. 'You're not on your own are you?'

He was pleased to see her and had recovered from the shock of her being there. 'I am at the moment,' he said, 'but where's the *Mary Ann*?'

'There,' she told him, pointing to a spot about thirty yards along the dock. She laughed, 'You've been so busy you never saw us coming'.

He gave a slight start, conscious that she must have known he'd been struggling by himself for some time. 'How long have you been sitting there?' he asked, avoiding the candour in her eyes by adopting a casual attitude.

She laughed again, 'Not long, we saw you as we drew alongside. We were just in time to spot another boat leaving'.

'My word,' he sighed, 'Shifty has all the luck, I had to wait most of yesterday for a berth.'

'Ah, but Dad's got me!' she cried triumphantly. 'I'm his good luck charm, or so he reckons.' Then, a little cheekily, she added, 'You could do with a bit of luck yourself, Michael. Did you keep the piece of coal?' There was an unmistakable challenge in her eyes and a provocative tilt to her head.

He was shaken as much by her forwardness as her remark. 'What do you mean?' he asked, playing her along and pretending not to understand.

'No matter, Michael Havercroft!' she said meaningfully, before moving back to the ladder, smiling as she did so. 'I'll be back to see Maggy later.' Then, lifting her skirts a little higher than necessary, she climbed back onto the quayside and left him to ponder on her behaviour.

That she was teasing him was obvious, but Michael saw her go with regret. Lily had the power to make him forget his problems, even if she did create a turmoil in his mind. He smiled to himself. Perhaps if there was time during their stay in Hull he could ask her out for a drink. He would think about it. At this moment, he had more to do than dream of Lily, but try as he might he couldn't put her from his mind, she was pleasant to contemplate and lifted his spirits considerably. When Erik and Ollie returned twenty minutes later they found him hard at work, humming a tune to himself.

'Is your wife not too bad then?' Michael asked when Erik got down into the hold. 'How is she?'

'I think she will be alright,' but there was uncertainty in the older man's voice. 'You never can tell with these things, but Anna and Maggy are watching over her so we can come back.'

'I'm very grateful,' Michael said, but he couldn't ignore the worried expression on Erik's face. 'Are you sure you feel like working?'

Erik nodded his head, and sighed. 'I work, it takes my thoughts away. Maggy will come and tell me if I am needed. It is good we have Ollie to help us, it will make up for lost time.'

Michael was relieved to see them and without further ado set them to work again.

'Do you think we'll get her emptied today?' Ollie asked, as he helped Michael to place lifting ropes around a long iron girder.

'I should think so,' Michael panted, as he dropped the looped rope ends over the lifting hook. 'Are you still of a mind to come with me to Sheffield?'

'Definitely! Have you any idea when you'll be leaving?'

'That depends on what's available to take back. I usually get a mixture of goods from Africa once a month but the ship hasn't docked yet. I might have to take what I can if it isn't sighted soon.' With that he straightened up. 'Right, I'll go and work the crane. Will you two guide this girder so that it doesn't hit anything?' He climbed onto the wharfside, wound the girder up slowly, then set it down with others on the quay, just as Lily approached with a mug of tea.

Handing it to him, she said with a smile. 'I thought you could do with this, and I've nothing else to do at the moment.'

'Thanks, Lily,' he said, quite touched and grateful for her gesture, as it had been some time since he'd had a drink. He took a mouthful and rinsed his throat. 'That was good, I didn't realise just how thirsty I was.' He looked at her, noting how pretty she was with her clear lively eyes which missed nothing, and which seemed to be weighing him up. He wondered how she would react if he asked her out. Was she leading him on or just filling in time until someone else came along? Plucking up courage, he asked, 'Would you like to go for a walk tonight?'

'Why, Michael Havercroft!' she said, looking at him in feigned surprise. 'I thought you'd never get round to asking.' She had a way with her that made him wonder if she was flirting with him, or simply just teasing. Had he been more used to women he would perhaps have worked it out, but he wasn't, so decided the best course of action would be not to let her know exactly what he did feel. She sat on the same bollard as before watching him finish the tea. 'How long will you be here?' she asked. 'Have you got anything to take back yet?'

'I think I'll be here tomorrow at least,' he told her, cautiously, as Swifty could smell a shipment a mile off! 'What about you?'

'Dad's gone to look around while my brothers off-load.' She took the mug from him, knowing he had work to do, and looked again along the length of the keel, all the while delaying the parting.

'Thanks, Lily,' he repeated again, 'now I'd best get on, the others are waiting.' He daren't press her for a reply to his invitation in case she laughed at him.

'Where shall I meet you then?' she asked, and was about to leave when she saw Ollie straighten up, 'I see you've got yourself another hand,' she said, and settled herself down onto the bollard again.

Michael nodded. 'The big man's my new mate, the young one's his son. He's just helping out for a while.'

'Oh, he is, is he?' Lily remarked quite casually, but her manner conveyed something else, causing Michael to glance at her half-turned head. She seemed momentarily distracted, and he sensed that her thoughts were on something else.

'I'll meet you at the *Mary Ann* at eight,' he told her, not sure why her mood had changed. 'Is that alright?' he asked.

There was a moment's hesitation, then she answered, 'What? Oh, yes Mike, that'll be alright. How long will Maggy be?'

'I'm not sure,' he replied a little disappointed that she could flit so quickly from one subject to another. Perhaps she was already regretting agreeing to meet him, but it was too late.

'I'll get off now and leave you to it, Michael. See you later!' With that she left him with an encouraging little smile, causing him to wonder if he'd imagined her change of attitude earlier.

Maggy returned much later in the afternoon, as the three men were nearing the end of their heavy work. Rushing up to her, Erik asked, 'How is my Ellen?' She felt sorry for him, knowing how anxious he was, and quite shocked to see how drawn he appeared. He seemed to have aged in the few hours she'd been away.

Trying not to alarm him she touched his arm, gently. 'She's been asleep most of the time, but occasionally she does get a tiny twinge of pain.'

'That's not good!' he declared, a look of real concern on his face. This frightened Maggy, who immediately thought she might have said too much. He must have realised from her stricken look that she was probably unaware of the dangers that attended child-bearing, and in a kindly voice added with a sigh, 'We are in God's hands child, babies are strange creatures.' He walked slowly away to where Ollie was standing, his steps lacking their usual energy.

Sitting down on the cabin hatch Maggy watched the men working, her thoughts far away, and it was only when Michael approached her and made some comment that she realised how intently she had been studying Ollie.

'Will you make us something to eat, Sis?' he asked, once she'd regained her composure. 'Lily from the *Mary Ann* came round earlier to see if you'd go into town with her. She brought me a mug of tea.' Surprisingly, this news had little effect on her. 'Come on, cheer up, it's been a bad day for us all.' He was concerned at her lack of response.

'I'm worried, Michael! Ellen is so pale, and Anna's been crying. I had an awful feeling of helplessness as I sat with them, waiting. She's not well, do you think Erik should go home? I know you need him, but we lost Dad without warning.' Tears ran down her face, and he began to suspect that Erik's wife might be more seriously ill than he'd imagined.

'Alright, if things are that bad I'll tell Erik we can manage now. Ollie can stay until we get further news.' As Maggy made her way below, he went to where Erik was tying up some loose chains. 'Look, Erik,' he said casually, 'I'd feel better if you packed it in now. It's been a long, upsetting day, it's nearly dusk, and Ollie and I can manage what's left on our own. His being here has more than made up for a slow start. Besides, you look all in. Go on, off you go!'

'Yes, I would like that.' There was a tone of resignation in Erik's voice. 'My mind is not here, you understand.'

'I hope you find your wife feeling a little better,' Michael responded, feeling more than just sorry for the man. 'Let me know later, how things are won't you.'

'Thanks, Mike. I tell Ollie why I go,' Erik replied, and after having a brief word with his son he quit the keel.

Michael wondered if Erik held himself to blame for Ellen's situation, especially after Ollie's remonstration with him over yet another pregnancy. Prior to that he'd seemed quite happy at the thought of becoming a father again, after so long. Going up to Ollie, he said, 'I've sent your father home, he's exhausted and very worried.' He then felt compelled to explain further. 'Look, Maggy's not happy about your mother's condition, but I didn't tell your father that. Would you like to go home too?'

Ollie considered the offer, but obviously decided that for the time being he could do no good at home. 'That's thoughtful of you,' he said, 'but there's not a lot I can do. His being there will do mother more good. I'll do his share of the work and you can pay him for it.'

Maggy reappeared with some sandwiches and a drink she'd made for them, and she took the opportunity to talk to Ollie. 'I appreciate your helping my brother,' she told him, when Michael had moved further along the deck. She was feeling a little nervous as it was the first time she'd spoken to Ollie at any length, but went on, 'and I'm sorry about your mother, I hope she'll be alright'. There seemed no need to speak cautiously, or feel shy under the circumstances.

'When you left her, how ill do you think she was?' There was a deep concern in his voice and on his face.

A lump rose in Maggy's throat, and her eyes moistened, 'I'm very worried, she's so pale, and Anna keeps crying. I do hope nothing bad happens'. Then, seeing the despair on his face she hastily added, 'I'm sorry, I should have watched my words, she's your mother and you must be very worried.'

'I am,' he admitted, 'but it's not your fault. I think my father is lucky to be working for a man who is as compassionate as your brother.'

Hearing this Maggy warmed to him, for Michael never seemed to be fully appreciated for his true worth. He was reliable and kind, and not the rough, hard man that many were. 'He is a good man,' she enthused, 'and I would not like to see him hurt or taken advantage of.' Realising that these words might imply some criticism of Ollie, she prayed that he would not misunderstand her reason for speaking out so boldly.

'I should hope not,' Ollie agreed, not unkindly, although he had not in fact missed the intensity in her voice. 'I, at least, would not repay his helpfulness to my family by doing so. As for my father it is not in his nature to be anything but open and honest.'

Feeling guilty and awkward, Maggy sought to make amends for her remark. 'I did not mean that you would,' she stammered, 'only that now he is Captain there are people who would ride rough-shod over him if he was not alert to what they were up to.'

'Then he and my father should get on well, providing they keep their wits about them,' he said. 'Times are changing fast and competitiveness will be all important in the future. They will not have to be afraid to fight for what they want.'

Maggy was beginning to feel that she had misjudged Ollie, and looking at him now she thought she might owe him an apology. He was no more arrogant or overbearing than any other man she knew, and at least he understood what the future might be, even if he had yet to prove himself in it. In a more subdued voice she spoke again. 'I am beginning to like your family, and I do hope that we can continue to work together.'

'There's nothing I'd like better,' he responded. 'It would please me greatly to see my father employed permanently once more. This would leave me free to pursue goals of my own.' He saw that this statement raised questions in her mind but did not enlighten her, instead he changed the subject. 'I must get back to work. Thank you for the refreshments.'

'When you go home, will you send word to let us know how your mother is?' she asked quietly.

'I will, especially if she doesn't improve, but hopefully all will be well and Father can carry on tomorrow as normal.' He looked at her, contemplating something, then asked, 'Am I to call you Miss Havercroft, or Maggy, like the rest of the family?' There was a lightness in his tone, but his face remained grave. He knew that she was watching him also, summing him up, and he found this quite an enjoyable experience. He was aware that young women often found him attractive initially, only to discover later that he was rather too serious-minded for their liking. He realised too, that she had not seen him in a good light the day before when he'd remonstrated with his father on the quayside. He smiled at the memory, and Maggy was happy to accept this as one of friendship.

Smiling back, she said, 'I'm Maggy'.

'I suppose you know mine,' he replied, 'it's Ollie, short for Olaf.'

She watched him as he and Michael finished clearing the hold of the few remaining chains. He was obviously not the monster she'd thought him earlier, nor did his plans seem to involve the *Maggie Kelly* in the long run.

Later, somewhat easier in her mind, she set about preparing a meal for Michael when he finished work, quite unaware that he intended taking Lily out that evening. He was unusually quiet as he ate it and even seemed a little nervous. She found this strange and finally asked, 'What's up? I know it's been a long, disturbed sort of day, but you've done everything you needed, haven't you?'

He agreed. 'Yes, thanks to Ollie. I wonder how Erik's wife is though, perhaps you'd better call and see her again tomorrow, even if he does come to the keel.'

'I will, but you're up to something, Michael, I can tell. You've been playing with your food, not eating it. Is there something wrong with it?'

He swallowed hard. 'Maggy,' he said sheepishly, 'I'm going out tonight, with Lily.'

'What?' She gasped with excitement. 'Is that why she came? To see you and not me?'

'No!' he protested, with a smile, 'I asked her out, just before she went back to the *Mary Ann*.'

'So you do like her then. I knew it!' Maggy cried triumphantly, as he pushed his half empty plate away. He shrugged his shoulders as if indifferent to her comments, yet she could tell that he was quite on edge. 'Well, go on then, go and get washed! I'll get you a clean shirt out, you can't let her see you looking like that.'

'Alright, alright!' he laughed. 'I always get washed after tea anyway.' He took longer than usual to do so that night, but eventually with a clean shirt on and his hair tidied, even Maggy had to admit he looked quite handsome. 'Do I look clean enough?' he asked shyly, almost ashamed that his spare pair of corduroy trousers were far from new.

Teasing him, Maggy said, 'She'll hardly see you in the dark. Anyway, where are you going to take her?'

'I'm not sure. A walk round the dock I suppose, then I'll take her for a drink somewhere—what do you think?'

'If you don't know by now, Michael Havercroft, then heaven help you. And mind you don't have one too many like Grandma Kelly had, *and* remember to treat Lily like a lady!' He straightened up at this remark and looked rather grim. 'Oh! Go on, away with you,' she said, pushing him towards the ladder. Poor Michael she thought, after he'd gone. It was more likely that Lily would take advantage of him than the other way round!

She was left without company and little to do but read, so, curling up on the locker, she opened her well-fingered copy of *Jane Eyre*, and tried to immerse herself in the familiar text. Try as she might, however, she found concentration almost impossible, mainly because she knew the tale so well that she could almost recite it from memory, but also because of Michael. What, she wondered mischievously, was Michael up to with Lily? Swifty's daughter was perhaps a little too lively for him, but the company of a pretty girl would certainly be a tonic for him at this time.

She was so deep in her reverie that the knock on the cabin hatch quite startled her. Jumping to her feet, and conscious of being alone on the keel, she called out nervously, 'Who is it?'

'Ollie Erikson!' came the reply.

'I'll come up,' she answered and quickly drew back the bolt of the hatch, both puzzled and worried that he should call so late in the evening. She took her lantern and climbed up onto the deck, having always been told never to invite a man into the cabin when she was alone, for fear of inviting gossip, if nothing else. 'Michael's not here at the moment,' she told him, 'is there anything the matter?' She was unable to see his face clearly, but then as he turned into the light, she could see that something indeed was very wrong. 'What's happened?' she asked, cautiously, and much afraid of what he might say.

'Sit down,' he said. His voice was strained and his movements tired as he joined her on the hatch cover. 'It was not to be, the baby was born dead.' He was subdued and obviously shaken by what had happened.

'Oh, no!' Maggy cried, not wanting to believe him.

'I'm afraid so. Nothing could be done!' This time there was a tremor in his voice, and she felt immensely sorry for him.

'But, your mother,' she stammered, 'is she…?' She stopped abruptly, and looked at him with frightened eyes.

'No, no,' he interrupted, 'she's resting, but I won't be happy until she's up and about again. So many things can go wrong at times like these.'

Maggy sighed, not really knowing what to say to give him comfort. She sat beside him in silence, in the gloom, waiting for him to speak. When he didn't, she forced herself to do so but chose her words carefully. 'You must be very worried, and your father too.'

'Indeed I am. I have only seen him so distressed once before, and that was when my sister died.'

'His beautiful Sonja,' Maggy said wistfully almost to herself, repeating Erik's own words.

Ollie was startled by her soft tone and her obvious knowledge of their tragedy. 'He told you of her?'

'Yes,' she nodded, 'while we were waiting to see if the keel would re-float off Whitton Sands. When we thought we were in danger, he told us stories to keep us going, and chatted about you all. He has a way of talking which is difficult to forget.'

'I had no idea that you had even been in trouble, was there an accident? He hasn't said.'

'Well, we grounded in a squall and there was a fear that the keel was on mud and wouldn't re-float. My cousin, a young boy who was with us was terrified, that's why Erik tried to take our minds off things' she explained. 'It was about that time that I read your letter out to him, too.'

He looked at her in amazement. 'You can read that well? And you know so much about me! You have me at a disadvantage, Maggy.'

Feeling as if she had betrayed Erik in some way, she quickly tried to explain and defend herself. 'It was not done to pry, only to give him comfort in return for his kindness!' She was flustered now, 'I cannot remember much of what I read.'

'No matter,' he reassured her with a smile. 'I'm not angry, only surprised that you have learned so much about us in such a short time.'

'I really haven't,' she protested, 'we were all a little frightened that night, especially Patrick, and Michael can't easily make small talk. Your father sought to calm us, that's all.'

Waving this aside, he asked, 'But how did you learn to read and express yourself so well?' He was intrigued by her ability to hold her own with him, a virtual stranger.

She was keen to let him see that she was not merely a 'water gypsy' as many saw canal folk, but a member of a hard-working group of people. 'I have been to school,' she told him proudly. 'My father paid for my schooling even though he couldn't read himself. Poor Michael has always had to work and couldn't be spared to improve himself, but I have taught him to read and write as best I can. You see, my father knew that my brother would always have work with him and would eventually take over the keel, that in itself is more than many can achieve.'

'You do not have to defend your family to me, Maggy. My father too worked hard to improve our knowledge, but for Anna it was different; there was never enough money, and he felt it more important to educate us.'

Maggy bristled at this comment. 'What do you mean?' She spoke sharply, 'Do you think it would have been wasted on her?'

He was taken aback by her reaction. 'You misunderstand me again,' he remonstrated firmly. 'The fact is, that no matter how educated Anna was, she could expect no more than any other girl in her social position. She can read because I taught her, and is intelligent, but she will only be able to go into service, or get married. Unless we support her, I'm afraid she must work for other people until that time comes.'

He was right, of course, and Anna was no different to herself in that respect. What a bleak and dismal outlook it was for their future! She felt uncomfortable over her outburst. 'I'm sorry,' she said lamely, 'I thought that you meant to discredit her.'

'Far from it, but Anna is also rather shy, and she lacks confidence. Unlike women in a higher social class, she stands little chance of bettering herself. We're not rich enough for her to stay at home doing needlework as the well-off ladies do.'

Will I be able to? she thought, listening to facts which only emphasised the disquieting realisation she'd felt since her father's death. 'But I'm in that position as well! There's not much to look forward to, is there?' She was more annoyed with her own predicament than with him. 'My situation is even worse, for if Michael marries, then he would not be able to support me, nor could I accept my brother-in-law's hospitality forever.'

He had no answer to her problem and could only commiserate by saying, 'If it was in my power I would change matters for both of you, but I too must plan my future carefully if I am to support a wife and family at some time. A man has responsibilities which never go away, and he cannot marry to escape them.' Then, fearing that Maggy would misunderstand his meaning once more, he said, 'I mean no criticism in that, it is simply a fact of life'.

Considering his words she conceded that perhaps a man's lot was not much better than a woman's. 'We are all trapped by the restrictions of our upbringing to some extent. It seems there is no way out.' She sighed, resigning herself to a less than bright future.

'I do not intend to remain as I am,' Ollie confessed, with no hint of arrogance or that he had already achieved a modicum of success. 'There are ways of improving my chances, and I aim to try them.' He realised that they had been sitting outside for too long; the air felt damp and it was getting late. 'I think perhaps the events of the day have made us dismal,' he said. 'Please tell Mike that I called and will come again tomorrow. If he has to be about his business early then can you arrange between yourselves the best way for me to see him?'

'Yes, of course,' Maggy agreed, 'and do you think I might pay your mother a visit later in the day?'

'Come when you can, Anna will be there, and I'm sure mother would like you to call,' he said, before taking leave of her.

'Say that I'm sorry,' she said gently.

When he'd gone Maggy went below. She pondered on their discussion, one which had lasted almost half an hour. What must he be thinking? She had shown herself to be aggressive, dissatisfied and worst of all, gloomy. Never before had she spoken to anyone, other than Michael, of her doubts and fears, and then not in any great depth. She had no real reason to complain of her situation in life, it was better than that of many others. Her overactive mind, however, gave her little peace, and she knew she must learn to choose her words more carefully, as these could bring unfavourable reactions from others who hardly knew her. She was deeply impressed by Ollie's gentlemanly conduct, and his readiness to discuss things intelligently, treating her as an equal. She was tired now though, and wanted to go to bed, but she couldn't do that without leaving the bolt drawn for Michael's return. Not that he would be over-late, Lily's father would see to that; they all rose early each morning and Lily was needed to cook breakfast for her father and brothers long before townsfolk were up and about.

Maggy was afraid to spoil Michael's evening out but she had to tell him about Ellen, as it might effect Erik's availability for work. She seemed to sit forever in her night attire, listening for his returning footsteps. Where could he be? At last, she heard his pre-arranged signal tapped out on the hatch. By this time she was weary and apprehensive, and rather than greet him with cheerful inquisitiveness she was a little sharp. 'Where have you been, Michael? You'll have Swifty after you, keeping Lily out 'til this time.'

'It's no business of yours, Maggy,' he told her, firmly but not unkindly.

Rather annoyed at this remark, she retaliated. 'I couldn't go to bed until you came back, next time I'll leave you up on deck all night!' She knew she was being peevish, but it had been that kind of day. He said nothing, but for the first time in her life she saw a look in his eyes which made her hesitate. Somehow everything she'd said that day had been wrong, waspish or argumentative. She bit her lip, fighting back the tears and remembered her earlier resolve to keep a check on her own words and thoughts.

Michael too had not had a good day, and his evening had not gone well. He hadn't known what to talk about, furthermore he was tired, his leg ached and Lily had been strangely quiet. He could see that Maggy was annoyed with him, but he wasn't going to tell her about his problems. It was only when he saw the unshed tears in her eyes that he realised something was wrong, something more than his staying out late. 'What's up, Maggy?' he asked quietly, watching her keenly. 'There's been no trouble while I've been away, has there?'

'Oh, Michael,' she cried. 'Ellen's lost the baby.' Tears suddenly ran freely down her cheeks as she looked helplessly at him.

He drew his brows together, and a puzzled frown appeared on his face. 'How do you know?' he asked, as if doubting her statement.

She sniffed, trying to stem the tears, 'Ollie came earlier to tell us. He wants to see you, and says Erik may be late tomorrow under the circumstances.'

'Is Ellen alright?' Michael asked, deeply concerned now as the truth sank in. He was sorry to hear the news, although he had half expected that such a tragedy might occur.

'I think so, at least Ollie thinks she is!' Maggy was beginning to get a grip of herself now. 'It is dreadful, Michael, but there's nothing we can do to help, is there? Do you think it will stop Erik from working?'

Michael was downcast, nothing seemed to go right for more than a day or so. 'I really don't know,' he sighed. 'He's got enough on his mind, but he still has a family to feed and needs the money. Did Ollie say what he wanted?'

'He said, if you were going to be away from here in the morning, where and when could he meet you?'

'I have to go to the Dock's Office first thing. You stay here and tell him I'll be back by ten, if not earlier.'

It seemed inappropriate now to discuss his evening out, so with no more ado she wished him goodnight and went to bed, leaving him alone with his thoughts.

Next morning as she waited patiently for Erik or Ollie to arrive, Lily came by. 'Michael's out,' Maggy informed her, 'he won't be back 'til later!'

Lily seemed a bit edgy and there was a furtive look in her eyes. 'Nobody else about then?' Her voice was casual, but her eyes darted here and there along the keel and wharfside.

'Why no,' Maggie replied, unsure of her meaning. 'Mr Erikson's wife is ill, so he's not here yet. Did you want to see me yesterday?'

'I just thought you might have gone round town with me, that's all. Anyway, I'll be off, Dad's moving across the river to the new dock. Tell Michael I'll see him sometime.'

Maggy assumed that the disappointment in her voice was because she'd missed her brother. 'I'll tell him when he gets back, Lily,' she called out, watching her slim form move away. There was something about Lily that she didn't like, she was moody. She could be friendly and lively one minute, then quickly change and become very casual. Deep down Maggy hoped Michael wouldn't fall in love with her in case he got hurt.

Before either Ollie or Erik put in an appearance, Michael returned with a broad smile on his face. 'What is it?' Maggy asked, her spirits rising at his obvious pleasure.

He could hardly contain himself as he explained, 'The ship with the ivory's been sighted; she's just waiting for the tide, and I managed to get a consignment of guano as well for Thorne and Sheffield!'

'Yuk!' Maggy exclaimed, with distaste. 'At least it's not smelly old bones for the fertiliser mill.'

'It's the best dried stuff, Maggy, and it's bagged. I've also got a load of whale bones for the garment factory, leaving plenty of room for the horn and ivory. All I need now is help to load up. Has Erik or Ollie turned up yet?' He looked round hopefully.

'No, only Lily. Do you want me to go to Adelaide Street with a message?' she offered, 'only I did say I would go today to see how Ellen was. What time is it?'

Taking his father's reliable old time-piece from his pocket, he announced, 'It's ten o'clock,' and then he thought for a moment, 'I think it best if I went, you stay here in case I miss either of them. If they're not at the house I'll come straight back, so tell them to wait. You can go this afternoon.'

Maggy was a little frustrated at having to remain on the keel on her own, but she consoled herself with the knowledge that she would, after all, be able to go later in the day. 'Alright,' she agreed.

'Did Lily say what she wanted?'

'Only that Swifty was having to move to the new dock, and that she'd see you some time. She seemed a bit strange and didn't stay long.'

There was no sign of disappointment on his face and if he was at all put out by the off-hand message from Lily, he concealed it very well. He simply looked to where the *Mary Ann* had been moored and saw that a different vessel had already berthed in her place, and was being off-loaded. Ignoring her last comment about Lily's behaviour, he remarked. 'Swifty's probably got a load of timber over there by the sound of it.'

Before setting off for Erik's house he went below to put away the Carrying Agent's documents for his new cargoes, hoping that someone would put in an appearance soon, thus saving him the journey to Adelaide Street. As neither man arrived by the time he had finished his task he decided to leave. 'I'm off, Maggy,' he called, 'if either of them comes ask them to wait here. I shan't be long.'

When he arrived at the Erikson home, he knocked gently so as not to disturb the beleaguered family too much, and waited. Rain clouds were gathering but there was a chance that the strong easterly breeze would keep the threatened rain away, at least he hoped it would until he had loaded up the guano.

The door knob turned slowly at last, and as the door opened he saw Anna's pale face peer round it enquiringly. He was about to smile broadly at her in greeting and as a way of introducing himself properly this time, but was disturbed to see her shrink back when she saw who it was. She was plainly nervous at finding him there on the doorstep, and the look she gave him was not one easily described. She could have no reason to fear him and he was dismayed and disturbed by her apparently instinctive reaction. He saw that she was desperately trying to regain her composure, so, in a business-like tone, he asked, 'Good morning, Miss Erikson, is your father, or Ollie, at home?' He wanted to allay her fears which he presumed stemmed from the awkwardness of their first meeting.

Anna quickly concealed her emotions and replied, 'Do come in Mr Havercroft, you have missed Ollie, but my father is with mother. I'll fetch him down for you.'

'Thank you, I'm most obliged,' he replied, trying to be formal without being unfriendly. As she left the room he noted how delicate she appeared, no doubt taking after her mother, and so unlike Erik. He was annoyed that his presence may have caused her further distress, especially as he was not the original cause. To his relief, Erik came down immediately, looking tired and flustered.

'Good morning, Mike, has Ollie been to see you yet?' he asked wearily. 'I tell him to let you know how things are, before he do anything else!'

'He hasn't been to the keel this morning, but he came late last night, though, while I was away,' Michael replied, feeling sorry for the man. 'How is your wife?'

'I'm sorry about Ollie,' Erik went on. 'Ellen is very upset and I worry for her, but I think if there is no fever she will recover.'

'Good! Is there anything we can do?'

Erik shook his head, 'That's kind of you, but Anna can manage to look after Ellen and the children. Do you need me to help you load up yet? I told Ollie to find out if you get a load, then I come. I don't understand where he goes to!'

'No matter, you've enough on your mind. I do have a consignment of guano to load up if the rain holds off, and my ivory is due in on the tide. Can you make it after dinner?'

'Ja, I come then! Would you like coffee?' Erik continued, 'I need one myself.' Seeing that Michael was in two minds at this he called out, 'Anna, will you make the coffee for Mike and me, please.'

Whilst Anna busied herself, Michael sat on a chair wondering whether to speak directly to her or to continue his conversation with her father. He would have liked to explain to her that he had been just as embarrassed by her father's words on the quayside as she must have been, except that the subject was a delicate one, and Erik was present. As she spoke to her father he realised that his first impression that she was timid, even mouse-like, was wrong. She was obviously shy, her movements being graceful rather than slow, unlike Lily who was somewhat brash and whose liveliness caused a stir wherever she went. He was rather amused by these thoughts. Here he was, a man who couldn't think of much to say when he was with Lily, yet now wanting to draw out the reluctant Anna! The thought that she might actually be afraid of him, made him want to laugh out loud. Whatever would Maggy think of this contrariness?

He took the coffee and thanked her with real warmth, smiling as he did so, and tried to convey a feeling of respect in order to make amends. To his surprise she smiled brightly back at him in return, and he was tempted to ask her to call him Michael, rather than Mr Havercroft, but curbed the impulse in case it was too forward at this time. Besides, Erik was there also, and might make another embarrassing remark. Erik's mind, however, was far away, probably grappling with more important family matters.

'Maggy's hoping to call this afternoon,' he told Anna, as she sat down opposite him. 'Do you think that will be convenient?'

'Of course,' she replied, her eyes brightening, 'it will make a nice change, and I know mother will enjoy it.'

He tried to hold her gaze in a friendly fashion, relieved that she seemed to be relaxing in his presence. 'It's good for Maggy to have a friend here,' he told her. 'Life on the keel can be lonely for a young girl, especially as she doesn't know many people on the canal, not having travelled with us regularly in the past few years.' He paused. 'I suppose she must find life very dull with just me for company, now that Father's dead.'

A look of sympathy crossed her face. 'Maggy told me about your loss. I am very sorry,' Anna responded, 'and I understand how you both must feel.'

'Thank you,' he said, 'but having your father on board with us has helped.' It was only then as he looked around that he realised that Erik had left the room. 'Is he alright do you think?' he asked in a low voice, as he stood up. 'I can tell he's not himself.'

Suddenly there was a noise on the stairs and three lively children burst into the room. 'Father's sent us down,' Johann cried, relieved to be downstairs again where he could play. He saw Michael, and without any sign of shyness, said, 'Hullo, Mr Havercroft, can we come and look at your boat?'

'Mr Havercroft is too busy,' Anna reproved, glancing apologetically at Michael. 'Forgive them, they have been cooped up all morning doing jobs and have just spent a little time with Mother.'

'Can we go out then?' Johann persisted, not at all happy to be kept indoors.

'Go on then, but don't make a noise. Don't get dirty, and don't go beyond the corner of the street in case I need you.' Anna's voice was firm, 'And say 'Good-bye' to Mr Havercroft.

Michael smiled at this. 'If you want to come down to the dock with my sister later on I'll show you round the keel.'

'Can I come too?' Kristen's small voice piped up, before Anna could intervene.

'Mr Havercroft is a very busy man and cannot spare the time to deal with children! Isn't that right?' She looked at him for support, defying him to contradict her.

He was amused by her insistence that he was too busy to spare five minutes, but in order not to incur her displeasure, he merely offered, 'Maggy could show them round if I'm working, or do you have things for them to do here?' He could see that she didn't think he was being entirely helpful, so decided that perhaps he'd better not press the matter. However, the matter was not allowed to rest.

'Can we go, Anna?' Johann pleaded. 'We'll keep clean and behave all day!' His young face was full of anguish, lest this treat might be withheld, while Kristen could hardly contain her excitement.

Faced with such enthusiastic clamouring, and not really knowing why she was making such a stand against them going, Anna reluctantly gave in. Michael sensed this and thought it better to say no more on the subject.

As Anna busied herself with Lucy's shoes, he fell to musing on his changed circumstances. Until recently there had lain deep within him the firm, unwavering belief that if he harmed no one, and kept himself to himself, then life would go slowly but surely on in a peaceful way. This conviction, however, had been violently shaken with the death of his father. Now he was constantly facing new challenges from which there seemed no escape, some which would appear quite ordinary to other people. Here he sat in Erik's home, where the bustle of excited voices and the battle of wills, although not unpleasant, was very different to his own quiet world. To a stranger, Michael's nomadic and insular life on the keel would perhaps be unenviable, yet here within these four walls it was he who felt oddly out of place. His life in the confines of the small cabin was very private, but elsewhere it wasn't; even his daily wash on deck could be observed by all, whereas a man living in a house could leave it at dawn and return at dusk, almost unnoticed.

He had been so deeply absorbed in his reverie that it was a while before he realised the room had become quiet, and that the children had gone. Looking up with a start, he found Anna was watching him intently. 'I'm sorry, did you say something?' he asked, desperately trying to remember what had disturbed his thoughts.

'Only that the children may visit the keel when it is convenient to you and Maggy.' She leaned forward with concern, and asked, 'Has something troubled you?'

'Not troubled, but perhaps a bit overwhelmed I suppose. I'm not used to such lively surroundings, nor am I used to so many people around me. My cabin is so small and quiet.'

There was a look of understanding on Anna's face. 'Then you must find life a little lonely? It is different here, one hardly ever gets much peace, or indeed time to be alone, but it is very companionable.'

'Not so much lonely,' he replied, thoughtfully. 'I have Maggy for company, and your father is but a shout away.' The words actually belied his true feelings, for he knew that when Maggy finally stopped travelling with him, life on board would certainly be very different.

As if sensing that he was experiencing some inner conflict, Anna tried to lighten the conversation. 'You must enjoy being out on the water though, away from the soot and grime of the towns?'

'Yes,' Michael replied, pleased to put aside thoughts which disturbed him, 'when the weather is good, but it can be awesome in the fog and gales, though your father must have spoken to you of it?'

She laughed softly, 'Yes, many times, too many! So that when he was away at sea we would remember and fear for his safety, especially when we heard of terrible storms.'

'Then he must find working on the canals monotonous after such a life?' Michael commiserated.

'I think not!' A strong voice called out from the doorway, as Erik entered the room. 'My last journey on the estuary was not without excitement, no?'

Michael chuckled, 'No, I suppose not.'

'Now I think that there is work waiting to be done,' Erik continued briskly, 'nor can my daughter keep you here chattering all day.' He grinned, 'Come, let's go, I work with you now.' He had his jacket over his arm and ignored Anna's blushing cheeks. He seemed also not to notice Michael's look of annoyance at yet another thoughtless remark and added, 'Your mother is sleeping, Anna, I come back later to see how she is, and please tell Ollie I want to see him!'

Michael felt sorry for Anna who once again had had to suffer her father's unthinking bluntness for he found talking to her very pleasant. He thanked her for the coffee before making a hasty retreat after Erik, who was already standing outside on the pavement, waiting to leave.

'We get no work done standing idly about,' Erik said, as they walked quickly down the street. 'When I see Ollie I tell him a thing or two! He has no excuse for not telling you how things are.'

'He probably had business to see to,' Michael said, in defence of Ollie, 'and might even now be waiting for us at the keel.'

'Huh!' Erik growled. 'In my young day we make work our business, not dreams.' He was obviously upset, and as the whole family was having a difficult time, Michael chose not to remonstrate with him on Anna's behalf.

Knowing Erik a little better now, he accepted that in his blustering way he was probably unaware of the impact his words had on his sensitive daughter. Nevertheless, Michael had a business to run, and recalling his own father's advice that it didn't pay to get involved in other people's affairs, he resolved to be careful in the future. Sentiment must not be allowed to interfere with work. In spite of having made this decision, he was more than a trifle put out when he got back to the keel to find Maggy and Ollie laughing together and in the company of Lily, of all people! Maggy spotted him first and rose from the hatch top where she'd been sitting, causing the merriment to cease. He was not oblivious to Lily's lack of interest in his return, and wondered why this should be, and what she was doing there. She seemed also to be unduly familiar in the manner in which he'd seen her talking to Ollie.

He felt apprehensive at what she might have gleaned from her conversation with Maggy, as he knew that Lily's loyalty to Swifty was never in doubt. His acknowledgement of Lily was therefore less then encouraging, and as Erik had gone straight to the fore deck without saying a word, he said to Ollie, 'Your father wants a word with you, Ollie, and I need to get the keel into the other dock as soon as possible.'

Seeing that Michael was in no mood for further conversation, Ollie simply asked, 'Is mother alright?'

'Sleeping by all accounts,' Michael told him, and, turning to Maggy he added, 'Anna's looking forward to seeing you this afternoon.' He was about to say something more to Ollie when, almost as an after-thought he turned to Lily, and said casually, 'See you sometime, Lily.'

Taken aback by this abrupt dismissal, Lily scowled, but realising everyone was about to start work she gave up.' 'Bye!' she called, and with a quick wave she hurried off.

'That wasn't very nice, Michael,' Maggy said, after replying to Lily. 'And you've got a face like thunder. What's the matter?'

'Look, Maggy,' he replied, 'there's been enough delay as it is, besides, I'm not sure if I trust Lily. You didn't tell her anything about the ship from Africa coming in did you?'

'Well…,' she looked a little sheepishly at him, and Ollie decided to occupy himself elsewhere, out of earshot. 'I just said we'd got the guano and were waiting for the ivory, but it's only Lily, Mike. Swifty's gone across to get timber.'

'That's not the point, you can't be too careful. I thought you of all people would know that by now.' He hesitated. There was nothing he could do but hope Swifty had sufficient cargo of his own not to poach on his territory. 'Forget it this time,' he said, 'but watch what you're saying in future.'

She watched him prepare the keel for the move which would take them to where the ship containing the guano was moored. He was obviously annoyed with her, but there was more to it. His behaviour towards Lily was uncharacteristic and, strangely, she in turn had shown no pleasure at seeing him again. A lover's tiff maybe, yet his distrust of Swifty's family in general was disturbing. Until his arrival she and Lily had chatted happily with Ollie, laughing about many things, and she'd admired Lily's ability to talk freely in his presence. For a while all of her own troubles had been forgotten, then Michael had appeared and spoilt it all. Erik too was not disposed to talking in his usual blustery way, and from snatches of his conversation with Ollie which she overheard during the next two hours she realised there was trouble in that camp too. She was, therefore, more than pleased when Michael eventually released her to call on Ellen, especially when he said she could bring Anna and the children back with her.

As the three men loaded the bags of bird-lime that had been brought from the Galapagos Islands, Michael repeatedly looked for the ship carrying the ivory to enter the Humber Dock. He was prepared to leave the others at work the moment he saw her, in order to race to the Agent's office. Here he might be lucky to secure something in addition, which could fill any space left in the hold. Ollie owed him no explanation as to why he had not been down earlier, and he had worked hard alongside his father. Indeed without him, valuable time would have been lost yesterday, and possibly they would not have been able to load up again so quickly. For this reason Michael was willing to let things ride, and allow them to sort their problems out in their own good time, providing this didn't cause any upset on the journey.

He was greatly relieved when the main lock gates opened and he saw the masts of the sea-going vessel eventually coming into the dock. 'Can you deal with everything, Erik?' he called down. 'I'm going to the Agents' office and might be some time.'

'That's good, we can manage! Shall we stack the rest of the guano over there?'

'No, keep that area clear for the horns and ivory, that should maintain the balance. If we get anything too heavy we could place the horns on top, depending where we have to unload it.' He was keen to get back before the weather changed and held him up further as it would take the rest of the day to finish stacking the guano. This would, hopefully, then allow them to top up in the morning and sail on the afternoon tide.

The Carrying Agents' office bustled with activity as usual, and he waited nervously for the captain of the newly-arrived ship to register his cargo. This could take some time and Michael was impatient; he wasn't partic- ularly good at hanging around waiting whilst precious time slipped by. This was yet another side of the business he had to get used to now his father was gone. Nor was he the only one waiting; several men hovered in the corridor ready to seize any opportunity which might arise for business. At least the *Maggie Kelly* had a long-standing contract to collect and deliver the ivory and horn for Parker's; what he needed now was that extra load which would increase his profit margin. Not all shipments into Hull were destined for his Keadby to Sheffield run, many would go up the Trent to Lincolnshire and Nottinghamshire, others to Goole and elsewhere, thus his chances for a full load were reduced.

At length a clerk put his head round the door and called, 'There's a consignment of whale oil for Doncaster, about twenty barrels if anyone can take it.'

Michael thought quickly. There might be nothing else for him on the ship even if he waited longer. He hesitated, trying to calculate the amount of space he would have spare in relation to the ivory. It would, of course, create extra work to move the horn twice, but by then he would have delivered some of the guano in Thorne. 'I'll take it!' he called out, hoping his calculations were good enough. He was acutely aware that travelling light from Rotherham would probably mean taking on water ballast to get under Bacon Lane bridge, and wished there'd been more time to work it out. Well, it was too late to withdraw now, the clerk wouldn't appreciate being messed about, and the more experienced captains would no doubt think him a fool. Michael acknowledged again just how much his father had needed to juggle, and think quickly at the end of each journey to provide them with a decent living. He in turn was going to have to be just as alert in order to survive. Perhaps Erik had also found that working as an independent captain was very difficult. At least now he had a full keel and there might yet be an opportunity to fill up again in Thorne or Doncaster.

Having completed the necessary details with the clerk, Michael returned to the keel with a lightness to his steps and his mind at ease.

He looked at the vast array of masts and vessels that were packed in the Dock and noticed that most of the other captains were older than he was, and this gave him a nice feeling of satisfaction. 'The *Maggie Kelly* was in good condition, her hold would be full within twenty-four hours and, thank God, he would have several days in which to rest his leg.

Unknown to his crew, he stood and observed the keel from the cover of a pile of chests. It wasn't his intention to spy on his crew, more a desire to admire his possession and enjoy a brief moment of relaxation. Erik was methodically stacking the guano passed down by Ollie; he had the stamina of two younger men and rarely stopped to rest. His larger than life personality radiated loyalty and commitment and he could be forgiven the odd foible, for Michael knew he too had some funny little ways of his own for others to contend with. As for Ollie, he was different. He was certainly not frightened of work, but remained a mystery and yet was an added bonus to the fortunes of the keel, though whether this situation would continue remained to be seen. He was personable, quite good-looking and had a refined manner, but was very much a man not given to discussing his private thoughts or feelings.

Michael felt a little guilty watching the pair working so hard, although it had only been for a few minutes, yet in that time the sun had broken through the polluted sky, lifting his morale even further. Reluctantly he left his secluded spot, climbed aboard the keel and called Erik to the side of the hold to explain his plans for the following day.

Erik immediately looked concerned and queried, 'That soon we move?'

'Yes, is that a problem?' Michael asked, anxious lest something had happened during his absence.

'No,' came the reply, but there was doubt in Erik's voice.

'What is it?' Michael probed, realising that there was indeed something amiss.

Erik was worried. 'It is Ellen, I had hoped to stay a day or two more, to make sure she is well.'

'I can't help it, Erik,' Michael replied, sympathetically. 'I know it's difficult but I can't risk any more delay.'

Ollie had joined them by this time, and hearing this, remarked, 'I came last night Mike, to make a suggestion, but only Maggy was here.'

Erik rounded on Ollie, 'You didn't tell me!'

'No,' Ollie agreed, understandingly. 'I wanted to talk it over with Mike first.'

So far Michael hadn't mentioned Ollie's proposed trip to Sheffield to Erik, thinking it better that he should broach the subject with his father. 'What had you in mind?'

'Well, suppose I take Father's place on the keel for this trip, and that he comes with us only as far as Keadby, then gets a lift back. 'I'm not as familiar with the Humber as he is, it would be safer that way, and he'd not be away from Mother too long.'

Erik was speechless. He looked from one to the other then back again, his face a mixture of hope, expectation and doubt.

Instead of accepting immediately, Michael took time to consider the proposal. On the face of it the idea was a sound one and would save Ollie explaining his real need to accompany him to Sheffield. Choosing his words with care in order not to offend Erik's pride, he said at last, 'It sounds a good idea to me, Erik. What do you think?' He waited, giving him an opportunity to object, but then added, 'Can you do without the money, though?'

Before Erik could say anything, Ollie broke in, 'I'll only need enough in wages to cover my food. Pay Father the rest instead of me, I won't have to fork out for any lodgings and I'm capable of doing the work, as you can see. I owe him that much, at least.'

Somehow without them realising it, fate had taken a hand and Erik's face softened. He swallowed hard, and in a choked voice, said 'You're a good son, Ollie. I pay you back one day'.

With due respect, Ollie responded, 'Well, if you must, but there is no rush'.

'That is good,' Erik said, with great relief. A broad smile crossed his face, the first to do so in days. 'It is good for your mother, you understand?' He took a deep breath, 'Now it is back to work'.

As Erik walked away Ollie looked directly at Michael. 'I'm very grateful!' he said, before following his father. Michael was touched by the moment of rapport he'd witnessed between father and son; this revealed more about the pair than they realised. He was beginning to see that not only was Ollie no fool, but that he had a sense of decency and deep regard for his father.

With the guano finally stacked away and the hatches in place, there was little else to be done until morning. 'You may as well go now, Erik,' Michael urged, 'and if Anna wants to bring the children down later to look round it'll be alright. You might tell Maggy that I'm starving, though!' In fact he hadn't thought about food for some time, not since he'd eaten the sandwiches she'd prepared for him that morning.

'I'll catch you up, Dad,' Ollie called to Erik who was waiting for him on the dock side, and to Michael said, 'We'll be down first thing tomorrow, unless I come back later with Anna and the children?'

'Do that, then perhaps we can have a few words while your father is at home.' He was glad Ollie would be returning, as there were a few details still needing to be discussed before they went any further. He heard footsteps and saw Maggy approaching with a basket in her hand.

'Sorry, I'm late,' she offered with a smile. 'I've been baking a pie for us at Anna's, it won't take long to warm up again.' She saw that Ollie was about to leave, 'You'd best hurry back,' she told him, 'Anna's made one for you as well.'

'Right,' Ollie laughed, 'I'll probably see you both later.'

As he went, Maggy looked at Michael, 'Is he coming back?'

'Probably with Anna and the children to look over the keel, didn't she tell you?' He was suddenly disappointed to think that they might not be coming.

'Yes, she did,' she said, clutching the basket Anna had lent her to carry the pie in. 'They'll come as soon as they've eaten, otherwise it will be too dark to see anything.'

'This tastes good, Maggy,' he said later, as he ate the pie. 'No wonder you were gone so long.' It had been some time since he'd enjoyed a meal so much. 'This meat must have cost something. Did you offer to pay Anna for it?'

'Don't worry, Mike, I know they're not well off. Anna and I agreed to share the cost, so stop going on about it.' It wasn't easy cooking on the keel, especially in rough conditions, and she had welcomed Anna's suggestion to use her better facilities. Plus when on board, she never quite knew when Michael would want his meal if he was busy. She'd thoroughly enjoyed working with Anna and had been reluctant to leave the Erikson home.

Hiding a smile, Michael asked, 'Who made this one, you or Anna?'

Rising to the bait, Maggy pretended offence. 'Why? If I told you that we both did it, which bit are you going to leave, hers or mine?'

He laughed merrily, 'I'd better not answer that'.

'No, you'd better not!' Then she looked more closely at him. 'You're in a good mood. Did you manage to get us some more work?'

He nodded, 'I'm well satisfied, and it means we'll probably be able to leave with the tide tomorrow afternoon, or first thing the following morning. The earlier the better.' He saw her face fall a little. 'You've enjoyed being here, haven't you?' He was pleased to see her happy and had to admit that even he was looking forward to the children coming later.

Maggy studied him, amazed by the change. He certainly must have struck a favourable deal at the Carrying Agents' Office otherwise he would not have been so cheerful. She smiled to herself, thinking he deserved a bit of luck after all he'd been through.

'We'd best hurry or they'll be here.' He pushed the empty plate away from him. 'You tidy up and I'll have a quick wash,' he said, as he took a clean shirt from the cupboard. Although he hadn't remarked on this to anyone, it pleased him when the children made a fuss of him. He'd seen little of Patrick and Danny as youngsters, and now they were almost strangers, as he had lately found out.

It wasn't long before the children could be heard scampering along the wharfside, and were soon peering cautiously down at him as he tidied up on deck. The loaded keel was now much lower in the water and could only be boarded by climbing down the iron ladder fixed to the wall. He straightened up and moved quickly for'ard along the gunwale to join them. Anna stood by the children watching him, but seemed to hold back, as if unsure of herself. Taking care not to ignore the excited children he made a point of greeting her with a smile, and said, 'That was a good pie you and Maggy made'.

She was unused to receiving compliments and replied shyly, 'I'm pleased you liked it. I'm afraid the children are very boisterous, they've been waiting all afternoon to come.'

'That's alright,' he assured her, 'but I don't know how we'll all get into my cabin at once, unless we sit down.' She looked warily down at the ladder. 'Come on, I'll help you,' he offered, and was about to take her hand to assist when Johann started to climb down. Michael was a bit concerned at his enthusiasm, but on seeing what was happening Maggy hurried forward in case he fell. 'Don't let him go too near the edge,' he called out, and, turning to Anna he apologised, 'I'll be back in a minute, once they're all safely in the cabin.'

After helping first Kristen then Lucy down onto the deck and making sure they were safe with Maggy, he went for'ard again. 'I won't come if you don't mind,' Anna said, remaining where she was on the quay. 'I'm not very fond of water.'

He didn't laugh at her, he could see that she was afraid, so he climbed up and took her hand. 'Come, I won't let you fall,' he promised, with such genuine concern that she allowed him to lead her towards the ladder. 'I'll go first, slowly, and you follow. Just trust me.' He guided her small booted feet onto each rung carefully, and talked her down the face of the dock wall as she endeavoured to modestly control her skirt with one hand, while clutching the ladder with the other. 'I know it's silly,' she said defensively, once she was safely on the keel. 'Me being the daughter of a sailor and a sister to two more, not liking water, but it's so filthy.'

Michael was puzzled. 'Did you never go on the *Martha Jane*, then?'

She shook her head. 'No! I don't mind being on large vessels far above the water, but here…' She looked down at the dark, scummy and debris-strewn water in the dock and shivered, much as Patrick had done before.

'I've been on water all my life,' Michael explained, 'so it's second nature to me. Yet you, I believe, can swim—I can't!'

'Father made us learn in the shallow waters of the estuary. Yes, I can swim, but it's the darkness of water that I fear. It's like a beckoning grave.'

'Indeed that's just what it can be,' Michael agreed, 'and I must admit, looking down into this cesspit I should hate to fall in. Even so, without help I would drown but you could save yourself.' He moved slowly along the deck, making sure she didn't falter.

'Then you really should learn to swim,' Anna admonished him, 'anyone who works on water should learn. So many people die needlessly every year.'

'I must get your father to teach me,' he agreed, as she bent to grasp the upstand edge of the hold. 'Here, give me your hand and stand upright,' he said, and in spite of her hesitation, he took it. 'Now follow me and don't look down at the water, you'll be quite safe.' Her hand was cold and trembling in his. 'We're nearly there now,' he assured her. As they reached the spacious aft deck and the safety of the taffrail he let go of her hand. 'I thought Ollie was coming with you?' he asked.

'He's coming later, and will escort us home as it will be dark soon.' They could hear the children below, with Maggy trying to answer two or three questions at once. Anna, who was feeling safer now, remarked, 'Aren't they noisy!'

'Well, they're enjoying themselves by the sound of it. By the way, how is your mother?' Michael asked, wishing he had done so earlier.

'She's a little uncomfortable and now we know that when she fell she must have sprained her ankle, instead of just bruising it. She's very upset over losing the baby, and Father keeps trying to tell her it was just not to be, but it doesn't really help her very much.' She stood quietly beside him, 'I think we had better help Maggy,' she said, and he realised that she still wanted to get away from the water, and go below.

'You go first then, and I'll follow when you're down.'

The children were now hidden behind the curtain which concealed a bed in the wall of the cabin. 'I see you've lost the monsters,' Anna laughed, and then an excited Kristen giggled, giving the game away. She quickly threw back the curtain and cried, 'Got you!' causing the child to squeal with delight.

The glee and mischief displayed on each face brought a sudden lump to Michael's throat. Often as a child he'd concealed himself from his mother in a similar fashion, on wet, boring days when there'd been nothing else to do. Sadly those days were long gone, she was now a muddled shadow of her former self, and he vowed to pay her a little more attention next time he called to see her.

Anna saw the flicker of emotion cross his face, and though she didn't know the cause, she immediately exhorted all three children to quieten down, in a tone they knew well. 'Now sit over there, at once!' she commanded, and pointed at the locker. Clambering down, they did as they were told and tried hard to sit still under her watchful gaze.

They managed to control themselves for some time, but it wasn't long before their voices were raised again with questions. 'I think I'll take Johann on deck, and let him peep into his father's cabin,' Michael suggested. 'But you can't go down,' he warned the boy, 'even I won't do that unless I'm invited, or there's a problem.'

With the older boy out of the way, some sort of peace settled over the cabin, and the remaining two children were content to sit and look at the interesting things surrounding them. 'It's very cosy.' Anna exclaimed, as she noted the polished wood of the cupboards and the compact stove. 'Where do you sleep, Maggy?' she asked, thinking that there was just the one bed.

Maggy chuckled knowingly. 'In there, behind that curtain where the children were. Michael sleeps behind the sliding doors at the back of you.'

'It can't be very comfortable for him,' Anna said with concern.

'It's larger than you think,' Maggy explained, 'quite snug, believe me.'

Anna then saw several ornaments made of ivory on a small shelf. 'Those are nice,' she said, getting up to look closer.

'We ship ivory and horn as you know, and if ever a piece was broken off Granddad could usually buy it cheaply and work it.'

'They're lovely,' Anna cried, 'especially this one. How did he get the ball inside there?' She had spotted a lantern-like cage with a little ball inside it. Maggy took it down and handed it to her. 'Where are the joins—how did he do it?' Anna asked, as she examined the intricate piece of work.

'He carved it from the outside, there are no joins,' Maggy explained proudly. 'It's an ancient craft which can also be done in wood. Granddad taught Michael to carve ivory too, look at this.' She took down a small model of a keel from behind the upstand of the shelf. 'There isn't much to do in the winter, and Michael doesn't read, so he carves. He usually sells what he makes but this piece is a little damaged, so he decided to keep it.'

Anna carefully held the model and enjoyed the feel of its smooth, cool surface. Then, examining the neatly wired repair on the mast, she said, 'What a pity, after the hours he must have spent on it.' She turned to Maggy, 'May I show it to the children?' She held it gently towards them and said, 'Look how clever Mr Havercroft is!'

The smell of guano surrounded the keel and mixed with the evil-smelling vapours coming off the water into the damp night air. Johann held his nose. 'Phew! What a smell! What is it?' he demanded of Michael, who laughed at his outburst.

'It is a bit strong, I admit! It's guano,' he explained, 'bird lime from an island where the stuff has lain many feet deep for hundreds of years. It's an important cargo nowadays, and people use it as fertiliser on farms and gardens. You ought to smell it when it's wet, it's even worse! Maggy doesn't like it either but it's not as bad as the smelly old bones we sometimes carry for the grist mill.' He'd quite enjoyed talking to the boy, and had just finished touring the keel with him when he saw Ollie approaching along the quay.

As he helped Johann down into the cabin, Anna was about to put the damaged model back on the shelf. She was a little flustered when she saw Michael watching her, but managed to disguise this by complimenting him on his carving skill. Somewhat surprised by the warmth of her praise, he thanked her, then announced that Ollie had arrived and that together they would show the other two children around before it became too dark.

With this finally done and the children safely returned to the cabin again, Michael felt it was time to have a discussion with Ollie about the journey ahead. Light was now fading quickly and he lit the lanterns before joining him as he leant against the winch. 'Your father hasn't changed his mind then, about leaving us at Keadby?' Michael asked, not knowing what to expect.

'No, I convinced him that it's a good solution to the problem, and that he need not feel guilty on my behalf. I also assured him that I do not intend making a habit of taking over his job,' Ollie replied, straightening himself up. 'But I must explain why I was late this morning. You see I wanted to make arrangements with my bank in case I needed more money when I reach Sheffield. It took a little longer than I expected, but I knew it would be at least a couple of hours before you could begin to load up.'

'You intend sailing back with me from Sheffield I hope?' Michael interrupted, 'I can't bring her back single handed, especially on the Humber.'

Ollie was a bit put out at this suggestion. 'I have considered all that,' he said, defending himself, 'and since my father is to remain here, then I will certainly stay with you for the entire journey. I just need two free days in Sheffield to conduct some enquiries, while you acquire fresh cargo. As I said before, I will pay for any delay that I might cause and for any help you may need during my absence. How does that strike you?'

'It does seem that your father's problem has made things easier for you!' Michael couldn't help making this comment on Ollie's plans.

Ollie had to agree. 'It has, but then I wouldn't have my mother go through what she has just to please me.'

'I didn't mean that,' Michael apologised, accepting that his words had been rather too forthright.

'It doesn't matter,' Ollie hastened to add before anything else was said which might make matters worse. 'I will explain more later if you can trust me a little longer. Believe me, I do not intend to let my business interfere with yours, but I do need those two days.'

'I'm more concerned about how you will cope with the Humber on our return. Are you experienced enough in handling a keel?' Michael was having second thoughts the more he considered the finer details of the proposal, and these he intended to sort out now.

'Well I can certainly handle sails and rigging, and I'll do what you tell me' Ollie said. 'I suggest that once we are ready to leave Sheffield, and can estimate when we'll arrive at Keadby, I write and ask Father to meet us there. Anna will read the letter to him. He's no fool, and can judge if the weather is likely to delay us; he'll simply hitch a lift to Keadby in time for our arrival. It'll not be the first time he's slept in a barn for the night, or made a bed on someone's floor.'

'You certainly seem to have thought this through,' Michael said, still with some reservation in his voice. It wasn't that he distrusted Ollie, it was more that he was uneasy over these complicated arrangements on top of his normal worries. Either he was a fool to put himself in the man's hands, or Ollie had the makings of a good businessman. It was only because he knew and trusted Erik and his family that he was even considering going along with the idea, plus the fact that he would be worse off without any help at all. 'Don't let me down, that's all I ask,' he said, firmly.

'Ollie!' Anna's anxious voice called out to them. 'It's getting late and we should be getting back!'

'I'll not be a minute!' he replied, seeing no reason to hurry.

'Oh, please Ollie.' There was a hint of fear rather than anger in her voice. 'You know I don't like dark water.'

He sighed with impatience. 'I suppose I ought to take them home. I'll just light this,' he said, picking up the lantern he'd brought with him.

Michael hesitated. He would have liked to question Ollie more about his intentions, but, understanding Anna's anxiety, had to accept that this would have to wait. Nevertheless, he was disappointed at parting company with his visitors so soon, especially as he would be leaving some time the next day.

'Honestly, Anna,' Ollie chided in a brotherly fashion, as he assisted Kristen from the cabin. 'What's the hurry, how on earth can you fall? There is only a small gap between the keel and the wharfside anyway.' Anna said nothing, her mind and energies being occupied in getting the children up on deck. 'You stay there until we get the children up and onto the quay,' he continued as though she were a child herself, 'though why you fret, I don't understand.'

Feeling sorry for Anna, Michael butted in. 'Will you go up onto the quay, Ollie? Maggy will guide the youngsters along to me, and I'll start them up the ladder.'

With the children safely off the keel, Maggy joined them on the quay and Michael went back to fetch Anna.

'Thank you kindly,' Anna said, as she allowed him to help her out of the cabin. In the gloom it wasn't easy to walk the narrow deckway back to the ladder, and instinctively she reached out to take his arm.

'Here, give me your hand,' he insisted, and, giving her no time to refuse, took it and found it pleasantly warm but trembling. He felt a strong desire to protect her and, without realising it, wrapped his fingers tightly around hers. 'It'll be easier to move this way, you'll be quite safe,' he gently assured her as he led her along. However, when they reached the ladder on the wall he saw that she was pale and apprehensive.

She paused, composing herself, but did not attempt to remove her hand from his. They stood there in the quiet stillness for several seconds, Michael's fingers still holding hers, neither uttering a word.

'Are you coming up, or not?' Ollie called down, breaking the spell in a rather exasperated manner.

Michael quickly released Anna's hand. 'Are you ready?' he asked a little huskily, wishing he hadn't responded to Ollie's call like a guilty youth.

'Yes,' she answered softly, 'and thank you again.'

'Then hitch your skirt up a little as you go, I'll be right behind you all the way.'

'Please look the other way,' Anna begged him.

He was quietly amused that in spite of her fear she was still conscious of the need for modesty, and what he might think of her. To Anna, the number of rungs on the ladder seemed never ending as she clutched at her skirt and gripped each rung as she climbed slowly upwards, Michael following close below. He'd seen Maggy and other women scramble deftly up and down such ladders so often in the past that he'd never really appreciated the skill it took to do it. There was no way in which he could assist Anna without actually touching her familiarly, and so embarrassing her; all he could do was catch her if she fell.

'At last!' Ollie declared when she finally reached safety. 'I was about to throw you a rope and haul you up.' There was laughter in his voice as he fondly teased her, but Anna was too preoccupied to appreciate his humour. 'Well, Mike,' Ollie said, 'thanks for showing this lot round, I'll be here first thing in the morning.'

As they parted, only Michael saw the look of gratitude on Anna's face when in a low whisper she said, to him, 'Thanks for being so understanding.'

'She's nice, and you're a fool, Michael Havercroft.' Maggy commented, as she joined him. The little group was gradually disappearing into the evening gloom, and only the flicker of their lantern could be seen in the distance.

'What are you on about now, Maggy?' he asked, puzzled over what could be wrong. 'I don't know that I've done anything to upset anyone, have I?'

She paused before descending the ladder, and looked up into his face. 'You'd be better off with Anna than Lily. At least you'd have intelligent conversation in an evening to keep you company, instead of Lily's moody ways.'

'Stop that, Maggy,' he said abruptly. 'Anna's a sweet girl, it's not fair for you or anybody else to go match-making for her. Lily can stand to be teased, but Anna can't.' He was startled by the strength of his reply. The evening had been a pleasant one and he was grateful that darkness concealed the emotion which must be obvious on his face. 'I'm not looking for a wife! Besides, she can't stand water so she'd be no good to me!' These last words were firmly spoken, perhaps more so than he'd intended, but necessary if only to stop Maggy's speculations.

'Oh, you're so touchy these days,' she complained, and climbed swiftly down to the keel, muttering as she went.

Michael followed slowly, sadly recalling his all too brief moment alone with Anna. The situation really was hopeless and perhaps the less he saw of her the better it would be for all concerned. He held her in great esteem but anything more would be impractical, unworkable even, for those small soft hands were not meant for keel life. As for Lily, she was young and immature; only time would tell what kind of wife she might make. At twenty-eight, he was still a young man with a future to be decided before he could even consider taking a wife. Perhaps, if instead of being shy he'd taken Lily's hand once or twice as he'd done Anna's, she might not have seemed so disinterested earlier that day.

He had no idea where Swifty's keel was now, or when their paths would cross again, but he resolved to be kinder to Lily when next they met. He hadn't walked her very far the night before, and had been careful to keep within the confines of the busy dock area, nor had he taken her hand for fear of gossip. Water folk were a nosy, gossipy lot, close knit, and to have gone that far might have conveyed more than he wanted. As a result, she had been moody and skittish, and they'd parted in a strained, awkward manner. She was an impulsive, more worldly person than he, and deep down he feared that if he once started an affair with her, he might not be able to control the outcome.

True to his word, Ollie arrived with his father at the crack of dawn the following morning, and by noon the keel was ready to sail with the tide. It seemed that Ellen was far from well, and this made the decision for her husband to return immediately they were free of the Humber a sensible one. Loading had continued without a hitch, the hold was full, and Michael now wanted nothing more than to be on his way. With four hands aboard and fair weather, the keel performed well and made good time up the estuary.

These were the days he loved best, when everything seemed to be going in his favour; even Maggy with her hair blowing in the wind appeared happy to be on the move again. For once Michael felt strangely disappointed to be leaving the Humber, and the challenge it brought with it. Time truly was a healer, and the memory of their previous journey had almost disappeared. The lure of the water, no matter how perilous, always drew mariners back, and to the end of his days he never forgot the feel of a vessel beneath his feet.

With all four of them, there was the same sense of exhilaration as they sailed swiftly along, the spray from the keel's blunt bow blowing in their faces. This is my life, Michael thought, it must remain so and nothing must be allowed to change it.

'A wonderful run, no?' Erik called out, beaming from ear to ear. 'I feel it in my bones that Ellen will be well.' He was the eternal optimist, bouncing back when all appeared lost, and Michael was going to miss him when he left for Hull, for however short a time.

'I think you're right!' Michael responded happily, feeling that today nothing could go wrong. Such was the case, and they were able to find a safe mooring at Keadby just before twilight.

After their evening meal, they gathered in the lantern light on deck, laughing and chatting for some while until firstly Maggy, then Erik decided to retire for the night.

'I get up very early and walk to the lock,' Erik announced, as he knocked his pipe out over the water. 'Then I catch the first boat home.'

'You'll stand a better chance that way,' Michael agreed, and added, 'good luck!'

'You too, and don't let my Ollie mess you about!'

'Take no notice of the old man,' Ollie laughed. 'It's too early for me to turn in though; how about you?'

'I like this time of night, out here,' Michael told him, 'the isolation; and the gentle movements of the *Maggie*. It's so quiet you'd think there was no one else in the world. I'll give it another half hour then go below.'

'It's too calm for me,' Ollie replied. 'It's safe enough, but I enjoy the swell of the sea and its sense of power. Even in stormy weather I actually enjoy it.'

Michael swiped casually at a moth attracted by the light. 'That's not for me, I'm afraid, but perhaps I have no spirit of adventure.' He paused for a while, listening to the lapping of the water against the hull, then spoke again. 'How strange,' he said, 'that in a sea-faring family such as yours, Anna is afraid of water.'

'Anna fears many things,' Ollie replied, 'but she's kind and gentle and needs a push now and again. Father molly-coddles her, I do not.'

Ollie was obviously fond of his sister, yet Michael thought him a little hard on her sometimes, and offered a few words in her defence. 'Perhaps she's not used to the rougher ways of life,' he said. 'Maggy doesn't travel with us as often as she did, but she's been brought up with all the inconveniences that canal work brings.'

'I'm not decrying Anna, you know,' Ollie replied, 'but until Father came on hard times she stayed at home, sheltered from the world; yet when I returned from America two weeks ago I found her on her knees, scrubbing at that wretched little tavern in Silver Street.'

'Not the Black Boy?' Michael was appalled at this news, and greatly put out at the thought. 'Things must have been bad.'

'I saw how miserable she was, skivvying like the fishermen's wives of Hessle Road, and there should have been no need for it. That's one of the reasons why I was so annoyed with my father when I met him on the wharfside.'

It was not easy for Michael to imagine the gentle and modest Anna having to mingle with the sort of characters that used the place, and his heart went out to her. 'I can understand your feelings. I'm afraid that Maggy too will have to find work soon, and domestic service seems to be the most likely job for her. Let's hope they both find work with better class families, until they marry.'

To this Ollie responded, 'I think Anna is too shy, she'll need a push in that direction if she's to find a husband, I don't doubt.'

This remark reminded Michael of the first disastrous meeting with Anna, and of Erik's thoughtless words at the time. He was irritated and greatly disturbed by Ollie's statement, particularly when he thought of either girl being subjected to hardship and servitude until they were able to find husbands. He resolved to keep Maggy on the keel as long as possible, while ever he could afford to do so, in the hope that someone would find her desirable as a canal wife. He knew that Joe, the lock keeper in Mexborough had cast his eyes in her direction, so a little contrivance there might not go amiss.

The conversation between the two men gradually turned to less controversial things, until at last they found the night air too damp and chilly, and they retired for the night.

Michael rose next morning in time to see Erik walking towards the lock at the junction of the Trent with the canal. Later, after his breakfast, he was pleased to see him standing on the deck of another keel, waving cheerfully and calling out to them as he sailed past.

Once through the lock, their own journey continued without incident. The weather was pleasant, but Ollie was inexperienced in handling the keel so it fell to Michael to take the tiller more than he'd hoped would be the case. This would not have been so bad if his leg hadn't started playing up again. Whilst in Hull the comparative rest he'd enjoyed had helped, but now he began to wonder if, in fact, the position in which he habitually stood at the tiller might not be the prime cause of his trouble. The occasional jar it received when handling cargo probably didn't help much either. It was, therefore, a relief to reach Thorne and complete the off-loading of the guano without mishap. The smell of guano was quickly dispersed by the down-draught of the sail and, with Thorne and Stainforth behind them, they soon entered the River Don. Ollie was in his element here, for to him this was another challenge after the restrictions of the canal. The now blustery wind offered frequent defiance to the set of the sail, especially when rounding a bend in the river, thus requiring constant adjustment to the rigging, and he and Maggy did a good job. He was quick and nimble, which was fortunate, as with the keel being half empty she was lively in the water. Consequently, when they reached Doncaster the three of them were more than ready for a rest.

This was the first time since Jim Havercroft's death that Michael had cause to stay a while in Doncaster, it was his favourite town. Here had been the only other home he'd known, apart from the keel, and although it had been some time since the old house had been sold, he still enjoyed walking along the town's busy streets. Never having been to London, he always imagined that Doncaster must have similar characteristics to the capital, for the Great North Road, which ran through it, had brought a wondrous assortment of travellers in the past. Many of these still came for the races but today they arrived by rail, bringing with them some dubious characters just as colourful, but of course less desirable.

The old Georgian squares, the pillars and ironwork of Bennetthorpe were all a world away from his own, yet he wasn't envious. He preferred, as he got older, the waters of the canal and river where it was quiet and certainly had fewer flies and dirt.

Today, however, there was no time for Michael to stroll through the town as he had work to do. There were friends and old neighbours who could be unaware that his father had died, so, thinking Maggy might be a little restless, he suggested she might like to call on them with the sad news.

Maggy, of course, was pleased at this, and gladly set off once she knew where Michael would be unloading and how long this might take. It was to the less salubrious streets that she went, where people were poor but straightforward and independent, and who made the most of their shabby homes. It was a community in which all knew everyone else's business, but out of loyalty made it their own when there was trouble. Unfortunately, at the houses where she called, one was boarded up and another had no-one at home. To Maggy's disappointment only Mrs Fidler was to be found, and it was she who regaled Maggy with all the gossip, after commiserating over her father's death.

'You've not been long,' Michael said, on her return. 'Were they all out?'

With a hint of sarcasm, Maggy replied, 'Mrs Fidler certainly wasn't! She told me everything that has happened since the last time one of us called.'

He laughed. 'I'm not surprised. Did she know about Dad?'

'Apparently someone told her last week—she sends her condolences. She also told me something that perhaps it's as well Dad didn't know, old Herbert Bones has gone into the workhouse.'

'Poor old chap,' Michael said sadly, remembering how, many years before, the man had tolerated his childish pranks. 'He won't last long in there, I'm afraid. It's a rotten shame.'

'Anyway, Lizzie Hemshall's getting married at last,' Maggy went on, 'and Mrs Fidler wants to know when you're going to get wed?'

'I hope you told her to mind her own business,' Michael replied a little more sharply than he intended. 'I never could stand that woman.' He remembered Lizzie Hemshall too. The ugliest girl in the street and the only one who'd ever fancied him! She'd made his life a misery every time they'd returned home from a trip with his father, following him everywhere. It had certainly taken her long enough to find a man, and no wonder.

'Now then, I've had a stroke of luck,' Michael went on. 'I've got a consignment of empty barrels which need returning to Sheffield. They've been waiting for a vessel with space for two days now. I've also got some vegetables.'

The load of empty barrels was just what Michael needed to give the run from Hull a good profit margin, and they were easy to handle. These, together with the consignment of farm produce, gave him the extra weight he needed. If the rain held off and the water level was low he might not need to take on water ballast to pass under Bacon Lane Bridge.

In many respects the journey onwards was an experience which opened Ollie's eyes. Familiar as he was with open seas and busy foreign ports, once beyond Doncaster's flat fertile plain he was fascinated by all he saw. The river now ran through deeply-wooded valleys and undulating countryside, and was canalised occasionally to avoid its weirs and shallower courses. As the keel travelled further inland along the valley of the Don, he was struck by the parallel of seeming to forge into unknown territory with that of his own pioneering into the hinterland of California. This illusion was shattered, however, when the ancient ruins of Conisbrough Castle loomed over them from the hill above.

He was intrigued also, when, on reaching Mexborough they abandoned mast and sail, and were towed from this point by horse and Marine. Steam-power was now the latest innovation in shipping, and to his forward way of thinking it wouldn't be long before it began to replace such archaic methods. The strange feeling of familiarity returned once more to Ollie when at Kilnhurst, the towpath ended, and it was necessary to put the horse onto a flat-bottomed ferry and cross to the other side of the river where it started again. This was much as he'd done when crossing the wide, clear rivers of the Sierra Nevada to mine for gold.

It was this sort of activity and the repeated negotiation of locks, that explained why, even in fair weather, the journey from Hull to Sheffield usually took five days and sometimes much more. His respect for the skill and hardworking life of the keelmen grew as each mile passed. He learned much from Maggy too, from her expertise, which she of course, took for granted. He concluded that the sailor who could never accept a woman mariner at sea would be astounded if he saw a young girl as capable as her in his crew!

In order to save time it was agreed that on reaching Aldwarke, Michael would make only a two hour stop, time enough for Maggy and himself to see Ma and get fresh clothing. They would then return on the dray with John, or Patrick, who would collect the food stuffs Michael had bought on the journey. Nothing exciting had occurred at the farm whilst they had been away, and much of their visit was spent telling Patrick what had happened since he'd left them. Having decided against the idea of Maggy going out to work as a servant, Michael had earlier told her that he would like her assistance for a little while longer, and was relieved when, without question, she agreed to make at least one more trip with him.

Ollie was now more familiar with the working of the keel and had been left alone to keep watch, whilst the Marine and his horse rested up on the high bank. He took this rare opportunity to relax, and lay spread out on the hatch covers in the spring sunshine, staring up at the sky. Within twenty-four hours he would be in a position to put the first half of his plan into action, and if at the end of the day this collapsed around him he would not be penniless, he was young and healthy, and at least he'd tried to climb the ladder of success.

So, with a trouble-free mind Ollie fell asleep, deeply so, and only the irritating touch of a fly disturbed him. He woke with a start, his eyes wide open. 'You were snoring,' Maggy laughed, still holding the feather which had woken him. 'You'll be glad you had that sleep,' she warned him, 'just wait until we get to Tinsley, you'll soon find out why.'

He made a half-hearted attempt to seize the feather from her grasp but Maggy whirled away, laughing, and went below, leaving him to ponder over her words.

Much later, when at last they'd climbed the twelve locks to the higher level of the canal at Tinsley, Ollie was in no doubt as to her meaning. Dusk was settling over them and his arms ached from working the lock gates. This was not the ladder he had expected to climb to earn success! 'That lot's incredible,' he said to Michael as they moored in the top basin for the night. 'You keelmen certainly earn your money. I would never have believed the work involved if I hadn't experienced it at first hand.'

'I suppose not,' Michael replied, 'and many a wife and daughter are expected to haul their keel when necessary, and work the locks themselves if money's tight. Maggy's done it all.'

'I'm not surprised, she's a remarkable girl,' Ollie conceded, before going on. 'When you said earlier this afternoon that we'd only got about four miles to go I thought we'd have been there by now. Obviously you lose a lot of time with this kind of caper.'

'The next three miles are easier, except for the bridges, but we're nearly there,' Michael reassured him.

Leaving Tinsley top basin shortly after dawn, the keel passed along the higher contours of the Don Valley, and then joined other craft in a congested mooring basin. 'What's the hold up?' Ollie asked, eager now to reach the end of the journey.

'It's t' Acky Duck,' Maggy told him.

He looked bewildered, and tentatively asked, 'Shall I get the gun?' She eyed him strangely. 'We could have duck for dinner,' he said innocently, a little puzzled by her look and how a duck could cause such a problem on a busy waterway.

She screwed up her eyes and after thinking for a moment, first chuckled, then laughed out loud. 'Daft thing!' she cried, 'it's not a duck, it's the aqueduct ahead, where the canal crosses over the road! Since I was a little girl I've always called it that.'

Ollie shook his head in amazement and then, seeing the funny side of it, laughed too.

Not being near enough to hear what had gone on, and thinking they were fooling around, Michael shouted, 'Come on Maggy, stop messing about.' Only later did he hear the story from Maggy, and saw the humour in it.

The total distance from Kingston-upon-Hull to Sheffield was about seventy miles—a comparatively short distance compared with Ollie's many sea-going journeys, but for him it had been an incredible trip. Leaving the remarkable aqueduct which crossed Darnall Road, in itself a feat of skill in construction, they pressed on through the deep cutting at Attercliffe, and although the water level wasn't high, Michael would still need to take a large quantity of water on board to pass under Bacon Lane Bridge when they reached it.

'I'll pump it out afterwards,' Maggy offered, as she went to open the brass sea-cock under the cabin floor which let water into the bilge. 'That'll leave Ollie free to help you unload at Parker's.'

The canal from here on was occasionally spanned by low stone bridges and flanked by tall factories, all standing under a canopy of thick acrid smoke which the sun couldn't penetrate. Once under Bacon Lane Bridge they headed for Parker's Wharf and off-loaded the horn and ivory, which left the empty barrels and vegetables for the quays in Sheffield.

'Here we are,' Maggy announced at last to the fascinated Ollie as they rounded the last bend in the canal, 'Sheffield Basin ahead!'

Chapter 4

Ollie was standing on the deck, looking as clean, smart and as out of place as a grinder at the Cutlers' Feast.

'Don't stand there for all to see,' Michael urged him, looking round the busy canal basin. 'Envy and jealousy can cause a lot of trouble in this business. They'll all wonder why a chap like you is working on my keel.'

'Sorry!' Ollie replied, none too apologetically. 'I just wanted to see if you thought I looked like a businessman. Anyway, how am I supposed to get off this floating tub to do what I need without being dressed for the part?'

'Just don't make it so obvious, that's all, especially when you come back.' Michael was more disgruntled at having him call the *Maggie Kelly* a tub, than anything else.

'Well, I'll be off then, and probably won't be back 'til late.'

'Good!' Michael muttered to himself as Ollie climbed off the keel and mingled with the busy workmen on the wharf.

Maggy laughed. 'You're jealous, Michael Havercroft, that's what you are'. She admitted to herself that Ollie did look rather too well attired for the basin, and wondered what he was up to.

Meanwhile, Ollie had left the yard and was walking towards the town, past the curve of terraced offices belonging to the coal merchants. He'd enjoyed teasing Michael, although he had to admit he ought to have been more discreet. It was too late now, however, and he would probably suffer a ribbing from some of the canal men when he returned.

He was confident in what he proposed to do, but then he felt he had a right to be so, having experienced at first hand the opening up of a new territory on the West Coast of America. He'd sampled the hardships of shortages and knew what items were much needed there. He was also very much aware of the fortunes that could be made, and lost as quickly, not only in mining for gold, but from trade. The very act of transporting goods across dangerous seas, barren plains and harsh mountain terrain was as likely to bankrupt a merchant, as gambling was to claim the spoils of the prospector.

He had also discovered that if one had sufficient capital to allow a man to ride out the storm when times were bad, very soon the tables would turn and leave him the richer. In such circumstances his own moderate pickings had earned him a considerable profit. Gold was not the only way to succeed, as he'd realised soon after arriving in California, it had simply given him the start he needed. He sometimes thought, on occasion, that he could still hear the bellowing of the cattle, not a few but more than three hundred, which he'd bought for 19 dollars a head and sold again two weeks later for 50 dollars each. The small piece of land he had bought for next to nothing, from someone in need, had been sold the same day for 1,700 dollars and had given him riches beyond his dreams. The fluctuation in the price of goods was incredible, and he counted himself fortunate to have decided to quit whilst luck was on his side. This much he knew, however, that men were desperate for razors, axes and knives, the latter being for protection as well as useful for hunting and hacking. Picks, shovels and pans were also needed as were crushing machines to extract gold from quartz. All were in short supply, for America was neither capable nor equipped to produce such things herself.

It had been apparent to him there, all those thousands of miles away, that a good Sheffield blade was much sought after, and if the appropriate knife was sold to the right man it would fetch a fair price. In fact, since returning home he'd actually read in the Hull papers, advertisements asking for supplies of crushing machines for the West Coast! At this time he wasn't particularly interested in fancy goods, they would come later, it was in the supply of straightforward necessities where he saw his opportunity to succeed.

The likes of George Wostenholm's knives were already well known across America, and it was at his establishment that Ollie decided to make his first call. He was soon informed where to find the works, and hurried nervously towards Wellington Street, rehearsing what to say when he got there. Having handled several knives with the IXL trade mark stamped on them he'd little realised how enormous a manufacturing concern their maker George Wostenholm owned. He was awed when he saw the imposing frontage of his Washington Works, and approached the main entrance feeling less than confident.

As he entered the reception office, he wondered if he'd set his sights too high, and his voice was hesitant as he enquired of a clerk, 'Would it be possible for me to see Mr Wostenholm, please?'

'Mr Wostenholm himself?' the man replied, eyeing him seriously through his small round spectacles.

'Why, yes,' Ollie replied. 'I don't have an appointment, I'm afraid, but I've recently returned from America and have a business proposition which I would like to put to him.'

'I'm sorry, Sir, but Mr Wostenholm is in London right now, preparing for the opening of the Great Exhibition in Hyde Park.'

'Oh dear, that's a pity. I have travelled from Kingston-upon-Hull to see him, and I'm sure he would be interested.'

'Well, Sir, if you would care to leave a message, I'll make sure he gets it on his return.' The clerk reached for a pen, dipped it into his inkwell and waited for Ollie to reply. 'Of course, Mr Wostenholm visits America regularly,' he offered, 'and is familiar with the market there.' He saw a flicker of surprise on Ollie's face. 'Indeed, we have an office in New York, and a representative in San Francisco.'

This news was a blow to Ollie, who had hoped to secure such a position with Wostenholm's for himself. 'It was on these matters that I wished to speak' he said, realising that he would need to re-think some of his plans. 'In view of what you say, I may not be able to assist him after all,' he went on, gathering his thoughts, 'but I have a mind anyway to buy a quantity of razors and knives from the company. Who then, should I talk to regarding this matter, as I would like to see a few samples of your products?' Ollie was determined to press on in spite of his setback.

'I'll see if the Sales Manager is available,' the clerk suggested. 'But he may be busy. Please take a seat and I'll be as quick as I can. What name shall I give him?'

Once alone, Ollie considered his position carefully. He was disappointed to learn that Wostenholm's already had a sales outlet in San Francisco, but he knew that men had to travel far out into new territory, ahead of commerce, in order to make good money. Initially, working alone could involve considerable risk to his capital, and he would need to buy at very competitive prices. This accomplished, the goods would have to be delivered to him in California via a reliable source. But Wostenholm's were hardly likely to supply him when they had their own agent there already! Here indeed was a predicament!

Ollie stood up as a gentleman approached him.

'Good morning,' the man said, shaking him by the hand. 'Mr Erikson?'

'Yes! Good morning,' Ollie replied. 'How do you do?'

'Now, Mr Erikson, what can we do for you? By the way, I am Mr Hall, the Sales Manager.' Having once heard Ollie's intentions, he said, 'Will you come this way?' He led him into a small room with a table at its centre, around the room were several showcases displaying a large range of pen, pocket and tradesmen's knives. The craftsmanship was excellent and Ollie knew that each item would fetch a good price in remote areas.

Ollie complimented Mr Hall on the array of samples displayed as the man placed a variety of knives on the table. He was then invited to examine for himself the balance, weight and finish of each. 'See for yourself, every knife is more than capable of doing the job for which it is intended. We pride ourselves on our workmanship and reliability.'

Firstly Ollie took hold of a hunting knife, and there was no denying the feeling of confidence the well-balanced, sturdy implement gave him. 'I must admit to having come across your knives before and I much admire them. Whilst in America I travelled out into the new territories where there are little or no facilities to purchase such important items. If all goes well I may eventually travel the wider world in a trading capacity.' He paused and, seeing no sign of opposition on the man's face, he continued. 'I would require a regular supply of items to be sent to Hull via the canal, and I have a keel available to collect them on a regular basis. Do you think this could be arranged?'

'Providing goods are paid for on despatch from our warehouse, and you do not work in direct competition with our established agents, we could supply you. I would seriously suggest you insure all goods transported, as the sea must be one of the world's best customers.'

Ollie laughed. 'A pity she doesn't pay for the goods,' he quipped, only too aware of the pitfalls of shipping.

'Exactly. However, the western part of America has its own hazards, as you no doubt know. Once the railroad reaches the West coast trade should boom'

'I'd like to buy a collection of samples in the first instance if you have no objection,' Ollie said, and set about selecting a number of items which he knew were in demand both for personal security and as hunting or everyday tools. He also took a cut-throat razor, but knew that providing they did their job well, other makes would be just as acceptable. After all, in order to buy at a good price, there were many other manufacturers in the town on whom he intended calling. He was, indeed, slowly coming to the conclusion that Wostenholm's might not be his sole answer, as they were too well represented in America already. He paid for the items selected, knowing he could re-sell them without difficulty if necessary. He asked if the manager would send him a quotation for the supply of various items at wholesale prices, with discounts reflecting the size of the order. This done, Ollie wished him a courteous farewell and walked briskly back into the centre of town.

Although a little daunted at the knowledge of the competition he might face, he knew that there would still be an opening for the early entrepreneur for some time to come. He resolved to call at a number of smaller, less affluent producers of quality products in the town during the rest of the day, as the visit to Wostenholm's had gone well enough, even if not as expected.

Ollie now needed somewhere to sit and contemplate his next move, so, enquiring where the nearest book shop might be, he set out to obtain a copy of a trade directory for the area. Thus armed with the thick volume, he found an eating house in nearby Fargate and seated himself in a quiet corner, eager to peruse its pages. To his dismay, over nine pages of cutlers and associated businesses were listed. He closed the book with a sigh, bewildered at the proliferation of firms producing knives of various kinds for the world market.

Eventually Ollie observed a smartly-dressed gentleman sitting at the next table, and nodded in a friendly, though not over-familiar greeting. 'Good day,' he remarked, trying to engage the man in conversation.

'Good day, to you, Sir,' the man replied cordially enough, 'a fine one too!'

Risking a rebuff, Ollie ventured to engage the man further. 'I wonder if you could assist me, Sir?' he said in a respectful voice. 'I'm a stranger to Sheffield and have bought this trade directory, but it is so comprehensive that I would greatly appreciate some advice.'

'I don't know that I can be of much help, but I will certainly try. Who are you looking for?' the man asked, with growing interest.

'That's very kind of you, Sir,' Ollie said, 'may I join you? I have no wish to disturb everyone else.'

'Please do,' the man agreed, moving his hat and gloves from the adjoining chair to make room for him.

'I wish to buy a quantity of knives in the town, and find it difficult to know where to start,' Ollie said as he seated himself at the table. 'There are so many listed here,' he indicated the directory. 'I was well aware of the quality and renown of Sheffield products, but not that there were so many manufacturers.'

His bewilderment seemed to amuse the man. 'Most of them are Little Mesters' he explained, but seeing that Ollie did not understand or grasp the implication, he continued. 'These are mainly one or two-man businesses, buying in and skilfully assembling knife parts. Few of them make a piece from start to finish, but each has a skill peculiar to himself. Some actually rent workshops within the premises of larger companies.'

Hearing this and looking again at the book in his hand, Ollie asked, 'Where then should I start, and how can I best discover who is likely to supply good quality goods, apart from people like Wostenholm's?'

A smile appeared on the man's face. 'There are few bad Little Mesters in the trade, most have served seven year apprenticeships, nor could they survive for long if they turned out shoddy goods. They buy in the best steel blades and parts to assemble or work on.'

Ollie eyed him cautiously. 'Are you in the trade?' he asked, suspecting the man was being over-zealous in his praise.

'You could say that!' There was a twinkle in his eye. 'I work for the Company of Cutlers in Hallamshire. I'm merely a clerk, but I know as much about the industry as do some of the managers. Take your pick out of any of the names listed, and examine their products, but remember three things. How well does the knife do the job it is intended to do, how long will it perform and how many times will it stand resharpening? These are the best tests of a good product. Knives here are more often than not made partly by out-workers, and finally stamped with the marks of the major companies, although smaller firms do have their own marks. Each finished item has usually been handled by a dozen or more different craftsmen, all equally skilled at his part of the process.' The man went on for several minutes, perhaps because Ollie was a good listener, explaining the complicated construction of pen and pocket knives. Then he leaned back in his chair. 'You have drawn me out on a subject close to my heart,' he said, 'but it still doesn't answer your first question.'

'You have proved me a novice on the subject,' Ollie responded with some humility, 'but have given me very sound advice, Sir, and I can see that I shall need to select my choice of suppliers with care. It would probably be best for me to find two or three companies of moderate size, who supply finished items; then purchase samples in the first instance, so that I can compare them.' He explained a little of his plans, taking care not to bore the man, or give too much away.

'May I suggest you take a journey to the Great Exhibition of Works in London? Believe it or not, we have nearly three hundred exhibitors going from Sheffield, many in the cutlery trade. There was a tardiness and lack of enthusiasm when the idea was first mooted, but in the end, as usual, Sheffield came round to the idea. Now there is an air of expectancy and excitement in the town, for the exhibition opens at Crystal Palace this week.' Always being one to encourage trade for the town and admiring Ollie's determination and interest, he added, 'Now, I shouldn't really do this, but if you have a pencil I will mark several smaller, competent firms which produce quality knives whom you might try. Then I must leave you, time is getting on.'

Ollie handed him the directory. 'I really am grateful for your time and advice. I count myself lucky to have fallen in with you today.'

'I never mind talking to someone who is willing to listen and learn,' the man said, turning the pages and pencilling a cross against several names. 'I live alone and as a consequence enjoy an interesting conversation.' He picked up his hat and gloves, then rose to leave. 'Well, good luck young man. You'll find Sheffield a friendly, well-meaning place, often the men are outspoken and blunt, but it is just their way.'

'I'm much obliged,' Ollie said, as they shook hands. 'I'm sure you've set me on the right track. Thank you.'

When the man had gone, Ollie looked carefully at the names he had marked with crosses; now his only problem was to find the premises selected. He decided against calling on such firms as Unwin & Rodgers, Mappins and the like, when he saw that they too had already established markets on America's East coast as far back as the 1760s.

By late afternoon, weary of foot and with his two satchels laden with samples, Ollie had visited most of the cutlers recommended by the stranger in the eating house. He had been astounded to find many of these working in small, cramped, ill-lit conditions, yet they were producing goods of the finest quality. At others he'd found rows of men crouched over benches doing intricate handwork, and some grinding in an atmosphere of dust and grime, all working quickly amidst great noise and clatter.

With the promise of several very competitive quotations which would be sent to Adelaide Street, he returned to the keel, but not before removing his coat and hat, and ruffling his hair a little to avoid attracting too much attention. Tomorrow he would seek out manufacturers of the tools and equipment that were in greatest demand by prospectors and settlers, and hopefully find a maker of small ore-crushing machines.

Seeing the heavily-laden and somewhat jaded Ollie climb back onto the keel, Maggy felt a little sorry for him. He'd obviously had a long and busy day. 'Would you like a drink?' she offered, and, reluctant to enquire too deeply into his activities merely asked, 'Did things go well?'

'I think so,' he sighed, placing his satchels on the deck. He was warm and felt grimy and unkempt. 'I'd love a drink, Maggy, that would be grand!' He sat wearily down on the hatch. 'Where's Mike?'

She looked round, 'Somewhere on the wharf, he can't be far away.'

'How did he do today, any luck with a shipment?'

'No,' Maggy said, 'there's not a lot doing, we might have to wait several days yet, who knows? You never can tell.'

'He could do with more guaranteed, regular work,' Ollie commented. 'He needs to call on a few large companies still using the canal, and arrange fortnightly pick-ups.'

Maggy was well aware that her father had always dealt with these matters, but was grateful that in spite of his tiredness Ollie still wanted to assist Michael, 'Would you like a bite to eat, as well?' she offered in a motherly tone.

He smiled ruefully. 'You're a wonder, Maggy, I'll not say no!' He looked at his shirt, 'Look at this,' he complained bitterly, 'you'd think I'd been working all day in a workshop myself to get in this state. I really don't understand why everything is so grubby.'

'There's always soot and grit in the air here. I don't wash anything until we get past Tinsley,' she informed him, 'and I'd certainly hate to live here all the time. I suppose a sailor never gets that dirty.'

'You'd be surprised,' he said, reflecting on times when he'd been cutting up whale blubber. 'But it's not usually this kind of dirt.'

Michael returned later to find a much refreshed Ollie standing in working clothes and chatting to Maggy, but noticed how tired he looked. 'Has it been a useful day?' he enquired. 'You look all in.'

'My mind's in a bit of a whirl I must admit, but this is a very hilly town and I feel as if I've tramped up and down every one of them! Still, I've accomplished quite a lot.' Then, changing the subject he said, 'You got the barrels off, I see, and Maggy says you're still looking for business?'

'Yes,' Michael admitted. 'It seems to get worse each time, that's why many are going straight for coal.'

'I can see it's a problem,' Ollie conceded, wisely refraining from offering advice to Michael for fear of upsetting him, especially after his comment about the *Maggie Kelly* being a tub! He intended giving the matter more thought though, when he had the time, in the hope of easing Michael's burden. 'Fancy a drink later?' he asked. 'I've not much time to spare as I want to study today's findings, but I'm certainly looking forward to a quick one.'

'Why not! I wouldn't mind a break either,' Michael agreed, having forgotten Ollie's earlier remark. He wasn't one to bear grudges, nor did he have the same forceful drive that Ollie had; he wasn't very adventurous either, but he had a steely inner strength which came to the fore when needed. He'd no desire to be a rough diamond either like many on the canal, nor did he want Maggy to become like Lily. Michael had no patience with the fighting and the resulting upheaval that sometimes occurred amongst keelmen, and was content to mind his own business and leave them to it.

'I have a mind to go to London to the Great Exhibition of Works,' Ollie told him later, as they sat drinking in the Maunch Vaults. 'I might take Anna with me, if Mother is well enough.'

America, San Francisco, London, thought Michael, it was all a world away from his own life. 'Maggy will miss Anna,' he said, without thinking, a little envious of Ollie's freedom to direct his own affairs.

'It will be for business ideas, not just for pleasure you understand,' the younger man interrupted Michael's thoughts. 'Probably for a week. The papers predict that the world will be there, showing wondrous things not seen before by ordinary people. It will open Anna's eyes a little. I'll buy her a nice gown and spoil her for a change.'

For no reason that he could think of, Michael was irritated by this and wondered why poor Anna would need her eyes opening at all. He knew he was being unreasonable, and also that if Maggy was asked she would jump at the chance to go as well. Several times since leaving Hull, he'd felt the need to defend Anna when Ollie seemed to speak disparagingly of her. It was foolish of him he knew, for Ollie was clearly devoted to her in his way. Perhaps his own regard for her was because she was shy and trusting, and had, in some respects, a similar character to his own.

However, Ollie's mind had passed on to other things. 'Tomorrow I won't be able to carry all the stuff I buy, I may need to have deliveries made directly to the keel while I call elsewhere. Is that acceptable, and will someone be at the keel all afternoon?'

'I won't be going far,' Michael said, finishing his drink, 'but I'll make sure one of us is there.'

'Now remember, Mike, if you need to hire help tomorrow I will pay for it. After that I can do my share.'

'That's fair enough' Michael responded, 'but there won't be much to handle, except some small items first thing, and those I can probably deal with as they arrive on the wharf side. Any large consignments will have to be loaded on Thursday morning if I can't arrange any help. Will you be bringing anything which might need a lot of room?'

'Not this time, Mike, though I may be able to put some work your way eventually, if things go well. I'll not say much about my plans until they're final, that way I won't make a laughing stock of myself if I fail.'

Michael shook his head. 'I somehow don't think you'll do that, and from what you've told me already I'm beginning to get some idea of your intentions. They're more than a little beyond my ambitions, but I hope they work out for you.'

'Before I'm through, Father will think I'm a spendthrift,' Ollie complained. 'However, no one can start a business without spending some money first, to investigate all the possibilities and pit-falls. If at the end of the day it doesn't work out, at least I've tried and can abandon the plan before coming a real cropper. Most of my outlay I should get back at that point anyway.'

As Ollie continued to confide in him, Michael began to understand him a little more. 'It all seems sensible enough to me,' he admitted, 'thousands do make money on a large scale, and they all had to start somewhere I suppose, although it's not something I'm likely to experience.'

'Well don't forget that without people like you who produce goods or carry them, nobody would get anywhere!'

After a while they left the tavern and returned to the canal basin. 'I'll say, good night,' Ollie said. 'I'd best prepare for tomorrow, then turn in early.' He went to his cabin and stored his well-wrapped bundles in a locker, then planned his activities for the next day. There would be time later to examine his purchases more closely and, when the quotations arrived, make comparisons then. He thumbed through the advertisements in the trade directory, and selected half a dozen makers of tools, including the firms of both Samuel and Ralph Skelton. He also decided that the people most likely to manufacture quartz crushing machines of the size he wanted might be Davy Brothers of Park Iron Works.

Next morning he set off early again and spent hours trudging through the damp and drizzle of a cold late April day. When he eventually returned to the basin in the afternoon, he found the keel moved from her mooring. He was wet and chilled through, and unless Maggy had kindly kept his stove going it would be some time before he could warm himself and dry out. He stood for a few moments wondering where the vessel might be, then decided he'd have to walk the length of the wharf in an effort to find her.

He at last came upon the *Maggie* in one of the small side basins, low in the water, indicating that Michael had been in luck that day. 'Hello!' he shouted, climbing on board. 'Is anyone about?'

Several seconds later, Michael climbed from the aft cabin, his face beaming, obviously pleased with himself. 'I thought you'd gone,' Ollie remarked. 'She's so low in the water I didn't see her straight away.'

'I'd hardly leave you behind,' Michael chided. 'Anyway, we're ready to move off first thing, and we've got a Marine lined up. How did you get on?'

'Another quite good day, apart from this dreadful weather. Did my goods arrive?'

'Two cases came soon after mid-day, and one later. How many did you send?'

Ollie looked relieved. Had they not arrived he could hardly have asked Michael to hold back until they did. 'Just those,' he said, 'I have the small stuff here with me in these bags.'

'You look wet through,' Michael observed. 'I hope I did right, I told Maggy to keep your stove going this afternoon.'

He gave Michael a grateful smile. 'I was hoping you would, Mike, thanks. I'll go below and get changed, then afterwards when I've had a rest, would you join me. I'd like a chat.'

'Why not join us?' Maggy will be pleased as she's had a dull day, what with the weather.'

'I'd like that,' Ollie replied. 'However I'd like a word in private some time, if you don't mind. Business, you understand? Perhaps we could go for another drink later?'

Michael agreed to this and Ollie went to his cabin. The warmth there greeted him, and although there were ropes and equipment stored in it, leaving little space to move about, he was pleased to be alone with his thoughts. During the last two days he'd used all his mental and physical energies to further his hopes and plans, and now there was little more he could do until they returned to Hull. Hanging up his damp clothes, he put on fresh ones, and relaxed on his locker. An hour and a half later Michael had to knock loudly to wake him.

'Are you alright?' Michael called, a little worried by the silence and Ollie's failure to appear earlier.

'Oh! Yes, yes...,' Ollie shouted back, his voice a little shaky. 'I fell asleep. I'll be there directly.' When he arrived on deck the damp evening air woke him completely; he shivered and hurried to the aft cabin, having lost any desire to go further that night.

'You must have been tired,' Maggy said, as he climbed down the steep ladder, stepped onto the locker, and then to the floor.

'I'd no idea where I was when Mike woke me,' he explained, 'my mind whirled like the mist outside.'

'Sit down for a while,' Michael told him, moving some things to make room.

'You're not going out tonight are you, Michael?' Maggy asked, putting down the book she was reading. 'It looks horrible outside.'

Michael looked at Ollie, 'Do you still want to go?'

'Not really, I've had enough bad weather for one day!' Ollie chuckled ruefully.

Seeing Michael's relief at this response, Maggy suggested, 'Why don't you have a drop of your hidden supply? One tot 'll not hurt you, and I'm sure Ollie won't say no!' Ollie looked a little puzzled at this. 'Michael only takes a sip of brandy when his leg is paining him,' she explained, 'he's not a drinker really.'

'Give over, Maggy,' Michael protested, with a grin.

'Actually, nor am I,' Ollie confessed, 'I don't like to drink a lot, I've seen too many men waste everything that way. Father drinks more than I do.'

'We had a grandmother who drank too much!' Maggy said with a giggle, which brought a look of disapproval from Michael.

Ollie's admission, however, had pleased Michael and strengthened his growing respect for him. 'I like to keep a clear head,' he said, 'and people can laugh all they like. One beer is enough for me.'

'I wouldn't mind taking a drop with you, though,' Ollie remarked. Then, when Michael had poured out the brandy he asked, 'What did you manage to pick up today?'

'Iron pipes, gas lanterns and some girders, all for Hull, and I've some ropes and canvas for Thorne as well, making a full load,' Michael was proud to announce.

'You were lucky. Tell me what I owe you for not being here when needed, and I'll square up tomorrow.'

'It all came straight off the wagons, I only had to give the carriers a tip for helping.'

'Well, let me give you that, then,' Ollie insisted, stretching his long legs towards the stove.

'What do you think of Sheffield, Ollie?' Maggy asked later, as they ate some sandwiches.

'I had no idea what to expect, and the hills surprised me. As for the people, I've never seen so many dirty faces before.'

She smiled, 'There's a saying here, that where there's muck there's money. Not that you can see much evidence of it, the money I mean.'

Ollie laughed, 'Only the muck!' She thought he was amused at her, and pouted at him. 'You do have some comical expressions, Maggy,' he said, not unkindly. 'I've not laughed as much for years as I have since we left Hull.'

She wasn't sure whether this remark was meant to be critical or simply his way of complimenting her. Remembering Michael's words of caution about her behaviour some time before, she blushed, feeling a little silly. Ollie seemed not to notice this as he chatted with Michael, so she picked up her book and pretended to be engrossed in its contents until eventually he left, rather more relaxed than when he'd arrived.

Michael could see Keadby lock ahead. It was late afternoon on the day before he was due to meet up with Erik and he was pleased to have had such a trouble-free run. 'We can relax now, Maggy,' he said. 'You take a walk later if you like, and stretch your legs.'

'I might just do that, when I've washed up. What will you do?'

Michael smiled with satisfaction. 'I might simply sit and think a while, and maybe chat to some of the men on the bank. It's a long time since I've done that here.'

When the keel was near enough to the bank, Ollie jumped onto the towpath with a mooring rope, and slowly brought the vessel to a stop, securing it fore and aft to rings set in the path. Suddenly he heard a familiar whistle and looked up with a shout of surprise, as he saw his father coming towards him. He called to Michael, 'Look who's here!'

Erik's bearing gave no reason to suppose that anything was wrong at home, in fact rather the contrary. 'So, you keep me waiting all day' he complained. 'I'm pacing up and down thinking Anna got it all wrong!' Then, having clasped hands good naturedly with Ollie, he climbed aboard and joined Michael at the tiller. 'You have a good run?' he asked with a smile.

'As a matter of fact we did,' Michael replied, pleased to see Erik looking so cheerful. 'How's Ellen?' he asked, realising that it had to be good news.

'She is fine,' Erik's eyes twinkled. 'And my son, he works well, I hope?'

'No complaints,' Michael chuckled, 'but I thought we said be here tomorrow?'

Erik smiled again, 'I come last night just in case. The lock-keeper let me sleep in the outhouse'. He turned and called to Ollie, 'Hal's home!'

'Is that your other son?' Michael asked, trying to recall the name.

At this juncture Maggy came up from below to see what all the noise was about, and seeing Erik her eyes lit up. 'Erik!' she cried, delight clearly showing on her face. 'We didn't expect you 'til morning.'

'Ah, my Maggy!' he responded teasingly, 'I come early to surprise you. Besides, what are you doing here, I thought not to see you for some time?'

Her voice was suddenly serious. 'How's Ellen?' she asked. 'She is better isn't she?'

'My lovely Ellen is well now, thank you, and she will be very pleased that you come back.' He turned to Ollie who had joined them. 'You didn't ask about your mother, son.' There was a hint of reproval in his tone.

'Huh!' Ollie rejoined, 'I knew the minute I clapped eyes on you that everything was fine.'

Erik smiled. 'You know me too well, I fear. See, Maggy, they learn at school to read me like an old book.'

Although Michael, in his usual way, did not openly display his pleasure at seeing Erik, he was actually the one most relieved over his arrival as he had worried lest the letter Ollie had sent might have been delayed, or even lost in the post.

'There is much congestion in the docks at this time,' Erik informed Michael later, 'several days people are waiting to berth. The whaling fleet is home and taking up space, but there is much talk of demand falling off and that some whalers will not go for whales again.'

'That will affect your son, Hal, then?'

'Who knows? There are other ships and other trades; if they need a sailor then perhaps he gets work.' Erik paused to light his pipe, drawing deeply until the tobacco glowed red. He sighed before speaking again. 'If I had not lost the *Martha Jane*, he would have no need to seek work.'

'He might like going to sea,' Michael said, trying to relieve Erik of the guilt he was obviously feeling. 'Ollie seems to have enjoyed his travels well enough, besides, you were a sailor yourself.'

'That's different,' Erik interrupted as he tamped his pipe down.

'What's different?' Ollie asked, joining them.

'If I had not lost the keel, Hal wouldn't be forced to go to sea again.'

'It won't hurt him,' Ollie said adamantly, 'you mother them too much. Look at Anna!'

Michael's hackles rose immediately. 'What's wrong with Anna?' he nearly shouted, but turned away lest his angry reaction should be noticed.

'You wouldn't let her marry George,' Ollie continued, 'because he wasn't good enough. You keep her at home and pretend you want her to marry, then, when you need money you let her work at The Black Boy! She'd have been better off with George!'

Erik was far from amused by Ollie's outburst, and retorted angrily, 'He was too old for Anna, that's why, and if I hadn't lost the keel she would never have gone to work!'

'The keel, the keel, always the keel!' Ollie raised his voice so that it seemed to echo down the canal. 'Leave them alone, they'll survive on their own.'

'Hey, keep your voices down,' Michael urged, failing to understand why Ollie and his father always bickered when they'd been apart for a while. Turning towards him, both men spoke at the same time. 'Sorry, Mike!' Fortunately this union of thought served to lessen the tension, and Erik lifted his hands in despair. 'You see how alike we are,' he said, without a trace of ill-feeling or resentment.

'Oh, let's go for a drink,' Ollie suggested, shrugging his shoulders, 'Mike will think we're always arguing. You coming Mike?'

Michael shook his head, 'No, you two go, I'll keep Maggy company'. He watched the pair go, talking calmly, their row forgotten. Michael shook his head again, and smiled to himself, half envying them their companionship and their ability to let bygones be bygones. They were indeed powerful men in their own ways, yet he suspected that Ellen could control them both. He fell to pondering about Anna. She was a complete contrast to the two who'd just left, perhaps she was content to live in their shadow, for both were fond of her. On the other hand, she'd displayed a quiet determination when her mind was made up. But, who was George, he wondered? Whoever he was he hadn't suited Erik, that was for sure. He could see Anna's face in his mind; the warmth in her eyes when she smiled, and he could hardly imagine a cross word passing her lips.

'Have they gone yet?' Maggy's quiet voice called up to him.

'You can come out now,' Michael answered, understanding her caution. 'They've gone to the tavern as if nothing had happened,' he said, then explained what had taken place. 'How old is Anna, anyway?' he asked, after telling her about George.

'About twenty, I think, and she's a very nice girl, Michael. She adores Ollie and her father, no matter what has happened.'

'Even so, they're an unusual family, although I have to say they are hard working.'

Maggy agreed, 'Well, with them around life is never dull these days, is it? They seem to cast a spell over everything. We've known them less than two months and yet it's hard to imagine life without them.'

'You're right,' he confessed, 'but I don't think the keel, or I, could stand having them both on board at the same time for long. But you seem to get on well with Ollie, what do you make of him?'

'Oh, he's alright,' Maggy replied, without hesitation. Michael looked keenly at her and she laughed, 'I don't fancy him, I just find him very interesting to talk to. He's done so many things, yet I get the feeling his life is just beginning and that a very different man will finally emerge.'

Her assessment of Ollie's character confirmed his growing belief that Maggy had a good brain and better understanding than many had. 'Ollie's not bad, Maggy,' he told her, 'but when you do find someone, make sure it's a man who can give you a good life. Don't marry just anyone and waste yourself.'

'Hark at you, Michael Havercroft,' she replied, snuggling her head up against his shoulder.

He put his arm affectionately round her. 'We've come this far, Maggy. I think we're going to make it, don't you?'

With four hands aboard the *Maggie Kelly* again, the estuary presented less of a threat than usual, although the wind had freshened considerably. Two members of the crew were, of course, happy to be returning home, and even Michael had a pleasant feeling of elation as they entered Hull's outer basin. He'd no idea why this should be as he had been there so many times before, whereas Maggy was simply pleased to back in the lively port again.

It may have been this slight relaxation which made them all slow to react, when the unexpected happened as they were being penned up in the lock leading into the Humber Dock.

A sudden gust of wind caught the unladen keel behind them before she was fully tied up, and thrust it violently forward onto the *Maggie Kelly's* rudder.

'Fanden!' Erik yelled, as the tiller jerked violently and nearly knocked him over the taffrail. The sound of the impact and the shudder of the keel shocked Michael badly, and he had to grab the winch post for support.

'What the devil's happening?' he bellowed as he righted himself and tried to help Erik to his feet. He let go of the winch, leaving Ollie and Maggy to tether the boom of the sail which they were lowering.

Erik was badly shaken. 'God knows!' he cried, and then, seeing that they'd been hit by the other keel, shouted angrily at the crew. 'Can't you control you own ship?'

As Erik appeared to be uninjured, Michael leaned over and saw to his dismay that their rudder had been damaged, but how badly he couldn't tell. 'Helvete!' Erik cried, when he also saw the damage, and was about to shout again, when Michael cautioned him.

'Calm down, Erik, it won't help now. Are you two alright?' he called to Ollie and Maggy.

When Maggy quickly answered, 'Yes, but what happened?' He turned his attention back to the damage.

Although he was angry, he knew that creating a scene would not help matters or assist him in obtaining any sort of recompense from the other captain. He turned to Erik. 'Look,' he said, 'you're shaken up. Go below and have a mug of tea.' By this time a small crowd had gathered to see what was going on.

The other captain leaned over the bow of his vessel to look at the top of the *Maggie Kelly's* rudder. 'Sorry,' he said, 'a gust of wind took us off guard. But it looks as if it's not too bad.'

Michael could now see that some banding had been disturbed, and replied, 'However bad it is it'll have to be repaired before I can sail again!' His voice was firm, and he knew full well that the captain would try to get away with anything he could. 'This is going to cost me time and money,' he said, determined to hold his ground, although he realised he'd as much chance of getting a fair settlement as he had of finding a berth that day. 'Do I get some recompense or do I fetch a Dockyard Officer?' Michael's tone was threatening, much as his father's would have been.

The captain grumbled something under his breath, watching Michael for signs of weakness. Seeming to accept that Michael was not going to give way, he said grudgingly, 'I'll give you a guinea to fix it.' This was a take it or leave it attitude, and Michael knew he would be lucky to get a better offer. He might spend days, even weeks, trying to negotiate a better settlement if the captain decided not to co-operate. Anything was better than nothing.

'I'll have it now,' Michael stated firmly, not wanting the matter to drag on once the lock gates opened up. The Dock Superintendent was probably fed up anyway with complaints of one kind or another and it would depend on his mood as to how seriously he took the incident.

With a look of distaste the captain reached in his pocket and drew out a coin. 'I'll have a receipt,' he said, reaching over and paying Michael. 'And think yourself lucky you've got witnesses.'

When Erik came out of his cabin with a mug of tea and heard what had transpired, he was far from pleased at the outcome, and cautioned Michael. 'Don't leave the keel unattended in the dock, he might appear to be a fair man, but don't take chances.'

Michael's nerves were on edge; standing up to the man had taken a lot out of him. 'Here, take this,' Erik said, handing him the mug, 'you need it more than me, I get myself another.'

Meanwhile, Ollie and Maggy busied themselves with tying up the sail, and Ollie was glad that Michael had been too occupied to notice when he got the boom caught up in the rigging. Maggy had gone immediately to help him, but she was still disturbed by the incident with the other keel and accepted that it was not her place to interfere.

By the time Michael had drunk his tea the lock gates were opening up to release them into the first of the town docks. Erik had been right, there was nowhere to berth. Fishing boats, sloops and keels were closely tied up side by side, causing a bottleneck and preventing other vessels from passing through to the other docks. They lowered the stabilising lee boards and worked the keel into the only area of clear water available, glided to a stop and waited. Eventually they were able to wedge the keel between two other vessels, a situation which could see them marooned for several days if they were unlucky.

'It's quicker to get from St Petersburg to here than from Sammy's Point through the docks.' Erik moaned. 'Now you find a chandler and see if he can get the rudder mended quick when we are off-loaded,' he suggested.

Michael nodded in agreement and turned to Ollie. 'You may as well go home,' he told him, 'you've done what you said you would, and thanks. There's nothing we can do here for a while.'

'Thanks, Mike. It's been quite an experience, one which I've actually enjoyed. I'll come and help you unload if you like, as I won't be leaving Hull for a few days.' He went below to collect what he could of his possessions, knowing that they could manage well enough without him.

Maggy was sorry to see him go. His conversation and occasional teasing had been very enjoyable and she felt a little empty inside, as she often did when a friend departed. But then they all travelled on sooner or later, that was life on the water.

'Can I leave some of my parcels on board until it's more convenient to get them off?' Ollie asked, as he prepared to cross over the next keel to get to the wharf side.

'They're not in the way,' Michael assured him.

Ollie gave Maggy a smile and a wink as he went. 'You'd make a good sailor, Maggy,' he told her.

'Bye Ollie,' Maggy responded with a laugh, 'we'll turn you into a keelman one day.'

Congestion within the docks had always been a problem, though it had been some time since Michael had seen it quite so bad as it was now.

There was nothing quite so boring as hanging around, waiting to 'liver, as his mother used to say. Until that was possible, and his rudder was repaired, he couldn't accept another shipment. With so much time on his hands he set about repainting several sections of wood affected by the winter frosts and ice. Every time other vessels moved out of the dock he was able to shift the keel nearer to where he needed to be, and would soon be able to arrange for a shipwright to assess the damage to the rudder.

At the end of their third day of waiting he was able to exchange places with a departing keel, and tie up at the wharf. Once this was done, he decided to stretch his legs and tell Erik himself that he would be needed the following morning. After warning Maggy not to leave the keel, he set off for Adelaide Street. Since the day of the incident, he'd seen little of Erik, or Ollie for that matter, both of whom he would have been forced to pay had they helped him, nor had he seen Anna and the children.

'Why don't you go and see Anna? he'd suggested to Maggy on the first day, only to be told that Anna had gone with her brother Hal to visit their grandmother somewhere near Ferriby. Whether or not this news disappointed him he failed to acknowledge, and as time went by his boredom led to day-dreaming. Nevertheless something had completely destroyed the buoyant feeling he'd had on reaching Hull. He became edgy and irritable, and tried to analyse his feelings, thinking that maybe he missed the company of a younger man, Ollie. Maggy obviously did, for she was also less than happy, and was moody and listless. He tried to think of Lily, whose path had not crossed his since their previous meeting here on the dockside, but it was only when Erik called by and imparted the news that Hal and Anna were back, that he realised he hadn't really thought of Lily for some time.

Full of enthusiasm now, he left the dockland area and made his way briskly to Adelaide Street, his spirits rising as he went. But what was he doing delivering messages when Maggy could have done it? He tried to convince himself that there was no ulterior motive in his visit, other than to see the newly recovered Ellen. After all he had some time to spare, and wasn't it common courtesy to show an interest in the welfare of someone who had befriended him? A stir of excitement ran through him as he contemplated arriving at the house, especially with the prospect of Anna greeting him at the door. This was hardly what he should feel for his Mate's daughter, but who was he fooling? For days now the touch of Anna's trusting hand had haunted him, and he'd even dreamed of silly little things, always involving her. There was no reason on earth why Maggy should not have come to the Erikson's today in his stead, he'd simply seized the opportunity to go himself. He realised that nothing could ever come of a relationship with her, her fears were too great for that. He just couldn't rid himself of his desire to see her again, to talk to her, to make a friend of her.

The last time he'd knocked on Erik's door he'd seen a flicker of rejection on Anna's face, and if that reoccurred today, then he would consider it well deserved, his thoughts being what they were. He raised his hand and knocked quietly as if apologising for being there, and waited, never doubting it would be she who came.

'That'll be Mrs Christy,' Ellen called to Anna, thinking she recognised the knock. 'Go and get it, love.'

Opening the door wide, with no regard for her appearance, Anna stared at Michael in disbelief, then, clasping her hands excitedly, she gasped, 'It's Michael!' Her eyes this time were bright and her smile wide and happy. He now knew that he was a welcome visitor to the house.

Very conscious of her behaviour and having no reason to suspect that he had come for anything other than business, Anna blushed furiously and struggled to regain her composure. 'Come in,' she said with a tremble in her voice. Then, averting her eyes modestly, she added in an attempt to cover her confusion, 'Mother will be pleased to see you.'

'Come through, Mr Havercroft,' Ellen cried, 'Erik's out in the yard. Fetch him Anna, will you?'

Anna went obediently, glad to escape Michael's intent gaze, yet eager to hurry back to where he waited.

'Ah, Mike!' Erik greeted him as he came through the back door, his hands covered in fish scales and blood. 'I gut fish for dinner, you will stay?'

'Well...,' Michael was tempted to say yes, but recalled that Maggy intended buying fish in the market to cook later in the day.

'Why don't you stay for dinner,' Ellen broke in, 'it won't be more than half an hour.'

Without thinking, Michael looked hopefully at Anna who was standing half in, half out of the doorway. Ellen saw the glance and the way Anna had been watching Michael, and prayed that Erik hadn't seen it too. So that's the way it was, Ellen thought, a gentle smile crossing her face.

'You look happy, Mother,' Erik said with some satisfaction, assuming his wife was thinking of something that he was not party to. Turning back to Michael, he asked, 'Well, are you staying or not?'

In order not to upset Maggy, Michael reckoned he could eat fish twice in one day without complaining, so against his better judgement he accepted, adding only that he couldn't stay too long afterwards.

'Good!' Erik agreed. 'Now you come and talk in the yard while I finish off!' Michael followed him and told him that they would be able to off-load in the morning, first thing. 'Right, after that we see how much damage there is to the keel, no?'

'Yes, it'll be a relief to find out.'

'Well then, have a rest this afternoon. A man needs a bit of pleasure in life. Or do you never stop?' Erik had a philosophy that what was unalterable had to be endured, in as pleasant a way as possible. 'Perhaps we have a drink or two? You're a young man—be happy.' He took the fish which he'd finished gutting and washed it before taking it in to Ellen, leaving Michael standing in the yard staring at the mess of fish gut and blood. No wonder the docks stank so when careless fishermen dumped rubbish like this into the water.

Erik returned, cleaned up, then went back into the house where Ellen had poured out two mugs of coffee. 'Sit down and take this,' he said, handing him a mug. 'Now tell me, what is Ollie up to? I've seen the bundles he shipped back, and now he informs me he's off to London to this exhibition. I know he's not afraid of work—he's up to something, I just know it.'

It was embarrassing enough knowing half of Ollie's plans and having to keep them from Erik, but now to answer him direct was even worse. 'That's not for me to say, Erik,' Michael replied. 'Why not ask him yourself?'

Erik sniffed. 'I'll not ask, if he chooses not to tell me; but I know he's hiding something.' He was not pleased but pride apparently prevented him from satisfying his curiosity. 'He's not hard up, that much I am knowing,' Erik murmured, more to himself than anyone else.

'All you have to do is ask!' A voice rang out from inside the house. Erik spun round, startled and surprised to think he'd been listened to unbeknown. 'Or are you too proud?' Ollie's voice had a touch of humour in it. 'I haven't explained because I didn't know myself how things would work out,' he said, as he came into the yard. 'Perhaps I'm like you, a stubborn and proud old goat. Now I've got something to tell you, I will.'

'Well, it will have to wait,' Ellen called from behind him, 'dinner is ready.'

Michael was pleased at Ollie's intervention as it saved him fending off Erik's questions. His return also meant that dinner with Anna would not be quite the ordeal he'd imagined. Once seated at the table, around which the whole family had gathered, he felt a bit guilty that Maggy was alone on the keel whilst he was enjoying himself. Ellen deliberately placed Anna next to her father, at the opposite end to Michael, in the hopes that the intimate glances she'd observed earlier would not be noticed by her husband. This way if Michael looked towards Anna, Erik would think he was in fact looking at him. She also thought that Anna's less than cautious display of interest would be unobserved in this position.

To Michael the time spent at the table was a mixture of purgatory and sheer delight. He neither cared nor even noticed whether the fish was good or bad, and was happy to be relieved of the need to speak often, because Erik made up for them both. It was Kristen who drew him out occasionally with her childish prodding. When he thought no-one was looking he glanced directly at Anna who responded immediately by demurely lowering her eye-lashes, but not before she'd momentarily met his gaze. They both failed to notice however, that they were quietly being observed by Ellen and Ollie, both of whom were enjoying the situation, and who were aware that a cat and mouse game was going on right under Erik's nose. Ellen had put her finger to her lips and shook her head to silence Ollie, after he'd raised his eyebrows in enquiry at seeing that something was afoot.

When at last the meal was over, Michael had no further reason for staying and rose reluctantly from the table, saying, 'Well, that was a fine meal, Mrs Erikson. Thank you, I'm glad I stayed, but now I must go.'

'That's a pity,' she replied, 'and a shame that Maggy wasn't here with you.'

'I feel a little guilty about that,' he confessed, 'she'll be wondering where I am. I'd best hurry back.'

Ellen smiled at him. 'Anna would love to see Maggy again, wouldn't you?' She turned to Anna; showing no sign of anything but motherly interest, and added, 'It's a lovely day, why don't you go with Michael to the dock? That's if Mr Havercroft doesn't mind. I can manage quite well here on my own.'

'Maggy would love that,' Michael quickly replied, and held his breath, hoping that Anna would accept.

She was hesitant, surprised by the turn of events, and looked anxiously at Michael before answering, unsure whether her company was being forced upon him. Her greeting of him earlier had been over familiar, with the result that he had watched her constantly throughout the meal with a strange look in his eyes. He stood waiting for her to answer.

'Hurry if you're going,' Erik broke in, 'he has work to do.'

With a start, Anna said, 'I would like to come. Could you wait for a moment first while I get something for Maggy?' She looked at him seriously, waiting for a sign of approval, and when he nodded she hurried from the room, to return with a bulky parcel and her shawl.

After they'd gone Erik winked knowingly at Ellen. 'You think I'm blind,' he said, with a chuckle. 'Well, I'm not!'

As Michael and Anna started down the street, it was she who was tongue-tied, being conscious only of Michael's presence and not knowing if he actually wanted her company, or if he had somehow been persuaded to take her along.

'Am I going too fast for you?' Michael asked, determined to break through her reserve, yet not wanting to repeat the awkwardness he'd experienced with Lily.

'Well...no!' she stammered, perturbed lest he might prefer to go on ahead. 'But if you're in a hurry and I'm holding you back, please do go on.'

'I'll try to remember to slow down,' he promised, then asked, 'but tell me, what's in the parcel for Maggy, am I to be let into the secret?'

She had been clutching the parcel so tightly that if the contents had been delicate they would have been broken by now. Releasing the pressure of her fingers she smoothed out the creased wrapping. 'It's a cushion I've made to brighten up the cabin,' she confessed, almost apologetically. 'It's really meant for both of you.'

'Well, thank you very much,' he said. 'The place could do with a little more comfort. Father and I put aside such things after we left Mother at home permanently. It made less work for the pair of us.'

'It won't get in the way, will it? I never thought that you might not want it.' She involuntarily clutched the parcel to her chest.

He shook his head and smiled, thinking how unlike Lily she was, sensitive and unassuming, her silence coming from shyness, not moodiness.

'I think it is time we brightened the cabin up, it's a nice idea and I look forward to seeing Maggy open it.'

They reached Monument Bridge and Michael paused for a while, apparently to watch the various vessels about their business. To a stranger this absorption might have given the impression that it was the first time he'd seen the dock, but in reality nothing over the bridge interested him, he merely wanted to keep Anna by his side a little longer. After their discussion about the parcel they had chatted like old friends. Anna had her own opinions which she expressed with quiet dignity, and could certainly hold her own with him. She had a ready smile which appeared whenever she spoke, and Michael had suddenly to admit to himself that he'd lost his heart to someone who was probably too good for him, as apparently George had done before him. He recalled Erik's words and wondered just how old George had been. This discovery made him despondent and a bit down-hearted, so he fell silent, and stared out across the dock. He would have liked to have known more about this George but could hardly ask Anna.

She became aware of this sudden change in him, and said, 'You look sad, Michael. Is something amiss?'

Pulling himself together, he smiled, a little forlornly. 'Oh, it's nothing for you to worry about,' he told her.

She placed a hand gently on his forearm. 'But I am concerned, we are friends aren't we? And friends should help one another.'

He bit his lip, thinking deeply. 'You must have so many friends, and I have but few,' he said glumly.

She squeezed his arm reassuringly, sensing that he was feeling low. 'Not as many as you would think.'

'No?' he asked, turning to face her. 'You have no one special?'

'No one,' she whispered quietly, not realising that he'd hoped she might consider him in that light.

Disappointed, he placed his hand gently over hers. 'One day someone will turn your head I'm sure.' Anna's heart sank at this remark as she had begun to see Michael as something special in her life. 'Come,' he said suddenly. 'We'd best get back to Maggy. She must be worrying where I've got to.'

'Oh dear, yes! Time has gone so quickly,' Anna agreed. 'You go ahead and I will follow.' She watched him go, despair creeping over her, as she accepted that what could have been was not to be realised. She was to be merely his friend, after all.

Michael walked away with hurried steps back to the keel, his own disappointment well concealed from passers-by. His mind was torn between what he would have liked to have said and the thought that if he had spoken out, his words might not have been welcome.

'Where have you been?' Maggy cried with concern, when at last he reached her. 'I thought you had met with an accident.'

'I stayed too long at Erik's, I'm sorry,' he said, and hastened to add, 'I didn't realise just how much time had passed.' He could quite understand her reaction on seeing him and blamed it on his own selfishness. 'Sorry, Maggy.'

'What would I have done if you hadn't returned?' She went on, angry and upset. 'And there's nothing for dinner 'cause I couldn't shop.'

'I'm here now, so calm down and listen. Anna's on her way, she has a present for you. Go and keep a look out for her, will you?' He wasn't sure if he could face Anna again. The happy feeling of anticipation which had accompanied him to Adelaide Street had now long gone; perhaps he'd expected too much, and it had left him feeling rather empty. 'You could take Anna shopping with you,' he suggested, anxious not to be alone with her. Maggy looked at him sharply. He was in a funny mood, but then he often was these days. He turned his head away from her, as if to examine a mooring rope, and said casually, 'Oh, and Maggy, don't get fish today will you?' He kept his eyes averted, 'I had some at Erik's!' Well, he thought, Anna would have told her if he hadn't.

'Ooh!' Maggy cried with exasperation, 'I've been sat here twiddling my thumbs, waiting for you to come back and you've been feeding yourself!' Her face was red and her eyes flashed with anger. 'I'm hungry, Michael Havercroft, and a fat lot you care!' At that she grabbed her purse and stormed up the ladder, leaving him feeling guilty and uncomfortable.

He could see her point of view, of course, yet the fire in her amused him. 'And I don't want any more sausages either!' he called after her as she stormed away indignantly, thus risking her wrath even more. She glared back at him with such contempt that he ducked quickly out of sight. He realised that Maggy was growing up fast. The dreamy, far-away girl had been replaced by a force to be reckoned with, one which his father would neither have approved nor allowed. To his dismay he saw that not only did she intercept Anna on the wharf side but paused only a moment, said something to her, then both turned and walked away, all without a glance in his direction. He kicked out at a rope fender and missed, catching his toe on a stanchion. 'Damn and blast!' he shouted, cursing himself on both counts. 'Damn, damn, damn!'

'Something wrong?' Michael spun round to find that Erik had returned to the keel unnoticed and witnessed his outburst.

'I've bashed my toe, that's all!' he said abruptly, unwilling to tell Erik the real cause of his annoyance. It never ceased to amaze him how Erik could appear from nowhere when he was least expected. He was about to remark on this when it struck him that he must be careful not to take his frustration out on Erik, who had no idea what was disturbing him.

'I see the girls have gone off together,' Erik said, grinning. 'They seem to get on well.' Sensibly, he said nothing else. The wisdom that sometimes comes with age told him that poor Michael was suffering from more than a bruised toe at that precise moment.

Michael realised he was stuck with Erik now for the rest of the day. He didn't feel much like talking, or drinking either for that matter; he also had a premonition that Anna would not return to the keel. In this respect he was right, as she had stayed in town for almost an hour before making her excuse and leaving Maggy to her shopping.

Soon after, Maggy made her way back to the keel, and found Erik trying to persuade a reluctant Michael into going for a drink. 'Come on, Mike,' he said, chiding. 'What you going to do 'til morning, sit moping about? Come, I take you to the Norwegian Tavern, meet some friends of mine.'

Realising that it would be churlish to refuse, and as he certainly needed cheering up, Michael agreed.

'Tell me, what you think Ollie is up to?' Erik asked, obviously trying to pump him again for information, as they walked away from the dock. 'He is very secretive.'

Michael had no wish to involve himself with the Erikson's affairs, and said carefully, 'Look, Ollie's told you to ask him, so why not do just that? I don't know enough, just a bit here and there. I might say something which could give you the wrong picture altogether, but I don't think you need worry, his head's screwed on the right way.' Erik shrugged his shoulders dismissively. 'You're a proud lot, that's your trouble.' Michael told him bluntly, intent on not becoming a pawn between them. 'Just ask him.'

'A'right, a'right, you win! Tonight I ask.' Erik gave in grudgingly.

For some time Michael had been aware that there was a man following closely behind them, and who appeared to stop whenever they slowed down. 'Don't look now, ' he said to Erik in a quiet voice, 'there's a chap behind who I'm sure is following us, and I think I've seen him somewhere before, but I can't think where.' He just managed to catch Erik's arm as he was instinctively about to turn. 'He's been there for some time.'

Erik waited several seconds, then said, 'Hold on a minute,' and bent down to re-tie the lace of his boot. He rose slowly, glancing casually at a passer-by before letting his eyes rest fleetingly on the man Michael suspected. They continued walking in silence for several seconds until Erik muttered quietly, 'It is the mate on the keel which rammed us. Do not worry, if he comes into the tavern I have friends there. He will not tackle us two at the same time, I think.'

The thought of trouble disturbed Michael. 'Look,' he said, 'we don't want a disturbance. I've never been involved in a fight and I don't want to start now. I'm no coward, I just don't like a scene.'

'It is more me he wants,' Erik protested, 'I see a nasty look in his eye before the captain intervened. He maybe has the money taken from his wages.'

Entering the Norwegian Tavern, Erik introduced Michael to a couple of men, then left him; as he did so, Michael saw the man who had been following them slip quietly into the tavern, where he leaned against the bar out of Michael's sight.

'He's here,' Michael informed Erik on his return, 'he's at the end of the room, behind those men.'

'Don't let him know you've seen him,' Erik cautioned. 'Believe me, once we go away from here he will not feel like following, and he won't want trouble on the wharf in case his captain find out. But don't leave the keel unattended in case he try something. Now, when I say, just get up and follow me.'

Michael was tense. He decided he didn't like the ale which Erik had chosen for him, and found it hard to make conversation under the circumstances. The longer they waited the more nervous he became.

'Now, follow me slowly,' Erik said, putting down his glass, and they made their way between the other drinkers towards the rear of the tavern. Once outside he muttered, 'That fellow not follow now.'

'How can you be sure?' Michael asked, 'He'll soon realise we've given him the slip and follow.'

'I think not! You see, he won't know that it is us teaching him a lesson.' He led Michael up a side alley and stopped just short of Dock Street where the front entrance to the tavern was, and waited, holding Michael back. They stood patiently for some time, and Michael wondered why Erik was so confident that something was about to happen. 'Here he is!' Erik chuckled triumphantly, as the man emerged swearing to himself, and somewhat the worse for wear.

Erik explained to Michael, 'When he gets up to follow us someone was to accidentally push against him and spill his ale. If he gets angry he get a clout! He is just small fry, I do not think he bother us again.'

By this time Michael had had enough. 'If you don't mind, Erik, I'm going back to the keel for a rest. You go in for another drink with your friends if you like, but don't get yourself into any trouble on my account.'

'I do just that,' Erik laughed. 'You go back, I see you tomorrow early.'

When Anna returned home her mother was quick to notice she was rather subdued. 'Did you see Maggy when you got to the keel?' she asked, gently probing. 'Did she like the cushion?'

'Yes, I went shopping with her. She said she wished she could sew as well as me.'

'And what did Michael think?'

Anna hesitated, wondering how to explain not having shown it to Michael without admitting her avoidance of him. 'He didn't see it,' she replied, with a tremor in her voice.

It was what she didn't say that warned Ellen to be careful now, as something was definitely amiss. This saddened her, especially after what she'd noticed earlier at the table. 'What a pity,' she said. 'Was he too busy? I would have thought...' She stopped, noticing that Anna was near to tears. So not to make matters worse she simply added, 'Well, I'm glad Maggy liked it, I'm sure Michael will tell you what he thinks when next you meet.'

That Anna should see Michael again soon was now foremost in Ellen's mind, so she prepared her plan carefully. When Erik left for work early the following morning she made sure that his sandwiches weren't ready for him. 'Go on, Erik, hurry up or you'll keep Michael waiting,' she ordered. 'I'll send Anna down with them.'

'Ollie can bring them—he's following me later,' Erik replied, rather puzzled as it wasn't like Ellen to forget his sandwiches. 'Are you feeling well?' he asked.

'Of course I am' she told him impatiently. 'Just leave it to me.' Once he'd gone she deliberately avoided mentioning the matter to Ollie, and sent him on his way empty-handed as well. She placed the cloth bundles in Erik's basket and left it plainly where Anna could not fail to see it, professing to be put out when she did so. 'Fancy Ollie going without it,' she complained. 'Be a good girl, love, take their food down to the dock when you've put the washing out, will you? There's another letter here for Ollie too.' Anna was taken aback at this as she didn't want to meet Michael again, but as there was no reason to refuse, she had to agree. 'You can take this cake to Michael as well,' Ellen added, 'and while you're there ask him if he needs Maggy this afternoon. She can come back with you and you can tell her about going to London with Ollie.'

Whilst Anna was excited at Ollie's invitation, she was apprehensive at the prospect of seeing Michael again. What could she say without in some way revealing her true feelings? She had never been able to easily conceal her thoughts and had developed a habit of modestly averting her eyes, or lowering her head. She wasn't quite as shy as everyone thought, but was acutely aware that her emotions were often plain for all to see. She decided to avoid personal matters when she saw Michael at the keel, and resolved to appear more interested in Maggy's affairs.

With this comforting thought in mind, she left the house with a quickening step. She couldn't avoid her excitement growing though, as she went along, and hardly noticed a small child crying on a doorstep, or the barrow-boy whom she nearly ran into. Neither did she glance at her own flushed face reflected in shop windows as she passed by. As a result she was almost out of breath when she approached the wharf side, so she slowed her pace and tried to compose herself. Ollie and her father were both hard at work unloading the keel, but of Michael and Maggy there was no sign. She stood for a moment or two plucking up courage before calling out to attract their attention, all the while refusing to admit that she was sad not to see Michael there.

'Hello, Anna!' A voice called from behind, making her jump with surprise. 'Sorry,' Michael said, laughing. 'Did I startle you?'

'Why…yes…you did,' she stammered, as she turned to face him.

'What have you got there?' he asked, with a twinkle in his eye, 'another cushion?'

She knew he was teasing her and smiled. 'No, no, just lunch for father and Ollie, and a cake for you and Maggy, from Mother.'

'That's very kind of her, and it was nice of you to go to such trouble with the cushion,' he said gently. 'You didn't come back yesterday so I couldn't thank you then.'

'No,' she replied shyly, 'I went straight home.'

He wanted to ask why but thought better of it. 'Shall I have the basket, or do you want to take it down yourself?' he asked with a laugh, then realised he was being a bit unkind to tease her, reminding her of her previous reluctance to descend the vertical ladder.

She shrank back a little, her lips parting, and her glance told him she thought that he was taunting her. He hadn't realised just how sensitive she was, and could have kicked himself for being so inconsiderate. 'Maggy's in the cabin,' he said, trying to make amends. 'Shall I fetch her?'

'No,' Anna replied, in a firm, decisive voice, 'I will go myself, if you will take the basket.'

Without a word he did so. He could tell that she was determined to prove that she could do it on her own, and it was all he could do to stop himself going forward to help. He stood and watched her, admiring her courage, knowing that she was quite frightened and was forcing herself to go down the ladder. When at last she stepped down onto the keel, Ollie clapped enthusiastically. Ignoring him, she turned and looked up at Michael defiantly. 'There!' she called up, 'I did it.' Nevertheless she made her way with shaking legs to the cabin, leaving Michael to follow her down the ladder, quite discomforted.

On hearing Ollie's applause, Maggy put her head up through the hatchway and saw Anna carefully making her way towards her, obviously a little distressed. 'What was all that about?' Maggy asked, concerned at the state her friend was in.

'They thought I couldn't come down on my own,' Anna was angry but still trembling, 'but I did it, Maggy, I did it!'

'Come down here and have a cup of tea,' Maggy offered comfortingly. 'You did well,' she said, 'but why are you so upset?'

As Anna sat on the locker she looked forlornly at Maggy. 'Michael thought I was too scared to come down onto the keel on my own. He was very unkind.'

'Michael unkind?' Maggy was bewildered. 'That's not like him at all!' She looked keenly at Anna, 'What did he say to you?' But before Anna could reply she heard steps near the hatch.

'Hush, he may be coming down,' Anna whispered.

It was Michael who appeared and the two girls fell silent, a sign to him that he'd been the topic of their conversation. Maggy looked askance at him, and Anna's face still had a pallor which told him she was upset. In his distress at having hurt her he'd forgotten the basket and was still holding it tightly. 'Here, Maggy, Ellen has sent us a cake with Erik and Ollie's lunch. Will you take their food through to them? There's nothing behind the hold door now so you can go through, it'll save you climbing up.'

Maggy thanked Anna for the cake, then, without further comment, she went through the small door leading to the hold and closed it firmly behind her, sensing that it might be better to leave the two alone for a while. Michael had had a strange expression on his face, one which usually meant he was in no mood to be questioned. She went forward to where Erik was working, and grumbled. 'I don't know what's the matter with Michael these days.' Holding out the basket, she said, 'Here, you appear to have forgotten this!' In her annoyance she might have seemed rude, but Erik took his lunch, concealing a smile as he did so. So Ellen hadn't spoilt the habit of a life-time, he thought, she had planned it this way! He called Maggy back before she could return to the aft bulkhead, and delayed her for some time with his genial banter.

When Maggy had quit the cabin, Anna made to stand up. 'Please don't go, Anna,' Michael appealed, as gently as he could. 'I seem to have upset you without meaning to.' She lowered her head. 'Look at me, Anna,' he begged, with a catch of emotion in his voice, and sat down on the locker, determined to make amends. 'I'm not used to teasing,' he said, 'I didn't mean to offend you.'

Anna realised that Michael was sincere in what he said, and looked at him. With a surging uplift of her spirits she saw no mockery on his face, only a look of contrite gentleness.

'I wouldn't hurt you for all the world,' he said, his voice husky and hesitant.

'No,' she said, shyly, 'I realise that now, perhaps I was silly to react so strongly. But I did it without help, didn't I?'

That it had meant so much to her surprised him. For several seconds he gazed at her, seeing the honesty on her face, and something else, something deeper. He was suddenly aware that it wouldn't be long before Maggy returned, and that this might be his last chance to have Anna completely to himself and in such intimate circumstances. He was nervous and his heart beat furiously in his determination to seize his opportunity. He was acutely aware that time was passing, precious time. In desperation he reached across the small folding table, 'Give me your hand,' he begged, fearing that she might spurn him. 'Please?'

Slowly obeying him, she lifted her hand from her lap and let him take it, her eyes never leaving his face. Tenderly cradling her fingers at first, he slowly tightened his grasp as his emotion strengthened. 'I have often thought of the moment when we last held hands, and dreamed of doing it again.' He leaned closer to her until they nearly touched and he could feel her soft breath on his face, a sweet, pleasant sensation. 'Anna,' he said, huskily, 'forgive me, I'm going to kiss you.'

Anna didn't move. She closed her eyes and waited as he leaned forward to place his lips lovingly on hers. It was a first, inexperienced kiss, sensitive, shy and trusting. 'Oh, Anna,' he whispered, drawing back for a moment, 'do you like me, just a little?'

Anna's eyes were open now, clear and bright, and she smiled happily at him. 'Yes,' she replied shyly, her head tilted to one side. 'Just a little.'

Suddenly, from above, Ollie's voice called, 'Mike, can I see you for a minute?'

With a start of alarm, Anna drew back, surprised and embarrassed. 'I'll come up,' Michael answered, smiling at Anna. 'Just a minute!'

'Fadern!' Erik cried, cursing himself. He had been so busy keeping Maggy occupied that he'd forgotten Ollie was working on deck. It was too late now to prevent him disturbing Anna and Michael in the cabin, and that was a pity. He wasn't blind, he had seen exactly what was going on just as much as Ellen had. He loved Anna and wanted her to be happy, and what he'd learned so far of Michael caused him to hope that at some time the two would realise that they cared for each other, just as Ellen and he had done years ago, when they first met.

Michael tried to appear calm and unruffled as he climbed up onto the deck, although he was far from that.

'I've had my final letter from Sheffield!' Ollie told him excitedly, oblivious to the flush on Michael's face, or that his mind seemed to be on other things. 'I've got all the information I need, now I can get off to London.' Erik and Maggy, having heard the fuss, clambered along the hold and stood just below him. 'If I ordered a quantity of tools and cutlery to be delivered to the wharf for when you get to Sheffield, will you collect them for me, Mike?'

'You arrange the details, I'll see to everything when I get there,' Michael assured him, much relieved that Ollie's exuberance would deflect everyone's attention from his and Anna's few minutes of intimacy.

'Thanks,' Ollie said, looking down at his father and waving the letter at him. 'I'll be off to London on Monday,' he called, his face alight with anticipation.

'London!' Maggy gasped, with equal excitement.

'He's going off to the Great Exhibition,' Erik explained, with some scepticism, 'and Anna goes too.'

Michael turned to Ollie, trying to muster some enthusiasm. 'We should be away ourselves then with luck, if the rudder is repaired.' This was a sobering thought, for with Anna enjoying herself in London she was hardly likely to think about him, and it might be some time before they would meet again. 'Look, Erik,' he said, 'we'd best get on, the shipwright said he'd call later this afternoon while the keel's high in the water.' So saying, he swung himself down into the hold, leaving Maggy to return to talk to Anna in the cabin about her forthcoming adventure.

Stepping through the hold door, Maggy found Anna sitting quietly as though nothing had happened. 'You didn't tell me that you were going to London,' she chided. 'But you are so lucky! What will you wear? How long will you be away?'

'Oh, Maggy, I was going to tell you about it, but everything's happened so quickly. I haven't had time to think about clothes or anything else yet, and now I learn we are to go on Monday! It'll be a long and tiring journey, and Ollie will be so busy at the Exhibition that I wonder he wants to take me at all.'

'If I were going I would be so excited,' Maggy enthused. 'Instead I will probably be leaving for Sheffield.' This steadied her. 'You don't know how dull and quiet it can be on the keel.' She was envious of Anna who seemed so undisturbed by her news, even somewhat preoccupied.

'I like to be quiet,' Anna confessed, looking wistfully around at the polished wooden panelling, her eyes finally resting on the small carved ship which Michael had made, 'and I'm not fond of crowds. When I have time to spare I walk down to the Humber and enjoy looking across the water, and at the seabirds.'

Maggy was now conscious of a wistful look on Anna's face, and said, 'But I thought you didn't like water?'

'It is dark water that disturbs me. If I can stand on land and just look at it, I don't mind so much,' Anna protested.

Maggy by this time was again becoming quite carried away in her enthusiasm for London, whereas Anna seemed unperturbed at the prospect. 'Aren't you even a tiny bit excited?' she demanded.

Anna smiled, 'Of course I am, but I don't always show my feelings like you, besides...' she hesitated, and became quite subdued, 'I shall miss you, and Michael.'

'But we won't be here,' Maggy pointed out, admitting to herself that she would miss Anna also, as she had become very fond of her. 'And I will have to find work soon, if Michael is to keep the keel profitable. What will you do?'

'I don't know, and we won't see each other very often, will we?' Anna's eyes moistened at this possibility.

Maggy looked at her in amazement. 'Why, Anna, you're crying.'

Brushing away the tears, Anna smiled weakly, 'Now that Mother is well again, and there'll be no new child to look after, I too must think of the future and find work.' She rose from the locker, 'Oh, Maggy,' she sobbed, hugging her closely, 'I wish you were coming to London with me!'

In the hold Michael worked on, lifting the pipes up to Ollie, although his mind was far away. He was desperately trying to find some excuse to catch Anna alone again, but gave up when he heard her speaking down to him from above. 'Are you going then?' he responded, trying to conceal his disappointment. 'Wait a minute, I'll come up,' and he climbed quickly out of the hold. 'Change places, Erik,' he called, 'and take a break for a minute or two.'

As he approached Anna he would have liked to have kissed her again, right there, if the wharf and keel had been deserted. She must have seen something of his thoughts reflected in his face, for quite deliberately she lowered her head. 'I must go,' she said, softly, 'I know you have work to do.' Slowly raising her eyes, which seemed even more gentle than he recalled, she added, 'I shall remember my visit with affection'.

'Come again soon,' he whispered in case Erik heard, but his words were merely a front for the message his eyes conveyed. Hearing Maggy on the cabin ladder, he said with a sigh, 'I have no excuse now to assist you up the ladder, not without giving your father reason to suspect something.'

She laughed merrily, 'That would never do, he would tease unmercifully'.

'Could we meet somewhere before you go to London?' he dared to ask quickly, before Maggy joined them.

'I'll try. But can Maggy come to the house today?' she asked, hopefully. 'She is so happy about my going to London that I fear she will find the wharf a little cheerless.'

Maggy had work to do, but if by allowing her to go it gave Anna pleasure, then it was the least he could do. Besides, he still felt guilty at having enjoyed himself with the Eriksons the day before, leaving her alone on the keel. 'Yes, alright then, even though it will mean I shall never hear the end of your preparations for London,' he replied.

Without her knowing it, Michael watched as Anna preceded Maggy up the ladder to the wharf top, and admired her new-found courage. Once safely there she gave him a cheerful wave, before both girls walked away.

'I am to buy some material to make a new dress,' Anna announced, as they linked arms. 'Will you help me to choose some this afternoon, Maggy?'

Once the two girls had disappeared from sight, Ollie approached Michael. 'Look,' he said, 'I'm afraid I can't help any more today, there are things I must get ready for Monday. You don't mind, do you?'

'I can hardly do so when you take such little recompense,' Michael remarked, 'and I hope your journey to London will be useful to your plans.'

'Thanks, Mike. But I do need to ask you something about my trip. Do you think you could allow Maggy to come with us? I may be very busy looking at engineering displays, which will bore Anna, and a companion would make all the difference to her enjoyment.'

Michael was quite surprised at this suggestion, and after a moment could only respond by saying, 'I don't know, business being what it is I don't have a lot of money to spare. I know she'd like to go, but I'll have to give it a lot of thought. How much will it cost?'

Hesitating for a moment, so as to evaluate the situation, Ollie finally said, 'Well, she could share a room with Anna, and our carriage wherever we go. There's the train fare to London, food, and a little to spend, and I don't suppose she has any suitable clothing here with her. Unfortunately, there's not enough time for her to go home to collect anything, but Anna is making herself a gown to travel in. Perhaps Mother could help out, she and Maggy are about the same size.'

Michael needed time to think, but his first reaction was to decline the offer. 'I don't know,' he said, 'there are bound to be other costs too. It's not a good time.'

'Has she no money of her own?' Ollie asked, trying to help, rather than pry.

'I'm not really sure,' Michael replied, shaking his head. 'It's not really my business.'

'Well look, I'll leave it to you to mull over. We go on Monday, that's four days ahead. I'll see you later this afternoon, if that's alright?'

Once alone, Michael had plenty to occupy his mind for the rest of the morning, and foremost was his relationship with Anna. This had progressed beyond his wildest expectations but now it was over-shadowed by the sad decision he felt he had to make regarding Maggy.

'You're quiet today, Mike,' Erik commented later, after they had been working in silence for some time. 'Is something wrong?' He'd seen Anna leave with a cheerful wave, and surmised that something involving Ollie had triggered off Michael's pensive mood.

'It's Ollie! He's suggested that Maggy should accompany Anna and himself to London next week, but it'll cost me a lot of money, you know.'

'Ah, so that's it,' Erik sighed. 'He has big ideas, but you, you have your feet on the ground.'

'Maggy won't see it like that. She'll just be very disappointed if she can't go. I suppose I can't blame her, it's a once in a lifetime experience, this exhibition and all that. But she's no clothing fit to wear in London either.'

'She can sew, can't she?' Erik suggested. 'Ellen will help her I'm sure. Ellen is good with a needle.'

Michael tried not to think of Anna going so far away, where she would taste and enjoy the finer things which he couldn't offer. Yet, if Maggy went too it might help her keep him in mind. He knew exactly what his father would have said, 'All stuff and nonsense, enough to turn a girl's head, getting above herself!' But he wasn't his father, and Maggy deserved more from life than their circumstances were likely to give her. Furthermore, until she married he felt she was his responsibility. She was a hard worker, and asked for little in return for the hours she worked on the keel. He felt a bit guilty on this score, and realised that she could hardly have much money of her own when he and his father had given her next to nothing, except her food and a bed; nor had she ever hinted that they should do more. He had a little put by, nothing to boast about, but he owed Maggy a chance to see something worthwhile in the world before she settled down.

His thoughts kept returning to Anna, wondering if he might see her again before he left Hull. He was still in a quandary when Maggy returned later, somewhat subdued, so he asked, 'What have you been up to with Anna?'

'Sewing,' Maggy replied, 'and helping Anna to make a gown.' She looked wistful, and he felt his resolve weaken further. 'When are we leaving, Michael? Has the man been to repair the rudder yet?'

'He's coming in about an hour. It doesn't look too bad now I can see it clearly. We could be off in a couple of days.'

'Oh, good,' she answered, but her voice was flat and despondent. Then suddenly, out of the blue she cried, 'What are we going to do, Michael? Things have changed so much since Dad died, sometimes I can't believe it's happened! I don't feel like the same person any more.' Michael could tell she was deeply disturbed, and she was right, in seven short weeks their lives had been turned upside down. He still missed his father, but without his death things would have gone on in the same old way, and of course he might never have met the Eriksons, and Anna. These thoughts caused him another twinge of conscience. He looked at Maggy, and made a decision. 'Maggy,' he said, smiling gently. 'Would you like to go to London with Anna? I can't spare much money but you've been a great support to me since Dad died, it would please me to see you enjoy yourself for a while.'

She looked at him, hardly sure of the words she'd heard. 'Me...go to London?' she whispered, a question in her voice. 'Me?' Then, as realisation dawned, the listlessness suddenly left her and her eyes were wide with excitement. 'Oh, Michael,' she breathed, 'can I really go?'

'Of course! Ollie thought you might keep Anna company while he is on business.'

'But I can't go like this!' she wailed, looking down at her dull, workaday clothes in despair. 'Even the clothes I have at home aren't good enough!'

'We'll sort something out, don't you worry.' Michael grinned broadly at her. 'Get Anna to go with you to buy some material, not too expensive mind, and then get busy.'

She looked at him fondly. 'I wish I could do something for you, Michael, in exchange!' There was real tenderness in her voice, mingled with excitement. 'I'll buy you something at the exhibition,' she promised eagerly.

He laughed at her enthusiasm. 'Well, you do me a good turn by taking care of Anna.' The minute the words were out he regretted saying them, and Maggy looked sharply at him, all suspicious. 'And yourself,' he added quickly, 'but that's what Ollie wants you to do, isn't it?'

He barely saw Maggy after that, she simply returned each evening to cook his meal, stayed the night, packed him a few sandwiches after breakfast each morning, then left to go back to Adelaide Street. Throughout the evening she happily regaled him with the events of the day whilst sewing by the light of the lantern. 'You'll spoil your eyes!' he warned her, watching her peering as she pushed the needle through the material in her hand.

Fortunately, the rudder was found to have suffered damage only on the iron rim, and Michael was immensely relieved when this was easily hammered back into place and strengthened with extra bolts.

He was intrigued to learn that Maggy had met the mysterious Hal who, it appeared, had decided to travel with them to London. As he mused on their forthcoming adventure, Michael felt a little bit excluded from the bustle of preparations going on, so busied himself as best he could with chores on the keel. However, his reward came on the third day when, having loaded the keel with Swedish iron ore and knowing he would have to leave the following morning, Maggy brought Anna back with her to spend the evening on some sewing. 'Michael will walk you home,' she'd offered, watching her friend carefully. For three days now she'd heard nothing else but 'Michael this' and 'Michael that' from her, and of course had not missed the touch of pink in Anna's cheeks when she'd spoken of him. Michael too seemed to mention Anna far more than he realised, leading Maggy to conclude that something was definitely going on!

Armed with a tasty meat pie and some freshly baked bread, they arrived just as he'd finished washing off the grime of the day's work. It turned out to be a pleasant evening, and as it drew to a close he looked forward to spending his last minutes alone with her as they walked home.

Beyond the confines of the wharf Michael slowed down his steps until they were barely strolling along, Anna's hand in his, and they chatted quietly as he guided her along the dimly-lit streets. 'I may be away from Hull for nearly a fortnight,' he said with a note of regret, 'and it will seem longer, knowing that you are far away in London where you will have no time to think of me.'

'But I will,' she protested, 'I will think of nothing but coming home.'

He stopped at that, pulled her back into a doorway, and drew her close. 'I'm glad you came tonight,' he whispered softly as he clasped her to him. 'I began to wonder if I had offended you the other day. I had no time to say much before Ollie called me away.'

She smiled up at him. 'I dare not come again without good reason. Mother is busy enough helping me make my clothes, it would have been thoughtless of me to leave her, yet I couldn't let you know.' She snuggled closer, enjoying the comforting pressure of his arms around her. 'It was Maggy's suggestion that I came tonight.'

He had placed his lantern on the ground, and now put her parcel there too. That done he drew her close once more. Her hair was soft against his cheek, and in the dim light she was all that mattered. He kissed her silky hair, then bending lower sought her lips with his own. This was not the shy, inexperienced kiss that he had bestowed before; the emotion that had built up inside him over the past days gave way to an urgency of longing that shook him. 'I shall miss you,' he said huskily, his face pressed once more against her hair.

For Anna, who had longed to see him again, it was too much. She clung desperately to him. 'I don't want to go,' she cried, 'I'd rather be with you.'

He cradled her head comfortingly against his chest. 'It won't be long, I promise, and I have to leave Hull in the morning anyway. You go and have a wonderful time, and I'll be back as soon as possible.'

The thought of their imminent separation cast a shadow over their new-found joy. 'Come,' he said sadly. 'We must go now, but remember this, you will be in my thoughts constantly until I see you safely returned from London.' He retrieved her parcel, and picked up the lantern. 'Let me hold your hand again,' he begged, 'until we reach your door. I don't care who sees us.'

They walked on, absorbed in each other, their fingers entwined. Michael thought of his long journey back to Sheffield during the next few days. There would be no Maggy to keep him company this time, only an empty cabin. Erik of course would be there to cheer him up, and for that he was glad, as his presence would remind him of Anna.

'I won't come in,' Michael told Anna as they reached the door of her house. 'Please explain to them all that I don't want to leave Maggy alone for too long. But really I'm in no mood to chat, when all I want is to hold you.' He dared not kiss her again for fear of watching eyes. 'Maggy will come first thing in the morning,' he said. 'Enjoy yourselves, and hurry back, for my sake.' He waited until the door closed behind her, then walked briskly back the way they had come, pausing only for a moment as he passed the doorway where they had stopped those few minutes.

Chapter 5

Watching the keel leave with the tide next day had a sobering effect on Maggy. She remained on the pier long after she'd waved Michael and Erik off on their journey, and felt a little afraid. Maggy swallowed hard; it would be almost two weeks before they came back for her, meanwhile she was to stay with the family of whom she really knew very little. She timidly knocked on the door, wondering if her presence would be an imposition on them. The Erikson household was, after all, a boisterous one within the privacy of its four walls.

Anna greeted her warmly, but seeing that Maggy was a bit low in spirits, tried to cheer her up in spite of the fact that she too had been miserable since Michael's departure. 'Ollie and Hal are in town making arrangements for the journey,' she said, as she led Maggy upstairs to the bedroom which they were to share. 'There's not much room I'm afraid, you are to have Kristen's bed, and she will sleep with me. The other bed is for Johann and Lucy.'

Maggy looked around the crowded little room, seeing that Anna had already brought up the few possessions she'd left on earlier visits. She sat on the bed. 'You can put your things in this drawer,' Anna offered, removing some of her own items.

'Thank you,' Maggy replied, 'but I do seem to be causing a lot of bother.'

'Nonsense, I'm pleased to share with someone of my own age for a change.' Then, trying to brush aside Maggy's fears, Anna asked, 'Did you finish the hem after I left last night?'

Opening the parcel she'd brought with her that morning, Maggy unfolded the dress. 'Does it look neat enough?' she asked, holding it up for Anna's approval. 'It's no good asking Michael, he's no idea at all.'

Anna smiled softly, savouring the memory of his strong arms about her, 'What a pity he won't see us in our finery,' she remarked wistfully.

Hearing this, Maggy said teasingly, 'I do believe you like him a lot, Anna!' At this Anna's face flushed, and Maggy smiled at her with affection. 'He's a good man,' Maggy went on, 'and I would like nothing better than to see him happy.' A small quiver of excitement ran through her at the thought that he might find this with Anna.

Ollie returned for dinner and informed them that he had been advised at the railway station that it would not be wise for them all to travel on the Monday as the capital was already over-crowded and accommodation in short supply. Seeing the crestfallen look on their faces, he quickly emphasised that he intended going himself anyway, and would secure suitable rooms for them all. They then should follow with Hal on the Wednesday. To help offset their disappointment he gave them both a little money for new bonnets to grace their outfits. Such luxury was hard to resist, and having more time now to prepare, Anna and Maggy needed no persuading to hurry off to the shops as soon as the meal was over.

Michael had been generous with Maggy but he had obviously no inkling of what constituted suitable attire for such occasions, for, when Maggy asked him for a little more money, he said in astonishment, 'Gloves, Maggy? And a wrap?' Michael was a keelman whose life was spent mainly on the canal, and he certainly had a lot to learn about women; nevertheless he was able to give her a few shillings extra. She thought it better not to ask for a bonnet as well, intending to dress her hair with ribbons. 'But that'll never do,' Ellen had declared on hearing this, and began to re-trim one of her own for Maggy. However, Ollie's generosity solved this particular problem and pleased her enormously. Fortunately also, she had brought a few worthwhile items from home and in particular, several petticoats to fill out her skirt in case an opportunity arose to use it. These Ellen now stiffened with starch to give a more fashionable shape to the gown Maggy had made. In the end the house reeked with the smell of ironing, and garments hung everywhere from hooks.

'Thank God I'm leaving in advance,' Ollie commented. 'I'm constantly being draped in women's clothing.'

Over the next few days it seemed of little importance that Hal came and went, where to no-one asked, and he never explained. He was always polite, yet Maggy felt he had a different personality to the others, and whereas Ollie was tall with a fair complexion, Hal was shorter and much darker. She'd no idea how old he was, but Ollie was obviously the elder and more dominant. She didn't think much about Hal's absences at first, believing these might be due to his long sea voyage, and his need to visit old friends. He was friendly and that was all that mattered.

The day finally came for them to depart, and rising early amidst a frenzy of activity they were soon off, leaving Anna no time for thoughts of Michael. Ellen and the children proudly accompanied them as they walked to the railway station, watched all the while by inquisitive neighbours, and they arrived at its low, canopied entrance ahead of time.

As none of them had travelled by rail before, not even Ellen, they stood chattering excitedly amongst the crowd of passengers eagerly awaiting the train's arrival. Looking round, Maggy considered themselves to be as well dressed, if not more so, than many of their fellow travellers, and if Michael could see her and Anna now, she was sure he would be filled with admiration, and consider his money well spent.

'Ollie says we are to take a first class coach,' Hal remarked with some satisfaction as he checked their tickets, 'and we are to guard our luggage at all times.'

'Do you think by now he will have found us a place to lodge?' Anna asked. 'And what will we do if not?'

Hal was looking along the platform, his mind somewhat distracted. 'Don't worry,' he said, 'if anyone can find a place then Ollie will.' Hal was smartly dressed in a knee-length frock coat and striped trousers, his attire completed by a tall top hat placed squarely on his head. 'I can see the train coming. Stand back!' he cautioned, gripping Johann by the shoulder and placing him firmly by Ellen's side. 'Keep him there, Mother,' he commanded, 'these are dangerous machines and you know what he's like.'

Amidst the clamour of voices, the awesome hissing of steam and the clatter of the wheels, Maggy felt that now her adventure was about to begin. They kissed the flustered Ellen and the excited children as Hal waited patiently by one of the carriages, to hand them aboard. 'It looks as if it'll be a long, uncomfortable journey, I'm afraid,' he said, when at last he joined Maggy and Anna in the small compartment. Indeed, the space available was severely diminished by the billowing skirts and cumbersome baggage of the party.

'There's hardly room to stretch our legs,' Anna whispered, as they were joined by three more travellers.

'It can't be helped, you'll have to take a walk along the platform each time the train comes to a halt at a station,' Hal quietly informed her, thinking that half the problem was the layers of stiffened petticoats.

As the rail line terminated in Hull they had to wait quite some time after boarding until an engine was attached to the leading carriage. Then, at last, the train began to move with disconcerting jolts and clanking noises. The two girls waved to Ellen and the children as best they could, before settling back in their seats with some trepidation as the train increased its speed beyond anything they'd ever experienced before. Hal's prediction as to their comfort was not exaggerated, and by the time they reached Selby, where they were to change trains, even he was glad to get out and stretch his legs.

The endless view of the countryside through the side windows of their compartment eventually became monotonous, and the constant swaying, rattling and creaking of the carriage made conversation difficult. To relieve their boredom they ate, with great enthusiasm, the tasty morsels packed by Ellen, and gradually, one by one, they began to doze uncomfortably, only to be disturbed by the movement of the other passengers. Many hours later and thoroughly jaded they reached the outskirts of London, the sight of which failed to impress Maggy, who had seen smoky chimneys and dilapidated housing before.

'We're to meet Ollie by the ticket office,' Hal informed them, as the train came to a shuddering halt in Euston Station, just as dusk was falling over the capital. 'If for any reason he isn't there, we are to enquire if there are any messages, but certainly to wait nearby until he arrives.'

'I cannot sit any more,' Anna groaned, 'I am stiff, I feel grubby, and I'm hungry.'

'Then let us hope that Ollie is there to meet us,' Hal responded, being just as glad their journey was over. He stepped down from the carriage, and was staggered by the large number of people also alighting from the train. After handing Anna and Maggy down onto the platform, he collected their bags. 'Keep together,' he urged, 'and watch your purses; this place could be a pick-pocket's paradise.'

Moving slowly with the crowd they eventually reached the booking office where Ollie, who had seen them coming, moved quickly forward to help carry their luggage. He looked every inch the businessman, and although dressed much the same as Hal, his extra height and bearing gave him an added air of confidence. Any stranger could be forgiven for thinking that he was already a successful man in the town.

He raised his hat to Anna and Maggy, and gave them a courteous bow. 'You both look very elegant,' he said, complimenting them in his usual polite way, 'and seem to have survived the journey well.'

'Thank you, Sir,' Anna replied, half teasing, yet happy to have such praise from her beloved brother. 'Have you found somewhere suitable for us to stay?' she asked anxiously, dreading that he might have failed.

'Well, I've found lodgings, although I don't know about them being suitable,' he quipped; but on seeing Maggy's worried frown he winked. Turning to Hal, he enquired, 'Were you able to do as I asked without too many problems?'

'Yes,' Hal nodded, 'everything went like clockwork, but I'm desperate for a drink right now, have we far to go?'

Ollie shook his head. 'No, we need a carriage though, and it might take a while to obtain one. Let's have a drink of coffee then leave the girls in the ladies waiting room with the bags, and see what we can find.'

On entering the waiting room, Anna whispered, 'I'm so proud of them both, Maggy, yet they seem almost like strangers, dressed the way they are.'

Maggy smiled at Anna's innocent pride. 'I feel like a stranger myself, and this bonnet has been irritating me for hours. Won't it be a relief to take them off and freshen up.'

It was quite some time before Ollie returned. 'Come on,' he called, having asked a young woman entering the waiting room to alert Anna to his presence outside. 'Hal's guarding the Hackney carriage for us.' He seized their two heavy bags and led the way to where Hal was waiting outside the station.

There was an eerie atmosphere in the building now; few people remained and the gas lanterns only half illuminated its gloomy corners. 'I've never been in a carriage before,' Anna said, 'have you?'

The streets outside were now almost deserted as they reached the station forecourt, and it all seemed a far cry from the farm and keel for Maggy. 'Yes,' she finally replied, 'several times with my sister, in Rotherham.'

'I didn't know you had a sister?' Anna cried with astonishment. 'You must tell me more about your family, Maggy, when we have a moment.'

Having installed Anna and Maggy in the carriage, Hal dealt with their bags. 'You get in,' Ollie told him. 'There's not a lot of room, and I have to meet someone and make a few enquiries. I'll follow later. We're lodging in a coffee house on a small street off the Strand. I've given the driver his instructions, and paid him in advance. Get a meal and a rest, I'll see you all before you retire for the night.'

'It's nearly dark, you'll be careful, won't you?' Anna pleaded, afraid that he might be attacked by footpads.

'Don't worry,' he replied, 'just go, we can't keep the driver waiting any longer.'

Once they were on their way, Maggy leaned back in her seat and relaxed. She looked at Hal in the gloom and asked, 'I suppose you're used to all this, having been a sailor and travelled so much?'

'No!' he replied. 'Not me, I was a keelman like your brother. I only went whaling because I couldn't get a job in Hull after we lost our keel. I've not been to exotic places like Ollie.'

'Oh, I didn't know you'd been with your father on the keel at all!' Maggy was quite surprised at this revelation.

'I didn't at first,' he went on. 'I worked as an errand boy at the dockside, then when Father bought the keel I went on it as mate. We were together for two years.'

This was the first time Maggy had spoken at length with him on anything but trivial matters. Previously he'd seemed remote, reluctant even to be more than just polite and helpful. 'I thought you had travelled, like Ollie!' she said, pressing him further.

He grinned. 'I know what you thought, or expected, but I'm just an out-of-work tar and I feel awkward in this blessed thing,' he plucked at his coat front. 'It was Ollie's idea, as usual!'

Maggy burst out laughing, causing him to smile broadly.

'Hal, behave yourself,' Anna remonstrated severely, trying to control the mirth but with little success. 'We mustn't let Ollie down, he's set great store by bringing us here, and he means well.'

'He's trying to turn us into something we're not, that's what!' Hal's tone, almost suggesting a slight resentment of his brother, struck Maggy deeply.

She'd never met anyone quite like Ollie before and had simply thought he was of a better class than herself. Acknowledging that she'd learned a lot from Ollie, and got on well with him, she had no desire to compare the two brothers, however. She could also see something similar between Michael's predicament and Hal's situation, and to lighten the conversation she remarked, 'It's good to know that you feel strange too.'

He laughed teasingly at her. 'So you're not the quiet little mouse I'd thought you were, then?'

'No,' she rejoined with some spirit. 'You ask Michael!'

'I must meet this brother of yours, one day,' he replied. 'If he can handle Dad and Ollie, he must be quite a man.'

'You haven't even seen the *Maggie Kelly* yet, have you?' she asked, thinking it strange that he'd not walked down to the dock during their stay in Hull.

'No, I've been a bit busy, looking for employment. I don't want to go to sea again, but it's not easy to find other work without having served an apprenticeship, unless I take a poor wage.'

Anna said nothing, but the mention of Michael had brought about a sense of longing which was hard to suppress. She let Maggy and Hal talk on, and looked out of the carriage window, her thoughts miles away. Suddenly, seeing a dimly lit sign, she interrupted them, 'It can't be far now, we're just entering a street called the Strand'.

Maggy was reminded that in spite of this being her first visit to London, she had not been taking note of the sights as much as she ought, so intent had she been in her conversation with Hal. Not that there was much to see in the gloom outside, and in the carriage it was even darker; perhaps, she wondered, this was the reason Hal had opened up as he had? In doing so he'd put her at ease, and she now felt there was common ground on which to build a friendship.

Turning off the Strand, they at last pulled up in front of a brightly-lit coffee house. After such a tiring day Maggy was vastly relieved at the prospect of a good wash, some real comfort and a good meal. In spite of Ollie's teasing she could see it was a respectable establishment, very old, with low ceilings and panelled rooms, and, in a way, reminiscent of the keel's cabin.

They were led up a dark oak staircase to a warren of passages and bedrooms, one of which she was to share with Anna. They found theirs to be simply furnished, yet retaining an atmosphere of the past. Anna remarked later, as she rested on the bed. 'It is so old,' she commented, 'that I wonder who else has slept here before us.'

'Probably no one of interest,' Maggy replied. 'At home the farm has similar beams and casements.'

Anna turned to face her. 'Maggy,' she said, 'there is so much that I don't know about you and Michael. I thought you lived on the keel all the time, and only called in home occasionally. Today I've learned that you have a sister, and live on a farm. Please tell me more, I truly would like to know. You rarely mention your family at all.'

'It's not a secret,' Maggy assured her. 'Sometimes it's like living in two different worlds. In the winter I stay at home, in fact in these past two years before Father's death I've hardly travelled at all. When the winter weather made it impossible to work, Michael and my father used to come home for a week or two, leaving the keel at a safe mooring. The farm actually belongs to my brother-in-law who has taken Mother and me in to live with them.'

'Your mother, what is she like?' It was the first time Anna had heard mention of their mother, and she realised again how little she knew about Michael and his family. To Maggy this question seemed more than just idle curiosity, and it intrigued and amused her, and she replied, 'She is older than your mother, and I'm afraid her mind isn't what it was. Mother is harmless enough, but must be taken care of. She's not capable of travelling any more, though now there is no longer any need for her to do so.'

'What was Michael like as a boy?' Anna asked, somewhat wistfully, needing to feel close to him, for the more she learned from Maggy the more distant he seemed to be.

Maggy was even more convinced now that Anna was extremely fond of Michael, and she wondered how she could bring them together when they got back. 'He was always quiet and took care of me because I was younger. Why not come and stay at the farm for a few days when we return? Now the weather is fair you would enjoy it. You could even travel on the keel. Michael could drop us off and collect us a few days later.'

Anna was chilled at the memory of the dark water surrounding the keel, and the joy Maggy's invitation had prompted was suddenly dimmed. 'I...I don't know about the keel,' she stammered. 'I think I might be too afraid.'

Maggy didn't press her, hoping that when she thought about it again, Anna might appreciate the very real opportunity she was being offered. She lay on the bed, her mind wandering from one thing to another, until a knock at the door broke her reverie.

It was Hal. 'Ollie's back,' he called out. 'He wants us to join him for supper, as we haven't eaten yet.'

'We'll be down in five minutes,' Anna replied, glad that in spite of their hunger they'd agreed to rest for a while before having to face a room full of strangers.

Now, washed and refreshed, Maggy was ready to devour anything put before her. It had been such a relief to untie the bonnet strings beneath her chin and to remove her dress in the privacy of their room. Having shaken the dust from its skirts and tidied her hair, she felt quite relaxed and was looking forward to the rest of the evening.

When they finally went downstairs, Ollie and Hal were already seated at a table, waiting to order their meal. The men rose politely to attend to the girls' chairs and, once seated again, Ollie regaled them with tales of his own journey south, then with much enthusiasm described the Exhibition, only part of which he'd yet been able to see, so large was the extent of it. The convivial atmosphere in the dining room did much to increase Maggy's confidence, and she thoroughly enjoyed being in the company of these young people. It was just a shame that none of them, except Ollie, knew what the future might hold, and for this reason she felt pleased for Michael. If he could with Erik's help keep the keel, then at least he had prospects although it would be hard work.

'I had no idea how big the exhibition was going to be before I arrived,' Ollie continued. 'I came because so many Sheffield manufacturers were to stand, and thought it would be easier to find them all under one roof, rather than go from one works to another. I actually found most of them in one court, but also discovered that manufacturers from London and Birmingham produce similar lines. Believe it or not, there are over 14,000 stands displaying quality products from all over the world!'

'Sounds impressive!' Hal commented. 'But difficult to imagine.'

'I'm not sure that you girls will enjoy the larger machinery on display,' Ollie warned, 'but there are many thousands of other wonderful items which I'm sure will more than please you. You'll not be bored, I can assure you! You may become tired, but not disappointed. I do suggest, however, that we retire early and make the best of the days we have here.'

'I agree,' Hal said. 'I shall probably divide my time between accompanying Anna and Maggy, and enjoying the latest innovations. How many visits to the exhibition do you propose we should make whilst we are here?'

'You will need at least two full days to see everything worthwhile, but the entrance fee is expensive, and you might like to see more of London. I think we must let that suffice.'

With the tribulations of the long train journey fast receding in her mind, and with the excitement of the day ahead to contemplate, Maggy found she could not sleep. 'It would have been better had I stayed up later, writing up my diary papers,' she told Anna the following morning. 'For when I did eventually go to sleep it was not at all restful.'

'That was obvious! You tossed and turned all night as though fighting the devil,' Anna responded, much refreshed by her own night's sleep.

'Sorry,' Maggy apologised. 'There is so much expectation in the air that I feel quite dizzy.'

'Eat a good breakfast!' Ollie advised as he escorted them to the table later on. 'Everywhere will be crowded and the roads so congested, that it will be far simpler for us to walk down The Mall to Hyde Park, than get another carriage.'

'It's not too far then?' Hal asked, thinking of Anna and Maggy rather than himself.

Ollie laughed lightly. 'For the gentry maybe, but we're used to walking. Once we've crossed over Trafalgar Square there's a pleasant path through the park as far as Buckingham Palace.'

Maggy had only vaguely heard of these places, and was amazed to see how large and fine some were as they progressed through the town.

'Come on you three,' Ollie called out, pressing them onwards as they paused to enjoy each new spectacle. 'We'll never get there at this rate. We can take a stroll another time when the exhibition is closed.' He led them through St James's Park, allowing them to stop only when a pelican appeared at the lakeside. Everywhere was becoming crowded as more and more people made their way towards Hyde Park, and Ollie deliberately took them on a path away from Buckingham Palace once they'd glimpsed it, fearing a further loss of time. Holding Anna's arm he hurried them on until reaching yet another busy road, he paused.

'Take Maggy's arm, for goodness sake, Hal,' he called over the noise of the vehicles and horses. 'It's not safe.'

Hal looked at Maggy, asking almost apologetically, 'Do you mind?'

In the hustle and bustle around her she was only too pleased to be guided safely through the tumult. 'Please,' she said, 'I would be grateful.'

There seemed no end to the passing wagons and cabs, and no break before more came along, until suddenly Hal grasped her arm more firmly and shouted, 'Now!' almost dragging Maggy across the road and missing a plunging horse by no more than a hair's breadth. 'Phew! that was close,' he said, grabbing at his top hat which had nearly been dislodged. He looked quite comical with it askew and she felt sympathy for him, knowing that he felt uncomfortable anyway in his fashionable garb.

'That's better,' she assured him playfully as she adjusted it for him, 'but just look at the state of our shoes now!'

When they reached Hyde Park it was hardly the open expanse which Maggy expected, instead it was covered by a blur of figures, coloured and moving like flowers in a gentle breeze. It seemed as if the whole country, from the lowest to the greatest in the land, was accompanying them towards the enormous glass structure which appeared to fill the sky-line ahead.

Maggy no longer felt self-conscious in her tightly-tied bonnet and her wide skirt amongst such a variety of costumes, indeed the four of them blended in very well. 'Let's go along the road to the main entrance,' Ollie suggested. 'It will be quicker than mingling with the crowd.'

Looking up in awe at the wondrous, almost fairy tale house of glass which towered above them, Maggy placed a hand on Ollie's arm and said, with a quiver in her voice, 'It's breathtaking. Thank you so much for bringing me.'

Touched by her unrestrained gratitude, Ollie pressed his hand over hers. 'It is wonderful, isn't it? You can see why they call it a giant glasshouse, can't you. Just wait 'til we get inside, then you will be even more impressed by the huge size of everything.'

Following the multitude up the few steps onto the main floor of the Palace, Anna gasped in amazement, 'How does it hold up? Surely it must collapse?'

'No, sweet sister, I assure you it will not,' Ollie answered her with a smile. 'It has a very strong iron frame with girders and pillars to support and link it together.'

'So much glass,' Hal said. 'It's a feat of engineering in itself.'

'This has to be the greatest showcase the world has ever seen,' Ollie continued. 'It's the first of its kind and surely can never be bettered. There are so many new inventions, and such fine quality. Prince Albert must have had a vision to have conceived the idea of such an enormous exhibition in the first place. The world can only marvel at our ingenuity.'

Hal gazed up into the arched glass roof, and then at the crowded upper floor and galleries, saying, 'It's going to be difficult to know where to begin, and once we've parted company I can see us becoming oblivious to time passing. Had we better arrange a meeting point, and a time to do so?'

'How about by the large glass fountain in the middle, over there?' Ollie pointed out. 'You can soon locate it by looking up and finding the blue fringed canopy over the dais where the Queen opened the exhibition.'

'How long do you think then? Say, two hours?' Hal queried, 'I think we'll need a break by that time.' Everyone seemed to be in agreement, so it was arranged accordingly. 'Where do you suggest we start?' he asked, knowing that Ollie had an eye for the exceptional.

'Stick to the lower floor first. I found that late in the afternoon the courts become a bit gloomy. You see there are no gas lights due to the threat of fire, and there'll be more light upstairs then. In fact the India display is the best place to start, over there,' indicating one corner of the main transept where rich silk drapes and tassels hung as a backcloth for a majestic, howdah-carrying, stuffed elephant.

'Good idea,' Hal said. 'I'll stay with the girls for now, then later when we've met up, I'd like to see the machinery you talked about.'

Ollie hurried off, intent on covering as much business as possible before rejoining them at the fountain. In some instances the exhibits which interested him most were displayed on stalls manned by assistants; it was simply a matter of returning when someone with more authority was in attendance. He'd proudly left his calling card where trade seemed promising, and his pocket-book was already half full with addresses, details and ideas, which might prove useful.

He could not have recommended a better first exhibit, for neither Maggy or Anna had ever seen an animal as large as the stuffed elephant before. They stood examining its thick, wrinkled skin with some curiosity. 'Wouldn't Michael find it interesting to see the ivory tusks actually on the animal,' Maggy exclaimed, clasping her hands in wonder. 'And to think that he and grandfather have carved beautiful things from such menacing objects.'

'Not tusks from Indian elephants, they haven't!' Hal pointed out. 'Their ivory is too brittle to shape. It's African ivory that is used for carving.'

Maggy looked at Hal, surprised by his knowledge. 'You would enjoy talking to my brother, it seems that you have much in common.'

'You must do that, Hal,' Anna urged. 'He's carved a model of a keel which is really beautiful.' There was no disguising her admiration for Michael; it was plain enough in her voice and on her face.

Hal and Maggy exchanged glances at this, and a few minutes later, when Anna was engrossed in studying the gold embroidered panels of the elephant's ceremonial robes, he whispered in Maggy's ear, 'Have I missed something? Is our Anna becoming fond of your brother?'

Maggy turned quickly but saw no malice, only amusement in his eyes. Lowering her head she answered truthfully, in a quiet voice, 'I think so, but I'm not yet party to any confidences'.

Hal leaned closer and, keeping an eye on his sister, again whispered, 'Then we might even become related.' He was close enough for Maggy to feel the warmth of his breath on her cheek, which she found was a little exciting, and quite disarming, leaving her too flustered to speak. 'Come on!' he called to Anna, as if nothing had happened. 'If we don't move on we shan't see much at all.'

It was quite some time before Maggy regained her composure sufficiently to speak again, such was the effect the brief moment of intimacy had upon her, and when she did it was very hesitant; fortunately Hal seemed not to notice, which was a help. Their attention was soon concentrated on the vast array and diversity of other exhibits, and their allotted time seemed to pass very quickly.

Judging by the satisfaction on Ollie's face when he walked up to them at the fountain, it was apparent that things had gone well for him. 'Have you seen much?' he asked, and without waiting for a reply added, 'I don't know about you three, but I'm hungry. As it's midday shall we go and eat?'

This suggestion was welcomed by all, especially Hal who had a very healthy appetite, and it wasn't long before they were dining on cold beef, pickles and bread. Afterwards, Hal and Ollie decided to visit the heavy engineering section, and as Anna's feet were tired from the heat, she begged to be allowed to sit and rest for a while under a large tree in the main hall. 'You go with them if you want, Maggy,' she urged, 'I'll be quite content to sit and watch the world go by. Besides, machinery doesn't really appeal to me.'

Although Maggy had a limited understanding of machinery, she knew how hard John had to work in the forge to shape pieces of iron, and could appreciate the benefits that could be gained by the use of mechanical devices. However, she was not prepared for the sight of such enormous machines, steam hammers and presses that were used to make the British goods now in such demand all over the world. Her interest and appreciation did not go unnoticed by her companions, and this prompted Ollie to remark, 'You would be surprised at our Maggy, Hal. She can handle the rigging of the keel as good as any man.'

Hal, looking at her in her charming gown, shawl and bonnet, found it hard to imagine Maggy on a keel at all. Through his experience on the *Martha Jane* with his father, he'd met many a captain's wife and daughters, but Maggy wasn't like any of such women he'd seen before.

Almost an hour had passed when Maggy suddenly remembered Anna sitting alone under the tree. 'I must go back,' she said, 'poor Anna will think I've deserted her.'

'I'll take you to her,' Hal offered, deciding that he'd seen enough machinery for one day.

'And I must call back at Wostenholm's stand before the afternoon's out,' Ollie informed them, looking at his watch. 'Let us meet again at five, near the fountain as before.'

As Ollie walked briskly ahead of them Hal remarked, 'He seems very pleased with his efforts here. Let's hope his money is well spent.'

'I think we shall all remember these few days for the rest of our lives,' Maggy said, 'so they could never be said to be wasted.'

'No, I agree!' They walked on through the meandering crowd until something suddenly caught his attention. 'Hang on a minute,' he said. 'There's Ollie now, talking to a man by that showcase.'

Seeing how engrossed Ollie was, Maggy was reluctant to interrupt him. 'Won't he be too busy to bother about us?' she asked.

'I suppose so,' Hal replied, looking closely at a display as Ollie moved away. 'My word, come and look at this.' It was no ordinary showcase but vertical and octagonal, a cross between a small greenhouse and a large dome and was taller than most men. Three rows of highly polished knives and razors by Joseph Rodgers of Sheffield were arranged in pyramid fashion within the case, the centre-piece being a knife of enormous proportions and complexity. 'It must be longer than my arm!' he exclaimed enthusiastically,' and the card here states that is has seventy-five separate blades!' He looked intently at the fanned out assortment of implements and much to Maggy's amusement added indignantly, 'I don't believe it!' He immediately set out to prove it while Maggy watched patiently. It was indeed a wonderful spectacle but she was more than willing to accept the information given on the showcard, rather than count them herself.

Twisting his head, he went on counting until, sensing her amusement he gave up. 'There's certainly over seventy as far as I can see.'

She smiled condescendingly, 'I'm sure there are. Now, how about Anna?'

'Good God! I'd forgotten her!' he exclaimed, 'I'll tell you what, we'll treat her to something nice.'

'I think instead of looking for a gift somewhere we'd best get back. We couldn't afford half the things here anyway, even if they were for sale.' By this time Maggy was getting edgy; she was unhappy to have left Anna alone for so long. 'We really shouldn't have separated,' she said, 'it was very thoughtless of me.'

Although pleased to see them, Anna hadn't felt lonely. On the contrary, she'd enjoyed watching the crowds pass by in the cooler atmosphere near the huge glass fountain. There was such a variety of fashion, colour and activity, the likes of which she might never see again, that she was happy to sit in the midst of them, viewing everything in comfort. Every so often the seat next to her became vacant, only to be occupied within seconds by another person seeking relief, and who more often than not was happy to pass the time of day with her.

Maggy returned flustered and apologetic, and Anna eventually grew tired of trying to convince her that she'd been better off staying put. She'd enjoyed a drink of clean, cold water from one of the drinking fountains, and was now quite refreshed and ready to move on.

Maggy kept close by Anna's side for the rest of the afternoon, while Hal stayed with Ollie after finding him again at another of the stands. 'What conclusions have you come to?' Hal asked some time later. 'Has it been worth all the expense and effort?'

Ollie was beginning to look tired, and his voice was hoarse through talking so much all day. 'I'll tell you all about it tonight,' he said, swallowing hard. 'I've got a bit of a sore throat and a breath of fresh air might do me good. Have you seen enough for today?'

Hal looked at his pocketwatch. 'It's four o'clock now and I'm through if you are. Should the ladies not be at the fountain we could certainly slip outside for a while.' Ollie was relieved at this suggestion as the atmosphere had been getting stuffier as the day progressed. Neither Maggy or Anna were at the meeting place, so the two men left the exhibition and strolled down towards the lake. 'Aspiring sailors all,' Hal laughed, as he watched the antics of the occupants of several rowing boats. 'I don't suppose any of them have ever been to sea.'

'What are you going to do with yourself when you get home?' Ollie asked in a low voice, trying not to strain it any further. 'Now Father's working for Mike Havercroft, you'll have to look elsewhere for work.'

'It's a problem,' Hal admitted, and he pondered for a moment. 'There are fewer whalers going out these days and that's a terrible job anyway. Fishing is growing apace now, but I'm no fisherman.'

'You could be,' Ollie remonstrated. 'Otherwise, why not come with me to America? You could work your passage, as I shall be doing. There'll be plenty of prospects as the land opens up, and once they get the railroad through to the West Coast, the first few years will be a bonanza for businessmen. I've no intention of staying there permanently myself, but I've learned enough of the ropes to safeguard us both, although no venture can be without risk.'

Hal was dubious. 'I don't know. I just want to work and get on with life. I'm not an adventurer like you. I'd have been quite content working the keel to the end of my days.'

'Just being Mate doesn't pay enough, unless you're on a family keel,' Ollie advised him. 'You've got brains, you can read and add up, and you can speak Norwegian. Why not try the Dock Office or some of the shipping agents? You're a steady sort of chap, and you'd make a good clerk.' Ollie's voice was getting weaker by the minute. 'Look,' he finally whispered, 'we'll discuss this later. If I talk much more I shall lose my voice.'

Looking at his watch, Hal agreed. 'We'd best get back anyway, it's a fair distance to walk and the weather's changing for the worse.'

They walked in silence until Ollie asked suddenly, 'I see you're getting on well with Maggy. Do you like her?'

Hal was surprised by this question. 'She's an intelligent young woman, why do you ask?'

'Nothing,' Ollie replied casually. 'It's just that I get the feeling she might become part of the family one day, that's all.'

Hal was perplexed by this, although most of what Ollie said and did these days left him bewildered. He hadn't realised that Maggy might be more than a friend to his brother, a man who normally kept his emotions well in check. He felt a pang of disappointment as he had enjoyed Maggy's company over the past few days, and had begun to feel a growing interest in her himself.

'Look,' Ollie said, as they turned and walked back towards the entrance. 'Would you mind going ahead and fetching the girls out here? I'd like to stay for a while and get some more air.' His face was quite pale, and very drawn.

Looking closely at him, Hal commented, 'You've overdone it, you had better take things a bit easy, so rest awhile. Have you the tickets to allow us back inside?'

Ollie took these from inside his note book and passed them to Hal. 'I'm sorry to be a wet blanket, but we shall be coming again tomorrow.'

It had been a tiring day and they had covered over a third of the exhibition. There were probably two miles of displays yet to be seen, and the prospect was daunting. Hal's mind was already saturated by the variety of artefacts he'd seen, and had he been on his own would have preferred a day ambling through the park, rather than walking the many galleries and courts again. These conclusions he kept to himself in case he should appear dull in the girls' eyes, particularly Maggy's. He could also find a better use for the five shillings entrance fee, and with these thoughts in mind he was in a sombre mood by the time he reached the fountain.

Anna saw him first. 'You look miserable,' she commented, noting the lack of humour on his face. 'Where's Ollie?'

'I'm just tired of the crowds and the stuffiness in here, that's all,' he answered, avoiding Maggy's eyes. 'Ollie's waiting in the park outside; he's got a sore throat and is losing his voice, so we think it best to go now before the crowds leave at six.' Maggy agreed sympathetically and with no more ado they followed Hal back to where Ollie was waiting.

'Don't you feel very well?' Anna asked anxiously, as she scrutinised him intently. 'He's very pale isn't he, Maggy?'

'I'm alright,' he whispered hoarsely, 'I'll be fine if I talk as little as possible.'

They retraced their steps through the park and busy streets to the coffee house, by which time Ollie was feeling quite ill. His head ached and he could hardly speak. 'I think I'll go upstairs to rest,' he said, putting his hand on the banister rail to steady himself.

'Go to bed!' Anna ordered him firmly. 'I'll have someone bring something warm and nourishing for you to eat. 'We'll only be here below, or in our room if you need us.'

Hal assisted Ollie up the stairway to the room which they were sharing. 'I'll see you comfortable first,' he said, 'then I'll have dinner with Maggy and Anna. If I were you I'd try to sleep this off, it sounds as though you've got a really bad cold coming on.'

'I couldn't care less what I do.' Ollie's voice rasped, as he tried to swallow. He removed his coat and sat on the bed, then weakly tried to pull off his boots.

Seeing him struggling, Hal bent forward. 'Here, let me help you,' he offered, and taking first one boot then the other he eased them off. 'Now put an arm on my shoulder, while I remove your trousers,' he ordered. He felt really sorry for Ollie who had set so much store by this visit to London. Seeing him now, helpless and dependent, made him realise that his brother might be more vulnerable than he liked to appear. Making sure Ollie ate the gruel which was sent up, and ensuring that he was settled down for the night, Hal went downstairs to join Anna and Maggy.

'I don't understand what has occupied him for three whole days already,' Anna queried as the three of them sat waiting for their meal to be served. 'Surely he hasn't so much money that he can purchase large quantities of anything that takes his eye?'

'Perhaps he's looking at everything that he thinks might be worth re-selling in America,' Hal suggested. 'His notebook seems to be almost full of figures and details, though I don't think he's actually ordered anything yet. It's cheap enough to simply look and compare prices and delivery.'

'You may be right,' she agreed thoughtfully. Then she leaned forward as though sharing a secret. 'This afternoon while I was sitting waiting for you all, I overheard a lady saying the Queen comes every day with her children, just to look at the displays!'

'I'm not surprised,' Maggy responded, 'I would never have believed that men could make such beautiful and fine things, had I not come to see them myself.'

Hal, although impressed by what he'd seen, had a very different point of view. 'Even so,' he said, indignantly, 'who can afford to buy them? Such finery is for the rich, and all we can do is look and admire. When men are out of work, and the sailors of Hull go to sea under harsh and repressive laws for so little payment, such luxury is almost obscene!'

Anna was quite put out by this. 'Hal, you're becoming cynical,' she cried, 'I think it is a privilege to see such craftsmanship.'

'He's right though,' Maggy spoke up, 'if it hadn't been for Ollie the likes of us would not be here today. Our sort can never hope to own what we have seen, we can only dream of such things.'

'Do you do that then, Maggy?' Hal asked, an amused twinkle in his eyes.

'Why not?' she laughed, glad that the conversation had lightened. 'Although I would hardly like a stuffed elephant or a large statue of the Queen on horseback in my home.'

'Marry Ollie and you'll probably get them all,' he quipped. 'Marry a sailor and you'll get none!'

'Thank you for the warning,' she retaliated, 'the first would be too much, the other too little.'

Anna tried without success to be severe with them. 'What rubbish you talk, there's poor Ollie sick in his bed and you make fun of him.'

'My dear Anna,' he bandied dryly, 'you obviously can't marry Ollie, but if you had a choice of these two alternatives, which would you choose?'

'I...' suddenly Anna's face became a picture of embarrassment, as if her thoughts had been discovered and, seeing their questioning looks, said shyly, 'Why, neither!' Then added quickly to cover her confusion, 'Why don't you two go for a stroll before it gets dark? I'll stay here in case Ollie needs someone'.

At this suggestion Hal forgot his sister's embarrassment, and turned to ask, 'Would you like to do that, Maggy? We could go back to Trafalgar Square or the small park we walked through earlier.'

'Go on, Maggy,' Anna urged, 'it will be a long evening otherwise.'

It was hard for Maggy to conceal her delight at the prospect of going out again, but not wanting to appear too eager, she asked, 'Are you sure you don't mind being left alone again?'

'Of course she doesn't, do you Anna?' Hal asked, determined to see a little more of London and escape the confines of the coffee house.

Maggy happily accepted. 'Why then, yes! I'd like to very much but I hope you don't mind waiting for a moment while I go and fetch my shawl. I'll be down again very soon.' She hurried off to her room feeling pleased at the prospect of a stroll, even though the early evening air was becoming cooler. It would also give her a chance to get to know Hal a little better. Since arriving at Euston Station she had noticed that although he appeared very different to Ollie, he was in fact similar in that both reflected much of their father's thoughts and personality. However, Ollie's character was of a more progressive nature than Hal's, which was practical and more sober.

It was only a short distance to Trafalgar Square, where this time they were able to view the tall monument to Horatio Nelson in comfort. 'Let's go on towards the park before it gets dark,' Hal suggested, after several minutes.

'It's a great pity about Ollie,' Maggy remarked as they set off. I do pray it's merely a cold and nothing worse.'

'He's healthy, and the symptoms are clear enough,' Hal replied. 'He'll no doubt be on his feet again tomorrow, but not in the best of spirits. Let's just hope that we don't all succumb to it as well!'

'Look!' Maggy cried, pointing to the lake. 'There's another pelican.'

Hal followed her gaze. 'They're strange creatures, aren't they? But look, there's a seat over there, why don't we sit and watch him for a while?'

'How do you know it's a him?' Maggy asked playfully. Then added, 'But of course, he is after all, a 'strange creature' is he not?' There was a teasing smile on her lips, and a challenge in her eyes. Hal hesitated, as if unsure how to take what she had said, and then laughed outright. It was plain to her that beneath the surface he did have a sense of humour, but it was dry, unlike Ollie's, whose quick wit matched her own so readily.

Hal smiled and, remarkably, his thoughts seemed to reflect her own, for he said, making no reference to the pelican, 'You have been around Ollie too long, I can tell. His humour is obscure too!' At the bench they sat peacefully looking towards the lake.

She was not offended by his remark. 'Do you really think so?' she asked good humouredly, barely suppressing her desire to make him laugh again and thus prevent him from resuming the stiff reserve which he sometimes adopted. In that earlier moment of intimacy by the showcase, when he'd whispered in her ear, he'd shown himself to be warmly human. This was something which Ollie in his dogged determination sometimes failed to show. Her thoughtful comparison of the two men was absorbing and she must have been studying Hal too keenly for she suddenly realised he was gazing at her intently, and his eyes met hers once again. His were a soft brown and often far too serious, yet in moments when he chose to reveal his thoughts they were warm, even merry. What, she wondered, did those same eyes make of her now? That, she acknowledged, was why she found the two brothers so intriguing. Ollie was exciting, it was he who intimidated her with his dynamic thoughts and behaviour, whereas Hal seemed wary of her, almost as if he found her occasional forthrightness too disconcerting.

How long they both sat there, quietly observing each other was probably only a matter of seconds, but there was no embarrassment, and she now felt she understood him a little better.

She looked again towards the lake in case he might misinterpret her silent observation of him.

'Do you often accompany your brother on the keel?' Hal asked, breaking the silence that had settled over them.

It had been a comfortable moment which she had been reluctant to disturb with something trivial, and for that reason she was grateful to hear him speak, but at the mention of Michael and the keel she felt a sadness welling up. 'Only since my father died two months ago,' she replied softly, almost in a whisper. He leaned closer trying to catch her words. This simple action moved her, and with a catch in her voice, she said, 'What am I doing here? Michael has given me money he can ill afford, and for what, for me to waste on pleasure?'

Hal was touched by the sudden change in her. 'He did something for you that pleased him,' he said kindly. 'Don't begrudge him that.'

'Poor Michael,' she said, mainly to herself, 'he's had so much to put up with since Father died. He even cried once.'

Although Hal couldn't see her face, the droop and gentle shaking of her shoulders told him that she was now crying herself. He was greatly moved to see her so distressed, and gently put an arm around her shoulders. 'It doesn't hurt to cry,' he told her, not knowing that for Maggy it was the only comforting touch she'd received since her father's death on the keel two months before. She sobbed, and he was grateful that the light in the park was slowly fading, screening them a little from passers-by.

He held her for some time, quietly murmuring comforting words to her, until at last Maggy straightened up with a sigh. Taking the handkerchief he offered, she said apologetically, 'I'm sorry if I have embarrassed you Hal, you have been so kind and understanding'.

'It's nothing,' Hal reassured her. 'I think grief is something that is better shared.' It was impossible for him to say more without disclosing how deeply her pain had affected him. 'Let's go now,' he said simply, 'it's getting dark here.'

On their way back he asked Maggy about her life at home and on the keel, and in return told her about himself, neither story being remarkable yet both were far from ordinary. He was a good listener and she drew comfort from being able to talk without fear of ridicule, knowing also that this was a man that would keep what he heard to himself.

By morning Ollie was well enough to get out of bed, and in spite of a streaming cold and a still weak voice, insisted on going back with them to the exhibition. 'I'm going to take it easy today,' he informed them huskily. 'Now I've done most of what I came to do I can show you where some of the better exhibits are, to save time.'

'Do we need to go to one of the main entrances?' Hal asked, pointing to a side door as they neared the Crystal Palace once more. 'Why go all that way only to walk back again once we're inside?'

Maggy agreed. 'That's a good idea and, as we cannot hope to see everything, perhaps we could select those exhibits which would give us the most pleasure.'

'I would particularly like to find the needlework displays, Ollie,' Anna stated. 'I know these won't suit you, but if I could only see some of the best examples I would be happy.'

'There is an extremely fine piece which you might enjoy,' Ollie answered, struggling to raise his voice to more than a whisper, 'but first I want to show you something really special. It's quite a walk but we will pass some good displays as we go.'

'We couldn't even get some of these pieces of furniture into our house, they are so large,' Anna declared in awe, as they stopped occasionally to admire items which caught their attention. They were too engrossed to notice the small group of people and children approaching, until Ollie suddenly put his hand on Maggy's arm and pulled her to one side.

A small woman walked sedately by. 'It's the Queen,' he whispered, restraining Anna also, in case she ran forward. 'I recognise her from the statue in the entrance, and those must be some of the little princes and princesses.'

Maggy was startled. 'But if that was the Queen surely she would leave by the main entrance?' she argued, as the Royal Party left the exhibition by a smaller door, not twenty yards from where they were standing.

'I believe she does that every day, to be inconspicuous,' he insisted, his hand still grasping her arm. It was a strange feeling to have Ollie touch her in this manner; she could feel his fingers pressing firmly through the sleeve of her dress, as though trying to convince her that he was right. She looked towards the doorway, excited at the thought that she had actually seen the Queen, and in doing so noticed Hal's expression change as he saw Ollie's hand on her arm.

Only momentarily distracted by this, she did not try to interpret Hal's gaze, instead she turned to Anna. 'Did you see her? She smiled at Ollie!'

'I think she was just being polite,' Ollie demurred, 'I could have been anyone.' Several minutes of lively chatter ensued before he suggested they should go upstairs to the galleries, where Anna might see examples of fine needlework.

'I'll wait down here,' Hal declared. 'I'm not sure I want to see such feminine works. Can we meet up later?'

Ollie turned to Hal, 'I'm not sure that I want to either,' he replied. 'I think I'll come with you. The girls don't need us, do you?' As Anna seemed to agree, he went on, 'Shall we meet at the foot of the stairs here, in an hour?'

Maggy, however, watched them go with some regret but she could hardly refuse to accompany Anna, especially as she had been invited to London for that very purpose. She concealed her disappointment and followed her companion dutifully upstairs. The quality and beauty of the festoons of hangings, shawls, silks and brocades impressed Maggy, of course, but she was grateful when they finally descended to ground level again.

'Apparently there is some tasty Yorkshire ham on offer in the dining court today,' Ollie informed them. 'Let's eat, then I'm sure you will like what I intend showing you this afternoon.'

'I think,' Hal remarked later as they sat eating, 'that if we were to return here every day for a week we couldn't hope to see everything. It would suit me personally to make the most of today, then perhaps tomorrow we could see something of London before going home.'

As an invited travelling companion, Maggy felt it wasn't her place to express an opinion on the plans of the others, and sat hoping that Hal's suggestion would be accepted, though not aware he was looking directly at her, obviously hoping for support. She knew he was tired of wandering around, looking at endless arrays of luxuries, as in fact was she. At first Maggy had been stunned by it all, now she would have given anything to be sitting curled up with a book on the keel or at home. Hal had been kind to her the night before and she would have liked to repay him by agreeing. Ollie sat quietly saying nothing, his face was pale, his whole demeanour very far from normal. Maggy felt sorry for him; she'd never seen him low in spirit like this and she realised that for once he was allowing someone else to make the decisions. She was about to agree with Hal, when Anna saved her the necessity.

'Hal's right,' Anna said, 'we've all seen some wonderful things but enough is enough, and I would be quite happy to go home soon. However, it is really up to Ollie; have you completed what you came for?'

Maggy breathed a sigh of relief and nodded at Hal, trying to convey that she would have supported him, but much to everyone's surprise it was he who spoke next.

'What do you think, Maggy?' he asked, but before she could answer went on. 'It's all very well but we have Maggy to consider too. What would you like to do?'

By this act of thoughtfulness Hal was actually forcing her to make her opinion known. 'I, too, would be very pleased to see a little more of London, and perhaps the river,' she replied, 'and the Tower of London, then go home.' Only after she had spoken, did Maggy realise that it wasn't Dalton she wanted to return to but Hull.

'I think it is a sensible decision,' Ollie broke in, his voice flat and tired. 'Best to leave London soon, and in any case the Exhibition doesn't open until noon on Saturdays.'

After mutually agreeing to spend one more day sightseeing, they continued eating, and Maggy quietly observed her companions one by one. They were each in their own way becoming very dear to her, and once Michael returned to Hull to fetch her she would rarely, if ever, see them all together again. Ollie would be going to America, and Hal's future was undecided. She was saddened by this and loath to part with any one of them, so, plucking up courage, she announced, 'I have asked Anna to come back with us to the farm for a few days, do you think your father would object?'

'Why should he?' Hal asked. 'If mother can manage without her then it's a very nice idea.'

Anna was listening intently, having already given considerable thought to the matter, and had braced herself to the fact that if Maggy's offer was in earnest, she would actually have to sail on the keel! Such a sacrifice would, however, be necessary, if she was to spend more time in Michael's company.

'But I thought you couldn't stand water,' Ollie said, eyeing her suspiciously. 'Wouldn't you prefer to go by train?'

'No!' Anna protested rather too strongly, 'I want to go with Maggy.' Then in a more subdued voice she added, 'I mean to conquer my fears'.

This last remark was said with such pathos that Maggy's heart went out to her, and in order to give comfort she responded, 'I'm so glad you've decided to come, it really isn't as bad as you think, and Michael will be pleased too'. At the mention of his name Anna blushed and addressed herself quickly to her meal, to give the impression that the matter was at an end.

'I feel a little better after that!' Ollie said, pushing his plate away from him. 'Now, when you're ready, I'll show you something very different which I know will charm you.'

'That's a relief,' Hal rejoined. 'One more statue, one more gilded mirror and I shall burst!'

'Hal Erikson!' Anna cried playfully. 'You are an ungrateful wretch!' To which her brother pulled a face making them laugh. 'And don't forget if there are any more samples of chocolate drops or sweets we must get some for the children.'

Leading the way, Ollie eventually reached the section he had promised they would enjoy. 'This is wonderful,' Maggy told him with real pleasure, as she peered into one of the many glass showcases filled with stuffed animals, 'and so unusual.'

'I thought you would like it,' Ollie smiled. 'Go and look at the weasels over there, all dressed up as men, in various poses.'

'This is better,' Hal laughed, having watched Maggy flit from one display to another. 'Come and see the mechanical birds,' he insisted, drawing her with him towards a case in which stuffed singing birds moved from one perch to another. A model depicting 'Rosenau Castle and Village' next caught his eye, and being as excited as a small boy, he exclaimed, 'And just look at this!' They watched this automata for some time, and were enthralled to see a group of small figures dancing round a Maypole.

'It seems cruel to stuff such beautiful creatures and then dress them as human beings,' Anna whispered as she joined them, afraid that an assistant might hear her. 'I just hope they don't kill them in order to do it!'

'I agree, I prefer to see them roaming wild on the side of the canal, or running free in the field,' Maggy replied. 'I hope to show you such things from the keel, or at the farm, when we leave Hull.'

'It sounds as though she will enjoy herself,' Hal remarked, enviously, when Anna had moved on. 'I miss the *Martha Jane*, but it's too late now.'

Maggy looked at him. 'What will you do, go to sea again?'

He shook his head. 'I hope not. Maybe Ollie's right, perhaps I could find employment as a clerk, or even go with him to America.'

'That would be a pity,' Maggy heard herself saying, without knowing why.

'Would it?' Hal asked, looking up from the tableaux he was viewing. 'Why?'

Maggy was shaken by his question for she had no valid answer to give, so to avoid making herself sound foolish she decided to be honest. 'I've just got to know and like you all,' she confessed. 'You feel like family, but we will all say goodbye soon and that will probably be the end of it.'

Hal dropped his gaze and appeared to be more interested in the postures of the stuffed mice and stoats than in what she had said. She had no idea what he was thinking, except that he seemed withdrawn. Perhaps he thought her over-sentimental, especially after the incident in the park the night before. Sighing softly to herself, she made to move away and leave him with his thoughts. In doing so her hand accidentally brushed against his, and the excitement she'd felt on the previous day when he'd leaned close to her returned. Without waiting for him to speak she hurried away, seeking the shelter of Ollie and Anna's company, unable to rid herself of the surge of warm emotion that the brief touch had engendered.

'Have you all had enough?' Ollie asked, assuming they were ready to leave. 'The weather is pleasant and we could take a walk by the lake, if you like.' Seeing that both Maggy and Anna approved he sent them on ahead, saying, 'You go on, Hal and I will catch you up'.

Still disconcerted and disturbed by her thoughts, Maggy was only too happy to escape, and even when the two men rejoined them she endeavoured to keep slightly ahead, pretending to be absorbed in whatever she saw. Not once did she allow herself to glance in Hal's direction for fear of meeting his gaze; instead she appeared to pay more attention to Ollie as a result.

As they approached the North Exit to the great building she paused and looked back down the main transept, trying to memorise a sight she would never see again. The magnificent leafy elms still proudly standing where they'd rooted so many years before, now covered by the beautiful arched roof, emphasised the impression that they were in a huge greenhouse. The larger than life statues stood as sentinels, dwarfing the milling crowds of visitors. What the future held in store for her only time would reveal, but these sights and all else she would remember for ever.

When they arrived at the lake, Maggy begged to be allowed to sit for a while so that she could sketch an outline of the Crystal Palace on one of her diary papers, to show to Michael.

'That's really very good,' Hal said, praising her warmly when she'd finished. 'You must let us see some of the other sketches you've done.'

'It's nothing,' she replied modestly, 'but it gives me pleasure. Sometimes I draw what I see along the canal, it helps to pass the time.'

Hearing this Ollie peered over her shoulder. 'She's good, Hal, I've seen some of what she's done already.'

Maggy rarely showed anyone her sketches, but Ollie had been present on the keel and had seen her working. Being unused to such praise she rolled up the paper and placed it in her bag. 'Perhaps when I get home and finish the sketches I might let you see them,' she said, determined that this was to be a hollow promise.

A line of ducks waddled by, one dawdling behind the rest as if in two minds whether to follow. 'There, Maggy,' Ollie laughed. 'Is that one of your t' acky ducks'?'

With sparkling eyes she laughed with him, enjoying a moment of shared memory which excluded Anna and Hal.

'What's this?' Hal enquired, hiding a touch of envy over their intimacy.

'Just something that happened on the canal,' Ollie chuckled. 'It would take too long to explain.' Seeing Maggy attempting to rise he held out a hand and helped her to her feet, leaving Hal to ponder on the undisclosed.

Maggy brushed the creases from her skirt and caught up with Anna who was now some distance ahead, leaving the men to follow. 'I'd like to take a closer look at Buckingham Palace,' Anna told her, as they made their way out of the park. 'It will round the day off nicely.'

The final day in London, however, did not turn out quite as expected. The Thames was murky and unattractive, and compared unfavourably with the Humber Estuary which was cleaned constantly by the tide. The splendour of the Cathedral Church of St Paul's was lost on them, after the magnificence of the Crystal Palace; and the crowded busy streets were dusty and dangerous.

There was also a change in Ollie's demeanour which puzzled Maggy; whether it was due to his cold or because he'd completed the task for which he'd come to London, she wasn't sure. His cold was loosening up, but this had left him with a cough which kept him awake for long periods during the night. Hal's sleep was affected too, leaving him quieter than usual. Strangely enough, only Anna appeared to maintain a buoyancy which seemed to increase as the day wore on.

'You're wearing me out!' Ollie complained more than once as she dragged them merrily along. 'I thought you wanted to go home?' Anna smiled but said nothing, her renewed spirits stemming from the knowledge that tomorrow they would indeed be home, where she would await Michael's return.

'I haven't much money,' she confessed to Maggy, while Ollie and Hal were some distance from them, 'but I want to take Mother and the children a small gift each.' She dropped her voice a little lower, adding, 'I would also like to take Michael something. What could I get?'

Maggy could tell by her manner, that this small gesture was of great importance to her, but as life on the keel was a simple one and needed no unnecessary adornments, it wasn't an easy question to answer. 'Let me think about it,' she offered, lowering her own voice so that the two men wouldn't hear. Then she had an idea. 'I can only think that he might like a handkerchief. Perhaps you could embroider something on it when you get home, in time for his return. He need not use it, merely keep it as a memento of your kindness.' Later she took heart from the fact that although Anna never referred to the incident, she did in fact purchase a gentleman's handkerchief, amongst a few other small items.

Ollie became unusually attentive as the day wore on, and she found herself in his company more often than that of her other two companions.

Eventually, tiring of the sight of churches, large buildings and monuments, they sat for a while in a small grassed area overlooked by a row of elegant Georgian houses. 'I have a lot of decisions to make,' Ollie said suddenly, as he and Maggy rested some distance away from Hal and Anna, who were watching several children at play.

Maggy sensed that Ollie wanted to talk rather than join the others. 'I have made plans to return to America as you know,' he said, taking her into his confidence, 'and I must do that soon. Once there I shall either make a good profit or I shall return no worse off than when I left England two years ago.' Maggy was surprised to hear him talking in this vein, as he had not discussed his business affairs with her before. 'However,' he went on, 'it is my ambition to return having established a future for myself as a merchant.'

'I'm sure you will succeed if anyone can,' Maggy told him with deep sincerity. 'I wish you good fortune. I shall miss your company and will often wonder what is happening to you.'

He seemed genuinely pleased by her remark. 'Will you, Maggy?' he asked intently, so that she had no option but to go on.

'Of course,' she smiled, 'I have grown very fond of you...' then, seeing his eyebrows lift quizzingly, she feared she had spoken too intimately and so added quickly, 'all of you!' Yet by doing this she seemingly confused the situation, for he looked hard at her, searchingly and said nothing for a moment or two. 'We get on well, don't we Maggy?' he responded at last, dropping his voice. 'And you must surely know that I've come to respect you a great deal.' He was hesitant, as though struggling to find words to convey what was in his mind. 'So much so...' Maggy became very still. She had a smile on her face but deep inside her was a growing fear that he was going to say something momentous, perhaps almost frightening. She sat anticipating the question that was plainly coming, and quite unable to prevent it. He hesitated again, 'I'm not good at this sort of thing, Maggy,' he said softly, 'but I would like you to consider marrying me before I go to America'.

Maggy was speechless. She sat staring at the ground, plucking at a blade of grass. There had been no words of affection, no expression of love or even passion, yet she knew him to be capable of such feelings, many of which she'd seen him display towards his family. At no time, however, had he shown any of these to her. They'd laughed and worked together on the keel and shared interests at the exhibition, but never had he intimated a special fondness for her, other than as a congenial acquaintance. Some men she knew were like that, rarely able to share their feelings openly, and yet they appeared to live happy married lives.

He was waiting for her reaction, rather than a positive answer, as if testing the water, cautious and a little wary. What could she say that wouldn't hurt or offend him? But she could sit there in silence no longer.

Looking at him with frank, kindly eyes, she answered, 'You do me great honour, Ollie, but it is such a surprise that I am bewildered'. She placed a hand on his arm, 'I must think, I didn't even know that you felt anything for me, apart from simple friendship. I am deeply honoured'. Her hand shook as he placed his own over it. It felt firm and confident, and seemed to offer great security, even perhaps a future beyond her expectations. 'I must think,' she said, feeling a great fondness for him. 'Please, may I consider the implications? You have obviously been thinking things over in your mind, but I haven't had that opportunity. You must realise that I have nothing to offer you in return, I'm not beautiful, nor have I any wealthy connections,' she lamented. 'You deserve someone better than me for a wife and companion.'

'That's just it, Maggy,' Ollie butted in eagerly, his face becoming alive again. 'You're capable of clear, sensible thinking, and you're like me, strong in purpose. It takes a certain type of pioneering spirit to conquer new fields and build an empire.' His enthusiasm was compelling, sending a thrill of excitement through her as she began to share his vision. 'I intend to build big, Maggy, and name the company "Erikson and Sons" he cried. 'It will be hard work, but we could do it together! Will you consider it?'

She nodded, her eyes reflecting her heightened emotions. 'I will Ollie, I will. Just let me think about it for a while, to make sure.'

'Good!' he laughed merrily. 'I would never let you down, we Eriksons stick together.'

Ollie was so exhilarated over not being turned down flat that for the rest of the day he seemed willing to fall in with anything his companions wished to do. He appeared not to notice that Hal was withdrawn, and took Maggy's quietness to imply she was in deep contemplation of his offer.

Anna was content simply to while the hours away and anticipate her return home, yet she was not unaware of Ollie's restored spirits, and presumed this was due to his feeling so much better.

Maggy, however, although flattered by Ollie's proposal, was in a quandary, for she knew the real reason for his exuberance, and was aware that a refusal would hurt him and severely shake his confidence. She had no real insight into the depths of his feelings, but accepted that for him to be so excited by his proposal, he must have some true affection for her. She was also finding that her friendship with Hal was becoming more and more strained, and wondered why he had become so subdued, even taciturn. Wrong words had not been exchanged between them, and she could not recall having done anything to upset him; there seemed no alternative but to respect his motives and let him come round in due course.

As the day progressed, Ollie's attentions to Maggy were becoming more obvious, and she was nervous lest Anna and Hal might suspect the truth; something she wanted to prevent until in a position to make up her mind. The atmosphere resulting from these diverse emotions left Maggy frustrated, so much so that by late afternoon, when everyone else's thoughts were of packing, she was close to tears.

'You're very quiet,' Anna remarked. 'I do hope you haven't caught Ollie's cold?'

'I don't think so,' Maggy mumbled, praying that they might all assume this was indeed the cause.

Accepting this and allowing her thoughts to move on, Anna continued, 'It must be very difficult, don't you think, being rich enough not to have to work, and instead be able to live a life of idleness?'

'You're not used to it, that's all,' Ollie replied, good humouredly. 'I could get quite accustomed to it!'

'I don't believe you,' Maggy reprimanded him. 'You have too much energy and too many ambitions for that to be the case.' Realising that she was dangerously close to revealing what had happened, she tried desperately to bring Hal into the conversation. 'What do you think, Hal?' she asked.

Hal shrugged his shoulders, seeming reluctant to give an opinion, and said only, 'I'm never likely to have sufficient wealth to find out. But it's as you say, he'd soon be bored'. There was a touch of irritation in his voice which increased Maggy's perplexity.

'It's merely a flight of fancy anyway,' Ollie commented with a laugh. 'But you all seem glum this afternoon. Am I right in thinking you've had enough of London, and want to get off home?' Seeing the answer clearly written on their faces he knew he wasn't far off the mark.

His comment made Maggy feel a little ungrateful and she quickly answered, hoping she spoke for them all. 'Yes, I think we are ready to go, but only because we are tired, having done and seen so many interesting things. Besides, there's a long and tiring train journey home to face which I'm sure we are all dreading. I fear I will make a wearisome travelling companion.' The latter was said almost as an apology to Ollie, who, although saying nothing, returned the look with sober, quizzing eyes.

'Maggy's right of course,' Hal broke in, watching them both closely. 'We'd best get back and pack if we are to leave tonight.'

The strain was beginning to tell on Maggy; everything seemed slightly unreal, and she wondered if she might indeed be developing a cold like Ollie. All she wanted was to be alone with her thoughts but felt compelled to put on a brave face lest she spoiled things for them all.

'Well, the night train leaves at nine this evening from Euston Station,' Ollie said. 'If we intend catching it I think we should pack, have our meal then rest until it's time to leave. We'd best be at the station by eight-thirty to ensure good seats; I'll arrange for a carriage for then.'

Maggy was greatly relieved when the party arrived back at the coffee-house and, as soon as it was polite to do so, she made her excuses and retired to her room to rest. Once there, she reflected on the things she'd seen and done since leaving home, and on Michael's generosity in making everything possible. She wondered where he was now and how he was managing without her and, more importantly, what his reaction to Ollie's proposal would be!

As it happened, on that same day, whilst waiting at the canal basin in Sheffield for one of Ollie's consignments to be delivered to the keel, Michael queried, 'Do you think they're enjoying their visit to London?'

Erik sniffed. 'They'll be having a good time if Ollie has anything to do with it,' he replied. 'Though what happens next is another matter.'

Ignoring the implication of this remark, Michael frowned and said confidentially, 'I wonder what my father's solicitor wants? My brother-in-law is supposed to have sorted everything out, and there didn't appear to be any problems.' With Maggy away, Michael had spent a good deal of time in Erik's company, and as a result he had discussed some things with him quite openly.

'No good fretting 'til it happens, I say!'

'It's not that easy, I always fear the worst when solicitors get involved.' Michael was given the official-looking letter when he had called in to tell his mother why Maggy had not returned with him. John had explained apologetically, 'I haven't opened it as it is addressed private and confidential to you personally'.

On reading it, Michael had the impression that although the letter seemed fairly urgent, the writer realised it could take time for him to receive it. Nevertheless, he was expected to call at the solicitor's office in Doncaster as soon as possible.

Erik interrupted his present thoughts. 'It cannot be so bad, or you would have heard more about it, perhaps you are going to get some money?'

'I doubt it,' Michael laughed scornfully. 'If only it were true! Anyway, I'll know soon enough.' He racked his brains, trying to work out what could be so important that it had not been revealed at the reading of his father's will, or in this mysterious letter, but find out he would when he reached Doncaster on Monday.

The journey north was a trial to Maggy. She had no concept of what was in her companions minds, but their gaiety had vanished and all were deep in thought. The night seemed never ending and the arrival of the dawn did little to lighten her spirits.

Hal must have noticed this, as, when they eventually reached Hull and he had helped Anna down to Ollie on the platform, he turned to Maggy commenting, 'It's back to reality, Maggy, back to reality!' He helped her to her feet, steadying her as she eased her stiff and aching joints from the long hours of sitting on the hard seat. His grasp was firm but gentle, almost fatherly, as if he knew and understood that she carried some kind of burden.

'It has been rewarding, though, hasn't it?' she responded, tiredly.

'For some, perhaps.' He looked rather stern and she thought the friendliness he'd begun to show her again was about to disappear once more.

Unable to control her sadness and disappointment, she looked directly at him and asked, 'Haven't you enjoyed it at all? I so hoped you had!' She would always remember his kindness to her that evening in the park, and now would have liked to touch his face gently with her hand as a token of her regard, and in reassurance that she valued his compassion and care for her. It had been a long and wearisome night; she'd fallen asleep once and woke to find her head pillowed comfortably against his arm. As she'd apologised for this she saw a look of amusement of his face, and it was then that something of his old self returned. Now he looked tired too, but his soft eyes were alert and watching, and she wondered if he was in fact aware of the nature of her problem. If only he had asked the question instead of Ollie, it might have been easier to answer. But what was she thinking? She stared at him with a helpless, defeated look on her face, and knew she could never marry Ollie. How could she, when she wasn't in love with him? How could she tell Ollie this, yet remain under the same roof for several days until the keel returned? Her eyes widened in panic. Hal, who had been watching her struggling emotions, in his wisdom made no comment, but determined at some more convenient time to get to the bottom of what was going on.

'Come on, you two,' Ollie called out impatiently. 'Have you misplaced something or other?' The sudden shock of hearing his voice brought Maggy to her senses. She stiffened and turned to climb out of the carriage, leaving Hal irritated and annoyed at Ollie's interruption.

He caught her arm firmly. 'Don't be too hasty, Maggy,' he whispered with a touch of urgency. That he suspected something, if not all of her dilemma was obvious now, but this was not the time to confide in him. She felt that Hal would understand if not approve of her hesitancy, and could give sound advice.

With a heavy heart she walked slowly with the others back to Adelaide Street, all the while wishing it was towards the keel. She had to escape from them all, and sadly but inevitably because of the circumstances, she would lose their friendship too. She would have to write to Ollie and tell him, as gently as she could, that she could not accept his offer.

After spending the weekend puzzling again and again over the letter, Michael was somewhat nervous as the keel approached Doncaster. He had made up his mind long before receiving it that if things continued well he would ask Erik for Anna's hand in marriage. Now, with this matter hanging over him he dare not allow his thoughts to dwell too deeply on Anna in case all was lost.

'Don't be so downcast, lad,' Erik said, trying to cheer him up as the wharf came into sight. 'I take good care of the keel for you, while you go and see.'

Michael was encouraged by Erik's ready smile. 'Thanks, Erik,' he responded. 'I suppose it's daft to fret so much. I'll be back as soon as I've sorted it all out.'

Leaving the keel in Erik's capable hands, Michael walked into the town. He'd only been to the firm of Mason's in French Gate once before at the death of his grandfather, and he entered their premises with some trepidation.

'If you can wait twenty minutes, Mr Mason will see you,' the clerk informed him, offering him a seat in the draughty, musty-smelling corridor. Almost half an hour passed before he was shown into an office where every flat surface seemed crammed with official-looking papers and books.

'Do come in, Mr Havercroft,' the solicitor said, as he rose to shake Michael's hand. 'Please do take a seat.'

'Thank you,' Michael replied, doing so and watching the man's face with some apprehension. 'What's the letter all about? I understood my brother-in-law, John Tradeswell, had sorted everything out regarding my father's business. The letter made it sound important?'

'I'm afraid it is,' Mr Mason replied. 'Something has cropped up about which I knew nothing until last week. Did you know that your father took out a loan some months ago using the keel as collateral?'

Michael gasped, and stared in disbelief. 'No! Why would he?' He stammered, bewildered at the very suggestion.

'Apparently he borrowed to buy new sails last autumn,' Mr Mason explained, 'and kept up the repayments until his death. Of course, once the April payment was not met the lenders contacted me forthwith. I explained that nothing was lodged with me regarding a charge on your father's estate and that, due to your travelling arrangements, it would take time to reach you, but the matter is of extreme importance if they are not to call in the balance, or take possession of the keel.'

Michael was shocked by these revelations and could hardly grasp all the implications. 'I had no idea, why didn't he tell me?' Michael said. 'He never let on that money was tight, I knew journeys were taking longer due to the shortage of cargoes, but not to that degree. How much did he borrow, how much is outstanding?'

'There is twelve pounds and ten shillings left outstanding, which must be paid in full by the end of the month I'm afraid. Under the circumstances that is quite fair, as one payment has already been missed. How do you stand yourself, financially?'

'I haven't got that much,' Michael admitted, nor can I lay my hands on any more. I've had one problem after another since Father's death, and it's a struggle until I get back on my feet. I've also the wages of a mate to find.'

'If I explain to the lender how this default has come about, could you raise a fair amount to offer them by way of good faith? That just might help.'

'I need something for my running costs and I was hoping to get married,' Michael said despondently. 'Even so it's not enough to pay off the loan, or even half I'm afraid.'

'Look,' Mr Mason commiserated. 'You have three weeks to comply. I can inform them that I have managed to make contact with you and that you will call in person before May 28th to resolve the matter. I really do suggest you try to pay off the loan completely rather than try to negotiate new terms, as their interest rates and charges do seem excessive.'

Michael was stunned. He'd never known his father to be so short of money that he'd found it necessary to borrow from anyone before. Had things become so bad that he'd not wanted to discuss it, even with him? The answer would probably never be known, and Michael had now to face yet another problem, one which he might not be able to solve. 'I have to go on to Hull with this load and return full, in order to pay my way,' he explained, 'but I will do my best and will return the minute I am able.' With that he left Mr Mason to write to the lenders on his behalf, aware that he would be incurring even more costs in doing so.

With dragging steps he made his way back to the keel, reflecting again on the strange sequence of events that had overtaken him in the past few months.

'It is bad news, Mike?' Erik said when he saw the look on his captain's face. 'Do you want to talk about it? It could help?'

'Not now, Erik, if you don't mind,' Michael said shaking his head. 'I need time to think and take it all in. I feel shattered at the moment.' He left Erik more than a little worried at this, and went below to try and reason things out before he continued their journey to Hull. All the anticipated joy of his arrival there was now ruined by the heavy burden that had been placed on his shoulders.

Chapter 6

he travel weary group returned home to a rapturous welcome. The rest of Sunday was spent unpacking and resting, leaving little time for contemplation. The children finally went to bed, thus ending their babble of excited questions, and a semblance of peace descended over the Erikson household.

'What wonderful things you've seen!' Ellen exclaimed with motherly pride, as they sat in the firelight before retiring for the night. 'I have thought constantly of you all but I'm glad to have you back safe and well.' Ollie wheezed and gave a tight, breathless cough which caused Ellen concern. 'You must watch your chest, Ollie, it sounds as though you could do with inhaling some steam. I'll prepare a basin of hot balsam for you.'

'Don't fuss, Mother, I'll be alright when I've rested,' he replied, looking round. 'Although it's a miracle I haven't passed it on to the rest of them. We thought Maggy might be coming down with it at one time, but fortunately she hasn't.'

'Did your cold hinder the business you went to London for?' Ellen went on. She had an insatiable appetite for news of their adventure, as did the children.

'Better than I expected, and now I feel I must go to Liverpool to arrange my return journey to America.'

'So soon?' There was disappointment in Ellen's voice. 'Will you be going for good?'

Ollie smiled, 'No, I don't believe I will stay there. I shall travel a lot but hope to make Hull my base for a business, eventually'.

A look of relief and pleasure crossed his mother's face. 'Your father would like that.' She turned to Hal, 'And what of you, Hal, must you go to sea again?'

'Not if I can help it. I've had one or two ideas over the past few days which might take shape and, if all goes well, could mean I can put the sea behind me forever.'

A sudden bout of coughing from Ollie raised Ellen from her chair. 'I'll go and get that balsam ready,' she insisted. 'It's best done before you retire if you want to sleep easier. I'll give you a call in a minute.'

'She's so kind,' Maggy was full of praise when Ellen had left the room. 'It's a shame we couldn't have taken her with us to the exhibition.'

'I wonder if Mother will mind my going home with you, Maggy?' Anna asked. 'It's still alright for me to come, isn't it?'

Nothing had been mentioned about Anna's visit since they'd left London, and Maggy now began to wish she hadn't invited her to visit the family at Dalton. 'Yes, of course, I'm looking forward to it,' she answered amiably enough, concealing her momentary qualms.

'How much longer do you think they'll be?' Anna queried, determined to draw Maggy out.

'Maybe two or three days yet, then I'm afraid I must leave, and you're welcome to accompany me.'

'Ollie! It's ready!' Ellen called from the kitchen. 'Come while it's steaming hot.'

'Bother!' he exclaimed. 'Look, Maggy, could I have a word with you before you go to bed? Will you wait up after the others have gone?'

Maggy nodded a little nervously, wondering whether she should tell him then that she didn't really love him enough to say 'yes', or to wait until Michael returned to advise her. She was no fool, and well aware that a man like Ollie came along perhaps once in a lifetime, and rarely would propose to a girl like herself. 'I'll stay,' she said with a smile, but immediately felt Hal's gaze on her, and was careful not to look at him.

'We may as well turn in,' Hal said. 'If we sit here we'll only get overtired and be unable to sleep.'

'I'll come as well. You won't be long will you, Maggy?' Anna asked as she made her way after him. 'See you soon.'

When Ollie returned, his face was hot from the steam. 'I hope it works, or Mother'll make me do it again tomorrow,' he said good-naturedly, and sat down opposite Maggy. 'Thanks for staying up, I know you're tired and need to rest, but I wanted to explain something before I leave for Liverpool and I might not get another opportunity to speak in private.' He leaned forward earnestly. 'I must have sounded very cold and uncaring when I asked you to marry me; that's why you needed time to think, I see that.' He lifted a hand, 'Don't say anything now, go home first then give me your answer when you get back. I've seen you looking at me as if you're not sure of my good intentions, but they are and I will take great care of you.' There was no doubting his sincerity, and she saw that to have spoken as he had, must have taken a great deal of thought. He seemed shy, even a little embarrassed. 'You do care for me, don't you?' he asked hopefully.

She could hardly say no when in fact she cared very much for him, as a sister might. His face was expectant, like that of a small boy. 'Of course I do,' she said softly, 'but America is a long way away and marriage is a big step. London was so exciting that it didn't seem real. I must go home and make sure that I am ready for such a responsibility.'

'So you haven't decided against me then?' Ollie said with some relief, and jumped to his feet.

'No,' she lied, avoiding his eyes. She sensed he was about to touch her, and wondered how she could avoid this, but he hesitated as though afraid of being too impulsive.

'You're very pretty,' he said lamely. 'I would be proud to have you by my side, but I won't force you into anything.'

'It is hard for me to think clearly, here in the warmth of your home, Ollie, and I love you all, but many marriages are not as happy as your mother and father's. I want that too.'

A wry smile appeared on his face. 'They are happy aren't they, and you're right, you must be sure. Come, you're tired and I'm keeping you up, but I await your answer with great optimism.'

Later, as Maggy lay in bed thinking of his words she felt torn between the prospects of an adventurous marriage and the unknown. Was the tender, deep and emotional bond created by Erik and Ellen unique? Her sister Mary and John had been married many years, and, although obviously content, were as ordinary as any other couple she knew. Perhaps in this extraordinary household she'd met the rare and nearly unobtainable, so was it fair to expect too much of Ollie? He was good and kind, respectable and fun to be with, whereas she was a young, insecure girl. Was her sometimes too active imagination taking her beyond what she ought to expect in life? With these thoughts she finally drifted into a troubled sleep, waking late in the day to find Anna busy with the children, and both Ollie and Hal out.

The two men returned together late in the afternoon in a happy frame of mind. 'You will be pleased to hear, Mother, that this has been a momentous day for the Eriksons,' Ollie declared as he entered the kitchen. He winked at Maggy who was helping Anna prepare their evening meal. 'I have this very day rented a small, dusty but secure lock-up warehouse, in which to store the items I order for America. Hal has agreed to handle any deliveries and despatches, and to keep accounts for me.' He was almost beside himself with delight. 'I shall have a small sign which I've ordered saying, "Erikson's Exporters",' he added proudly, as Ellen listened with great interest.

'And I have a job, Mother!' Hal announced with equal satisfaction. 'You see before you a clerk on the railways with regular hours and a steady wage!'

She teased them, 'So, the Eriksons are going up in the world, and not before time. So much luck in one day, but does this mean you will be leaving us again soon, Ollie?'

He nodded. 'Tomorrow I'm going to Liverpool to organise everything, and by the time I return, the keel will be here with some of the goods I've ordered from Sheffield. I would say that within a month I shall leave for America.'

'You won't go before I get back from Maggy's, will you?' Anna asked anxiously.

'No! Many of the items I ordered at the exhibition will be brought on the keel's next trip, and I shall need to sort them out before I leave. You'll have your chance then to say farewell. I may even surprise you further before I go,' he laughed merrily, glancing once more in Maggy's direction.

Maggy, afraid that he might say something revealing, deliberately turned to Anna to whisper innocently, 'I wonder what he means?'

'When do you start, Hal?' Ellen asked, noticing he had suddenly become subdued, and aware that he was often overshadowed by his brother's enthusiasm. 'Do you think you will like that type of work?'

Returning to the present, Hal said, 'Yes, I think so. I've been looking round the docks for an opening since I got back, but I was interested to see how the railways operated on my visit to London, so I decided to chance my luck and enquire at the station. It's not an important job but there will be opportunities for betterment if I work well. I start on Friday. Meanwhile I'm going to sweep and clear out the warehouse for Ollie.'

'Who knows, one day if I get established I may need your experience and take you into partnership,' Ollie offered. 'Keep trying the shipping offices, you might get a better job there and be able to put some business Mike and Dad's way.'

'Huh! Just give me a chance to get some experience first,' Hal retorted, shaking his head. 'You've got to prove yourself too, don't forget.'

'Hal's right,' Ellen broke in. 'I shall have more need to worry over you than Hal.'

The happy banter went on for some time all through tea, taking the pressure off Maggy who had no desire to get into a deep discussion with Ollie. He, fortunately, was too preoccupied with his plans to notice. She was quite interested to find out more about Hal's new job and when the opportunity arose, asked, 'What will you be doing at the station, do you know?'

'As I don't have a lot of experience in handling money or organising people,' he told her, 'I suppose I shall have to learn to keep books and fetch and carry; it's a very humble beginning, but there are prospects.' He was almost apologetic in his manner as if needing her good opinion of his hopes for the future.

Touched by this, she replied, 'You're very brave to try something new. Michael was worried what he would do if he had to give up the keel, but now he has your father things are looking up. You have an advantage over Michael because he only reads a little, and without having served an apprenticeship he has no choice of getting another good job.'

'You don't think I should have gone with Ollie then, and tried my luck elsewhere?'

She thought for a moment, 'Is that what you want to do?'

'No,' Hal replied without hesitation. 'I'm not very adventurous, just a dull fellow really. Ollie can have all the worry success can sometimes bring. Me? I'll be satisfied just working hard to gain my reward.' He seemed quite resigned, happy even to have settled his destiny. 'I'll help him all I can from this part of the world,' he went on, 'at least he knows he can rely on me, and that I won't do him down.'

'Who knows? One day your part here might be very important to Ollie, he can't be everywhere at once!'

'Maybe so,' Hal agreed. 'I'd say if he doesn't make it in two or three years he never will, but at least he'll have tried. Just so long as no one gets hurt in the process.' He was suddenly very serious. 'Remember what I said, don't be hasty!' With that he excused himself and went across the room to where his mother sat. Maggy was sure now that he understood her situation only too well, she would have liked to ask him to say more but knew that this would have been heard by everyone else in the room.

After a while Ollie suggested that Hal and he should go for a drink to celebrate, and both men departed to The Albert.

Maggy spent the evening chatting to Anna and Ellen, Hal's words never far from her thoughts, until in the end she decided to retire before he returned.

Next morning she deliberately occupied herself upstairs out of the way for as long as possible, and went down shortly before Ollie was due to leave for the station. He quite obviously wanted to speak to her more intimately than circumstances allowed, and the frustration in his eyes saddened her. 'Look after yourself,' she said warmly as he left, trying to convey simple affection in her words, for she did care for him. With his lively presence gone from the house she felt a sense of loss and an emptiness, and wondered if she should have offered to accompany him to the station, however to have done so would have disturbed her even more. Hal had already left earlier and time began to hang heavily on her hands. 'Would you mind if I went a walk,' she asked Ellen after a while, 'I'll fetch the shopping if you like.'

She found herself wandering around the Docks searching unwittingly for the keel. 'Where are you Michael?' she cried inwardly. 'I want to go home.' She thought of Ollie's pleading, parting look and of Hal's well-meant warning. The day stretched interminably before her and she swallowed hard, her eyes misting over, the happy memories of London becoming lost in her misery.

She returned to Adelaide Street with the shopping to find Hal dusty and tired, having come back from the warehouse a matter of minutes earlier. 'You look like a chimney sweep,' she teased with a grin, never having seen him anything but clean and tidy before.

He raised a dirty hand playfully as if to blacken her face, and Maggy feigned horror. 'And what have you been up to today, Maggy?' he asked, his eyes framed by the dust, quizzing her.

She was fascinated to see his face so disguised, and said, 'Not as much as you by the looks of it.'

'Do you mind if I strip off for a wash, Maggy?' he asked. 'I'm desperate to get this muck off.'

'No, no, I'll put the shopping away,' she replied. She could not easily avoid seeing him pull his shirt up over his head, revealing his sturdy figure, and the strange emotion she'd felt before returned to trouble her. She was acutely aware of a quickening of her pulse, and she averted her gaze lest he read her thoughts. She'd seen many a keelman washing like this on deck and never thought much about it before; in the privacy of the Erikson's home, however, the desire to observe Hal more closely was tantalising. There was an unusual silence in the house of which she was only now aware. Steadying herself she addressed Hal as he washed, hardly daring to look at him. 'Where is everyone? It's very quiet?'

'It is peaceful for a change isn't it' he replied. 'Mother's upstairs changing the beds and Anna has taken the children to visit Grandma in Ferriby.' He picked up a towel to dry himself and continued, 'She decided to treat the children to a ride on the train after Johann kept going on about railways'.

'When will she be back?' Maggy asked, watching him quite openly while his face was concealed behind the towel. She was hoping that Anna would return soon so that she would not be alone with Hal too long, and was relieved when she heard Ellen on the stairs. She quickly returned her gaze to the shopping and busied herself with it.

'I hope you're not making a mess of my sink, Hal Erikson,' Ellen rebuked him as she entered the kitchen, and then seeing Maggy said, 'Oh, you're back, Maggy! I was getting a bit worried after you'd been gone so long.'

'I went down to the docks not intending to hang about but time seemed to fly,' Maggy replied. This wasn't altogether true but she could hardly tell Ellen of her problems.

'We'll have a nice quiet tea before the children return,' Ellen said, as if this was her one luxury in life.

Preparing the table whilst Hal was upstairs getting changed gave Maggy a chance to recover, and the meal which followed was eaten in a leisurely, companionable atmosphere; one which soon changed with the arrival of Anna and the children.

When at last the children were beginning to flag, it was quite late. 'Make the most of it,' Ellen said as she ushered them up the stairs. 'Your father should be home tomorrow or the day after, then you'll be in bed at your normal time, or else!'

'Do you think they will be back tomorrow?' Anna asked Maggy as they helped Ellen tidy up.

'Possibly, but it may take days unloading and re-loading the keel before we can leave.'

'And do you think Michael will mind my coming?' Anna went on. 'Will I be in the way?'

'I doubt it, but Michael will have to sleep in your father's cabin, it wouldn't be right otherwise.' She saw a maidenly flush on Anna's face and smiled to herself, wondering just what was in Anna's mind.

Erik's sudden appearance at the house the following day at first brought relief to Maggy and hope to Anna. He was pleased to see them all safely returned from London, but taking Maggy to one side he said, 'Mike had some bad news and needs cheering up. I think you should go to the keel and see him soon'.

Maggy was aghast. 'Bad news? It's not my mother is it?' Her eyes widened with alarm.

'No, no! Something perhaps about the keel and money, but it is not for me to discuss it. I only tell you because I'm worried about him. He is very low. Please, go and see him! There is no need to pack, just go. He's at the far side of Junction Dock, by Postern Gate.'

Needing no further explanation, she did as he suggested and left the house immediately, wondering how on earth they could be in financial trouble so soon. At the Dock she soon found the *Maggie* exactly where Erik had said, and saw Michael busy on deck. 'Coo-ee!' she cried with the shrill call she used to attract his attention when he was too far away to hear over the noise of the dockland, and waved when he looked towards her.

He came forward immediately, crossing another vessel to reach her. 'Hello, Maggy, have you had a good time?' he asked, as he climbed up. 'It's good to see you.'

Brushing aside his questions, she asked, 'What's up? Erik thinks you're in some sort of trouble.'

'Don't shout, Maggy,' he cautioned. 'Let's get across to the keel and I'll explain all about it.'

Without another word she followed him, and once below in the cabin she asked again, 'What's happened?'

'It's serious, Maggy, more than you can imagine,' he said, sitting down on the locker. 'Did you know that Dad borrowed money last year, to buy new sails and some other things? You do the books sometimes.' Pointing to a pile of papers on the table, he asked, 'Did he say anything to you?'

She was puzzled. 'There was a bill for sails which I wrote down, and every month we sent some money out for these, but Dad never explained why. Don't forget, during the winter I stayed at home. Does he still owe for them?'

'Apparently so, but worst of all he borrowed the money on the strength of the *Maggie*! We've missed a payment already and are now in danger of being forced to pay the lot off or lose her!'

Her face fell. 'Then it's all my fault,' she wailed. 'I've entered up all the Bills of Lading, all the dock and lock dues, everything like I should, but I didn't realise that we were to keep making payments for the sails. Haven't we got enough to pay them off?' she asked innocently, unable to see the depth of the predicament they were in.

'Not enough...not now...' his voice trailed off. 'Besides, I've kept the paperwork up to date too. How were we to know? Even Mason's in Doncaster didn't until a fortnight ago.'

Maggy looked at him. 'You said 'not now'. Have you spent money we might have needed?' Her tone was almost impatient but Michael let it go.

'It's nothing, forget it!' he hastened to reassure her. 'But now we're short.'

'Come on, Michael, we're in it together, where's the money gone?'

He sighed. 'Well if you must know, I had a bit of spare money, which was rightly mine and...' he hesitated, 'I let you have some of it for your trip to London.' Maggy gasped at this but, before she could speak, Michael went on, 'If it hadn't been for Dad being so secretive we wouldn't be in this pickle, and it wouldn't have mattered! I wanted you to have a chance to see something, but I'm worried now that neither of us might have much of a future by the end of the month.'

'Oh, Michael, I'm so sorry. What can we do?' She sat staring at the papers, realising that amidst all that had happened since their father's death, the thought that these particular payment entries in the ledger should have been continued, had not occurred to her. 'Why didn't he tell us?'

'I think of late, Dad was beginning to slow up. It seems he wasn't well, and perhaps he was slipping in getting good shipments too. I can't understand why I never noticed anything! He looked pale and pinched sometimes, which I put down to the icy weather affecting him more as he got older. I really don't know which way to turn, Maggy.' He looked defeated and her heart went out to him; she felt partly to blame, and had to find some way of helping him. 'They want nearly thirteen pounds all told,' Michael explained.

Maggy blanched at this, knowing that few people earned this amount in a year. 'Could we ask Ollie for a loan?' she suggested in a whisper, afraid that he would be angry.

Michael bit his lip. 'We can hardly do that, not after what we've joked about, and I don't know how we'd pay him back anyway, not now I'm employing Erik.'

Lowering her head, she said, 'There is a way'. There was a catch in her voice, and he looked puzzled. 'I was going to tell you much later, but Ollie has asked me to marry him before he goes back to America.'

'Oh, Maggy!' Michael cried, brightening up. 'That's splendid! Why didn't you tell me your news earlier? I didn't know you loved him, I must be going blind or something.'

'I could tell him I have a few expenses to pay off, to clear the decks sort of thing. I'll think of something. Surely he'd give me a little money to buy clothes and essentials that I might need. I could bring some things from home and he wouldn't know the difference.' Such was the relief on Michael's face at this idea that she smiled wanly. 'I'm sure it would work. How much can we raise ourselves, how much would I need to ask for?'

'I've worked it out, and if I could find seven pounds I'd have enough to pay off the loan and still run the keel, but it's a lot of money, Sis.'

'On the other hand, if we lose the keel, Erik will be out of work again and you'll have to find a job as well! Everyone will suffer, even Mother!' The terrible truth of her words hit her with such force that Maggy realised, with an awful sense of finality, that there really was only one course open to her.

'Are you going to be happy though? You don't look over the moon about it. You do love him don't you?'

Maggy shook her head. 'It's the worry, that's all. Just think, Ollie will make his mark on the world one day, I've seen him organising things, and he works hard you know,' she said, trying to convince herself that the sacrifice was worthwhile. 'It will be hard at first but one day he's going to be successful. He's in Liverpool now and wants my answer when I get back from Dalton. It's very considerate of him to let me think about it, don't you agree?'

'As long as you're happy. I don't want this money to spoil things for you.' He smiled, knowingly, 'I agree he'll go far, and you seem to get on with him well. I'll let you into a little secret, I was going to ask Anna to marry me, but it seemed hopeless if I was to lose everything.' A big grin crossed his face, he looked so jubilant now whereas before he'd looked a doomed man.

'You and Anna,' she laughed. 'I don't think it's much of a secret, she's talked about you so much in London.'

'Has she?' Michael asked, his eyes lighting up. 'Maggy, I love her so much, do you think she will accept?'

'Of course,' she replied, seeing the joy in his face. How could she refuse Ollie now when so much was at stake? 'I have another bit of news for you. Anna is coming back to Dalton with us for a visit. Would you mind sleeping with Erik?'

He breathed a deep sigh of contentment. 'Everything's going to work out, I just know it.'

Maggy had never seen Michael so happy before, but she wanted to be alone. If she stayed any longer he would see the deep misery that was beginning to engulf her. 'I must go back and pack, tonight I will tell you all about our visit to London. I'll try to bring Anna back with me, that will give you something to look forward to. Don't worry about the money, it will be alright, and you are so lucky to have found Anna, I love her too.'

'But you say Ollie's gone off to Liverpool? Then what am I to do with the goods I've brought back with me? I've got to get them off the keel before I can reload!'

'He's renting a small storage warehouse nearby, Hal's there now cleaning it out. Do you want me to go and tell him you've arrived?' Maggy offered, making an effort to make amends for her negligent accountancy.

'That would help, although I don't know exactly when I'll be in a position to deliver. Just warn him, that's all. Erik's coming down later to see if I've got a berth. Are you coming back soon?'

'I'll come before dark, and bring Anna with me. You will walk her home afterwards, won't you?' she said, her eyes full of mischief.

'Now don't you go saying anything yet,' he warned. 'Anna doesn't know I'm going to ask her. I can't until we've sorted out this mess over the money.'

His words brought Maggy back to earth with a start. 'No, I won't,' she promised. 'I'll go now and tell Hal and then go to the house and pack.'

Although Maggy had no idea of the exact location of the warehouse, Ollie had explained to them that it lay off Myton Gate, a street which she knew well. Then, on hearing him mention Sewer Lane she'd laughed, saying it sounded disgusting, whereupon Ollie agreed, but at least the address had stuck in her mind. Sewer Lane was longer than Maggy had anticipated, and she began to wonder if she ought to have waited until Hal returned home, instead of trying to find him now. However, amongst a mix of properties she eventually saw one which proudly displayed the name 'Erikson', a sign which Ollie had ordered optimistically even before going to London.

She hesitated before the large arched door, uncertain whether to try the handle or knock, but decided on the latter, and waited. Hearing the sound of footsteps which she assumed would be Hal's, she took a deep breath in an effort to contain her rising excitement.

The door creaked open. 'Maggy! What on earth are you doing here?' Hal asked, surprised and pleased to find her there. 'Come on in!' Stepping into the large dimly lit storeroom she looked round. 'It's nothing much is it?' Hal commented. 'But it'll do the job and it's dry, that's the most important thing. Anyway, why are you here?'

'The keel's returned and Michael wants to know what to do with Ollie's goods. I told him about this place and offered to come and tell you.'

'Does he want me to get them now?' Hal was a little perturbed.

'No, he's still trying to get a berth and your father's gone home to see your mother.'

'Look,' Hal offered, 'I've nearly finished here, so why not wait and then you can take me to see this keel of yours.' As Maggy agreed he fetched a wooden crate, 'Here, sit on my jacket if you like, I'll not be long.'

As she sat in the cold, echoing room and watched him push a bench up to a wall, she wondered if he would approve of her as Ollie's wife. Her decision had been made spontaneously from worry over Michael's predicament. Now, as the harsh reality set in, she was bewildered and frightened. Could she really love Ollie enough to make him happy, or would she have to pretend for the rest of her life, and possibly make them both miserable in the process? There was nothing wrong with Ollie and he deserved more than she could give him. Could she learn to love him, or did she love him and not realise it? What was love anyway?

Hal was leaning on the bench he'd just moved. 'You're very quiet, Maggy,' he said. He'd watched her for some time without moving. 'What's up, missing Ollie?'

Startled she quickly replied. 'No!' Her reply was so sharp that he stared at her.

'No?'

'Well of course, I do—but...' She couldn't continue.

Hal came and stood in front of her. 'Something's amiss that's for sure. Want to talk about it?'

'No,' She groaned. 'Sorry, but no!'

'Then there is something. Look, Maggy, I've known you long enough now to see when you're unhappy. Can I help?'

She shook her head sadly. 'You can't, really you can't.'

'I did once before if you remember, in the park that evening.' His voice was calm and consoling as it had been then.

'I'm in such a quandary,' she confessed. 'But I can't talk about it to you or anyone else.'

'Why not?' he insisted.

'Because he's your brother, that's why!' she cried despairingly, wishing he wouldn't press her so much.

He said nothing but stood quietly watching her, and she became increasingly disturbed by the knowledge that he wasn't going to let it end there. 'Has he been pestering you?' Hal demanded, his face stern.

'He wouldn't do that,' she whispered, hoping she hadn't implied such a thing.

Because her voice was low and subdued, Hal took it to mean the opposite. 'He's been making a nuisance of himself, that much I can see. Don't forget, he's going away soon about his own business, what does he think he's playing at?' He was angry and his eyes fierce.

Frightened by the look on his face, Maggy cried hysterically, 'He hasn't, he wants to marry me, that's all!'

'Then, what's the problem?' He was beginning to lose his temper, convinced that Maggy didn't love Ollie and that there was something seriously amiss. 'Well, are you going to accept him?' he demanded.

Maggy couldn't answer for a moment, her hands were tightly clasped in her lap with tension. She couldn't look at him. 'I don't know… I think so,' she stammered, and rose as if intending to leave.

Hal turned and put his jacket on. 'You don't sound very enthusiastic.' His tone was caustic.

Maggy was suddenly angry and upset at having been drawn into making her confession. 'How do you know! What's it to you anyway?'

Hal had never heard her speak so rudely before and he was stunned. 'You don't love Ollie,' he said harshly, 'or you wouldn't hesitate, or treat him so coldly.'

'What do you know about love?' Maggy demanded, her eyes ablaze.

He stared at her in disbelief. 'I'll show you!' he cried, and pulled her roughly towards him. 'It's nothing to do with looks,' he said angrily, 'it's to do with feelings.' He stared hard into her eyes. 'You don't love Ollie at all! I have never seen such coldness between two people. You look at me with more feeling than you do him!'

Maggy was shocked by his anger and the depth of emotion in his voice. Was he going to hit her, she wondered, in defence of his brother? His eyes were cold and hard now, like those of a stranger. Bending suddenly, he kissed her full on the mouth. She struggled, trying to break free, but he refused to let her go. 'Stop it!' she cried, pulling her head away. 'Someone will hear!'

'I don't care,' he gasped hoarsely and kissed her again, and no matter how she twisted to free herself from his embrace, she could not escape. Thinking that if she offered no resistance he would release her, she became still, waiting for him to draw back, but as she did so Hal only kissed her with renewed passion, his arms holding her even closer.

With one final twist Maggy broke free and would have fallen backwards had he not caught her. 'Has Ollie kissed you like that?' he asked fiercely. 'Has he any passion in him at all, I wonder?' He grasped her arm again, to prevent her fleeing. 'If you want real passion, Maggy, come to me!' With that he let her go and walked to the door, leaving her shaken and bruised from his hands.

Maggy was trembling as she watched him step out into the street, aware of her weakness resulting from his assault. She took several deep breaths to regain her composure and wondered what to do, her face burning with the memory of what he had done, but she could not ignore the wanton, wild surge of excitement she felt. He'd wakened a response in her that refused to go away. The feeling she'd experienced before when they'd accidentally touched returned, leaving her amazed and even ashamed of her thoughts. She was afraid to follow him but couldn't stay in the warehouse forever, so, gingerly opening the door which he had slammed so vehemently, she stepped out into the sunlight, half expecting him to be waiting, but he was nowhere to be seen.

She no longer knew what to think as she hurried back towards Adelaide Street. Life was becoming a nightmare from which there appeared no escape. She had admitted to Michael that Ollie had proposed to her, this seeming to be the answer to their problem, and had now compromised herself further by telling Hal! How could she face any of the Eriksons again, and how could she tell Michael that he would have to find the money elsewhere if she didn't go through with it?

As she passed the town burial ground she knew she could not face Anna and Ellen, so went through the gate to seek solitude and peace in the graveyard. Amongst the sombre stones she wandered, pondering upon Hal's behaviour, aware again of the tingle she'd often felt at his nearness. This emotion seemed to consume her until, ashamed, she knew she must never again be alone with him lest he saw the desire in her eyes.

Drained and shivering Maggy eventually realised that if she did not return to Anna's soon, everyone would be alarmed and begin to search for her, and she would be forced to account for her distress.

Maggy continued anxiously towards the house, hoping to slip upstairs and pack once she had greeted Ellen and Anna. The problem was even more complex than she'd imagined. Anna would be expecting to accompany her home within the next few days, and, if Michael married her, how could she then sever her links with the Eriksons?

Hopefully Ellen wouldn't suspect that she was upset, only tired, but it wasn't that simple. The moment Ellen saw her, she declared, 'Oh dear, whatever's the matter? You look washed out. Sit down and I'll make you a cup of tea.' Maggy obeyed, having lost all will to resist. 'I suspect that you have caught Ollie's cold after all.'

Allowing Ellen to make this assumption suited Maggy, who immediately replied, 'I may have, I don't feel at all well'. Uneasy at fooling Ellen, she felt it better to do that than involve her in other matters.

'You really must go to bed and sweat it out, you can't go back to the keel in this state,' Ellen gently insisted, her face full of motherly concern.

Maggy felt trapped in the house, knowing that Hal and Ollie's return was imminent. 'I'll be alright soon,' she said weakly. 'But I must go, Michael has enough problems without worrying about me.'

'Don't worry about anything, Erik's gone back to the dock with Hal, and any help Michael needs they'll see to.'

Why had Hal gone to the keel? Was he looking for her? Maggy's mind reeled, and she looked at Ellen through a mist of tears. 'I'm a burden to everyone,' she cried, with such pathos that Ellen put down the cutlery she was holding and came to fold her in her arms.

'You're not,' she said gently. 'You're just not well, that's all.'

At this, it was as much as Maggy could do to prevent herself from giving in completely to Ellen's loving care, and pouring out her tale of woe, but enough mischief had been done already. The kindly woman who held and comforted her did not deserve to be deceived or disturbed in this way. Submitting to what seemed unavoidable, she merely said, 'I will go to bed then, and thank you, but I must talk to Michael, it is very important!'

'Don't you worry, I'll tell Hal to go back and fetch him as soon as he returns. You go on up now, I'll bring a hot brick to put in the bed.'

Dutifully Maggy obeyed, glad to escape. She wasn't ill, nor even tired, but her mind raced feverishly with questions. How could she tell Michael, how could she face Hal and what could she say to lessen the blow to Ollie? She lay there fretting, listening for the slightest sound from downstairs, on tenterhooks over who might arrive first. When finally there was a gentle knock on the door, it was Anna. 'Are you awake?' she called softly. 'Can I come in? I've brought the brick.'

Maggy peered over the sheets. 'It's alright, I'm not asleep.'

'Good, move over, I don't want to burn you.' Making sure all was well, she said, 'I'll come back later when you've rested,' and left Maggy to do so. The warmth of the brick allowed her to relax and she fell asleep to be woken a while later when Anna knocked again. 'It's only me,' she called. 'Are you feeling any better?'

Now over-heated from the warmth of the bed, Maggy was flushed. 'Come in, Anna, I'm a little better for resting.'

'That's good, because Michael's here!' There was a bloom about Anna's face and a warm sparkle in her eyes. 'Shall I let him come up?'

'Please do, and I'm sorry I can't take you down to the keel this evening. Perhaps tomorrow if I'm well we can go.'

'It's alright, Maggy,' Anna said with a beaming smile. 'Michael's going to have tea with us after he's spoken to you. Would you like a bit of something too?'

'Thank you, I would, but not too much,' Maggy murmured, concealing the fact that she was more than a little hungry.

Anna came closer to the bed, hesitated, then said, 'Would it cheer you up if I told you a secret?' she whispered shyly, 'Michael's asked me to marry him!'

The shock of the announcement made Maggy gasp for breath, and she began to cough to conceal her dismay. 'How, when?' she spluttered.

'I offered to go down to the docks to tell Michael that you were ill, to save Hal going back, but I got there after he and Father had left. Michael was so pleased to see me,' and she paused shyly. 'He said that he'd missed me so much that he'd be miserable if we were parted again.'

'What did you say?' Maggy asked, afraid that in his excitement Michael had assumed his money problems were solved.

'Oh, Maggy,' Anna laughed, 'I said yes, of course, how could I say anything else?'

'Have you no doubts at all? Don't you need to think about it first?'

'I have done nothing but think about him since I last saw him. What is there to think about?'

'Nothing, I suppose,' Maggy said lamely, thinking of her reaction to Ollie's proposal. 'Just make Michael happy, please.'

Anna was touched by this remark, 'I will, I will. He's going to ask Father tonight so please don't let on!'

When Michael's head finally appeared round the door, he saw Maggy's anxious face and said, 'My, you are flushed. Don't disturb yourself or you'll make things worse.'

'Close the door,' she whispered, 'I want to talk to you.' He did as she asked, wondering what was so mysterious and urgent that she had sent for him. 'Michael, what have you done?' she pleaded, keeping her voice down. 'Anna says you've asked her to marry you already, but surely you can't do that yet?'

'Why not?'

'Don't be silly, you know why. We might lose the keel if I don't marry Ollie, and I haven't told him I will yet!'

He laughed. 'To hear you anyone would think that's why you're marrying him, for the money.'

She looked at him sharply. 'What's got into you, Michael? Don't you see, I've sent for you to tell you, I just can't marry Ollie! Not even for the money! You've asked Anna without thinking it through!' Her voice was rising hysterically.

'Hey, hey, Maggy, calm down. Someone might hear you,' Michael said calmly. 'There's no need to go on.'

'But if I don't marry Ollie you'll lose the *Maggie Kelly*!'

'Look, I'm not such a fool. The money problem has been solved. It's alright, everything's fine and nobody's going to make you marry Ollie.' The smile left his face. 'Were you doing it just for the money, Sis?'

Refusing to meet his gaze, she nodded. 'It was the only way I could think of to help us. But how can you have got the money so quickly?'

He sat on the bed. 'Listen. Erik knew I had some sort of money problems and he thought I wouldn't mind if he told Hal about it. What he didn't know was that Hal still had most of the money he'd earned on the whaler. Anyway, Hal came round to see the keel, apologised for the fact that Erik had told him my business and suggested a deal, which I have accepted.'

'What?' Maggy broke in. 'What have you done?' She made to get out of bed, shocked and angry, then sat back and stared in disbelief as the truth sank in.

'What's got into you, Maggy?' Michael demanded. 'You haven't heard the deal yet. Besides, it's my business and I'll decide what's best.'

'But you'd have let me marry Ollie earlier, if there had been no other solution!' She could hardly believe what Michael was saying.

'I thought you wanted to marry Ollie. It was your idea, not mine.' He was becoming irritated now; this was not the sort of response he'd looked forward to from his sister. 'I wouldn't have wanted or expected you to do such a thing, even to save the keel. Now just listen, will you? It's a fair deal.' Maggy sat glumly in silence as he tried to explain. 'Hal's got a job now and says he can spare this sum from what he'd earned at sea, so for Erik's sake, he's bought a share in the keel. It's enough to keep us going, but of course he expects a return for his money, and providing he gets that, and we prove his investment's safe, he'll not bother us. We can have the cash tomorrow; it's the only way, and not a bad one Maggy. Erik's a worker and he trusts his son—besides, they'll be family soon.' He waited for her to say something but she said nothing. 'I don't know what's got into you, I really don't, did you want to lose the *Maggie*?' He was annoyed with her and had to remind himself that she wasn't well. 'It'll sound better when you're in a fit state to think about things, you see if it doesn't.'

'Hal! Why Hal? You could just as easily have asked Ollie for a loan? After all you feared about him wanting to buy the keel in the first place, you now take money from his brother. You don't even know much about him.'

'Oh, I can't be doing with this, Maggy,' Michael interrupted impatiently. 'He offered me the deal. Anyway, I'll come back later after tea, and have another word. Just think about it 'til then.'

When Michael had left the room Maggy sat upright staring defiantly at the walls, her resentment of Hal growing. Here she was, imprisoned in the bedroom through her own stupidity and his actions, whilst below so much was taking place. Between the announcement that Anna and Michael were to make, and the news that Hal had saved the day, she was party to none of it. Her anger and rancour at Hal overrode any gratitude she might have felt towards him, and Michael in his trusting way had placed her in a cleft stick. She was hungry and angry and, by the time Ellen brought her a meal suitable only for an invalid, it was all she could do to disguise her chagrin.

'We're going to have tea now,' Ellen told her gently. 'I'll pop up again later!'

'Thank you, you're very kind,' Maggy murmured dutifully, and once Ellen had gone, ate what she had been brought with unseemly haste.

She'd never dreamed that Hal had money or else, before their confrontation, she might have considered asking him for the loan. Now, however, she and Michael were beholden to him, he was a partner in the keel and with more say in its future than she.

'Quiet now!' Erik admonished the family seated at the table below stairs. 'Mike has something important to tell us. Come on lad, don't keep us waiting.'

'Well,' Michael said, turning to Anna for support, who nodded encouragingly at him. 'I've asked Anna to marry me,' he said hurriedly, relieved to be able to speak openly of his happiness, 'and she's accepted!'

The ensuing chorus of excited voices drowned each other out and Maggy guessed that something of importance had been said.

'This is good, is it not Mother?' Erik was looking at Ellen with a twinkle in his eyes. 'And who can we thank for such an outcome but you.' Michael looked at him questioningly. 'My Ellen she sees everything, Mike, so be careful,' he warned, with a broad knowing smile. 'She thinks I don't know these things. But now you promise to take care of my Anna, if not I am standing at the tiller and will see!'

Amidst the laughter, Michael took Anna's hand firmly in his and whispered, 'He'd better not or I shall push him off the keel!' At this, Anna broke into a giggle and squeezed his hand.

'Quiet!' Erik raised his voice again. 'There is more news, my new son-in-law has agreed to let Hal buy a share in the keel, so that I can keep an eye on these young people.' He raised his mug, his face suddenly becoming serious, and with a husky voice, said, 'God Bless you both'.

For several seconds after Erik's emotional words no one spoke, not even young Johann who could never keep quiet for long. Then in a quiet voice, Ellen said with equal sincerity, 'This has been a good week for the Eriksons.'

Half way through tea Ollie returned home and found the family in a jolly mood. 'What's going on?' he asked, and on looking round saw Michael at the table, which aroused his curiosity even more.

'Anna's going to marry Michael,' an excited Lucy informed him.

He grinned at Anna, not at all surprised by the announcement, just the timing of it, and then congratulated Michael. 'You'd better take good care of my little sister,' he told Michael cheerfully, 'or you'll have me to answer to!'

At this Michael promptly replied, 'Don't worry, I will!'

Then Ollie noticed Maggy's absence and when, after a while, she did not appear he asked where she was.

'Upstairs in bed,' Ellen informed him. 'We think you might be guilty of giving her your cold.'

'Oh dear, is she in a bad way?' he asked with real concern. 'I hope not,' he added, barely concealing his disappointment at this news.

'She'll live,' Michael broke in. 'She was becoming a little argumentative when I saw her just before tea, and that's a good sign, believe me.'

As Ollie and Hal were talking later in the evening, Ollie remarked, 'Well, this seems to have brought a few things to a satisfactory conclusion. It's just a shame that Maggy's not well, have you seen her today?' Hal appeared not to hear this, so he went on. 'She's missing all the excitement, do you think someone should go up and see her so that she knows we haven't forgotten her?'

'I don't know, ask Mother,' Hal replied irritably. 'Maggy'll get disturbed in a while anyway, when the children go to bed.'

'I suppose so. How's the clearing up in Sewer Lane going on?' Have you hit any problems?'

'Nothing to speak of, the sign's up and we can put the stuff from Sheffield in there as soon as you want.'

This news seemed to please Ollie. 'Good, then I can start sorting and packing things for shipping. I'll have to wait for the next lot to arrive before I leave but it's a good step forward.' He paused for a moment, then lowered his voice to add, 'It was a good move on your part to buy into the keel, I would have done it myself had I known Mike was of a mind to allow it.'

'Something cropped up which created the opportunity, and I thought it would give security to Dad as well as being a small investment. Now, with those two getting married it seems an even better move.'

'Once you get established in your job, and the warehouse is up and running, you'll be alright.'

'What will you do?' Hal enquired. 'Send the orders to me to pass on to the manufacturers?'

'That's right, then no one will know too much about my business abroad. Goods can be delivered here, or picked up by the keel, and you can ship them out to my instructions. You can do the paperwork and pay the bills from my bank, along with a sum for yourself, on a regular basis. It won't be a lot at first but once things build up you could do well.'

'Sounds fair enough, we'll go through all the details when we're on our own. Are you going to arrange to move the goods tomorrow if Mike's found a berth?'

'As soon as possible. By the way, I think I've managed to get a regular shipment of seeds and grain for Mike's return journeys. You yourself may be able to find them a few orders, once you get to know the market.'

Things were beginning to quieten down at this time, as the children were preparing to go to bed. 'Well,' Ollie said, looking at Hal, 'I may as well tell you something else. I've become quite attracted to Maggy recently.'

'So have I,' Hal rejoined bluntly. Ollie's eyes opened wide, he was taken aback by his brother's statement. 'I thought I'd just tell you, that's all.'

'I didn't realise,' Ollie said, looking cautiously at him. 'Look, I'm serious about this.'

'So am I!' Hal warned him.

'It could be a bit awkward,' Ollie declared as the two brothers eyed each other. 'There can only be one winner, the other loses.'

'In the past, you and I have faced many a challenge against each other,' Hal said, 'and you've usually won. This time I intend to win.' There was no mirth on Hal's face, simply an expression of fierce determination to succeed.

'One of us will lose, that's for sure, and I shall fight as hard as you,' Ollie retaliated. 'Shall we make a pact to remain friends as well as brothers, no matter what the outcome?'

With a wry smile, Hal agreed. 'In the end, Maggy will do the choosing and we will have to accept that.' He held out his hand, 'Are we agreed?'

Clasping Hal's hand, Ollie said, 'Agreed!'

Erik had been watching his sons for several minutes and recognised the old spark of a challenge in their eyes. 'What are you two up to?' he asked, good-humouredly, still pleased by Michael and Anna's betrothal.

The charade which Maggy had brought upon herself was becoming wearisome and the sound of merrymaking below revived her flagging spirits. She wanted to throw off the mantle of deceit and go downstairs, but it would have been impossible under Ellen and Erik's watchful eyes for they would know immediately that she had not been ill. There was nothing for it but to suffer in silence, and suffer she did. The more she considered her predicament the more she realised that both Ollie and Hal had forced her into the situation. This growing awareness increased her anger and determination to make them suffer equally, especially as neither had offered true love and affection. She was not prepared to become the object of their desire to fill the world with little Eriksons! A delicious quiver of excitement ran through her at the thought of teaching them both a lesson—she was ready to do battle!

At last Michael re-appeared at the door. 'I'm not leaving yet,' he said, 'but the children will be coming to bed soon and I thought I'd better see you before they do.' He looked down at her. 'You seem on the mend, Sis, there's a sparkle in your eye that tells me so.'

She ignored this. 'You've been having a merry old time of it down there,' she complained, but then softly asked, 'are they pleased about you and Anna?'

He smiled a cheeky grin, and sat on the bed. 'I think so! I just hope Ma behaves as well when I take Anna home with us.'

'She can't help but like Anna,' Maggy assured him. 'But where will Anna live when she's not travelling? Have you thought of that? John can't be expected to have her as well as Ma and me.'

He was suddenly flushed and embarrassed. 'For a while until Anna has a child she will travel with me, but when that time comes and during the bad winters she will stay here. I'm hoping eventually to rent a little place nearby.'

She smiled and said, 'I hope you'll be very happy together'. Then she said wistfully, 'This will mean the end of my travels, Michael, there won't be room on the *Maggie* any more. I knew it would happen one day, but not this soon.'

'You'll come and keep Anna company, on occasion, won't you, and stay perhaps with Ellen here sometimes? I wouldn't want Anna to be lonely when I'm away either.'

'Perhaps, when things settle down I will, and she could stay at the farm while you go on to Sheffield.' Her tone was becoming warmer the more she talked to him. 'You've got your life sorted out better than we'd expected, things really are looking up, Michael.'

'But what of you, Maggy?' He was concerned now. 'Your future is not cut and dried and I won't be able to keep us all for long, not if children come along.'

'As they will,' she said, squeezing his hand fondly. 'Don't you worry about me, I'm not afraid of work and who knows what might turn up. Now, you go below and enjoy tonight, it's a rare occasion and you should be with Anna! I'll see you tomorrow.'

'I'll help all I can, Maggy, you know I will. Things won't be quite the same ever again, but they may even be better. Let's hope so. By the way, Ollie's back!' he added with a grin, as he left her once more.

When the children came to bed, with instructions not to disturb her, she eyed them through half closed lids. Yes, she thought, each one in some way was becoming special to her; she had at least gained another family.

Refreshed by her long sojourn in bed, Maggy rose early the following morning bright and full of determination. No one had a hold on her and she was ready to exact her revenge on the two men whose overconfidence and complacency regarding her feelings was going to be rudely shaken.

Maggy's first resolution, to put Hal in his place, was tested immediately; he approached her the minute she left the bedroom, as though having lain in wait. 'Can I have a word with you, Maggy?' he asked in a friendly manner.

'I'm going back to the keel when I've packed,' she replied, dismissing him and trying to pass.

'Then let me carry your things,' he offered. 'I owe you that much!'

'No, thank you!' she answered haughtily, 'I can manage.' His face fell and she didn't enjoy being cruel, but then he deserved it.

'I've got to talk to you, Maggy! I'm sorry about yesterday, but I can't go into that with everyone coming and going.'

'I can manage!' she insisted, pushed past him and flounced down the stairs, only to bump into Ollie who appeared as she got to the bottom. 'Ollie!' she gasped, trying to avoid knocking him over. 'You're back!'

'Yes,' he laughed. 'You're feeling better I see!' Thinking his words unfortunate, and not wanting to be delayed, she stormed off into the kitchen, leaving him astounded. 'What did I say?' he asked as Hal also reached the foot of the stairs.

'Who knows with women? Perhaps we have offended her,' Hal suggested, who was similarly not wanting to stop and talk.

'Hardly,' Ollie retorted, 'I haven't seen her for days.'

'You look better now, that's good,' Ellen said in greeting, when she saw her. 'Did you sleep well?'

'I'm fine now, Ellen, and thank you both for looking after me so well.' She turned to Anna. 'We are to be sisters soon, I'm so pleased, and you've made Michael very happy.'

Hal and Ollie entered the room and immediately Maggy fell silent, refusing to look at either of them. The atmosphere in the kitchen cooled noticeably, Ellen realised this but kept silent too. Suddenly Hal spoke up, 'Maggy says she's going back today, and I've offered to carry her things. It will give me a chance to have another look around the keel'.

Maggy seethed inside at this remark, but she could hardly upset Ellen by saying she would rather struggle on alone than accept his help. She scowled at him when Ollie wasn't looking and saw a satisfied expression on his face. Ollie on the other hand looked downcast, and she wondered if things hadn't gone too well in Liverpool, or if her unwarranted abruptness was the cause. Was she being foolish to behave in such a childish manner when a more mature woman might lead them a dance with more subtlety? She sighed deeply, not knowing that Ollie was watching her closely and endeavouring to understand the change in her.

'I'm going to the warehouse first,' he announced suddenly, 'and then I will arrange to collect the goods Mike's got on the keel, when he's ready. Might I see you down there, Maggy?' He looked troubled, ill at ease even, for a man about to view the foundations of his future empire.

Taking pity on him, she made an effort to suppress her resentment at his previous lack of emotion with her. 'Later, I'll be there then,' and as an afterthought added, 'I'd like to see some of the things you've bought when you've time.'

The immediate effect of these conciliatory words transformed him. 'Right, I'll see you at the dock later.' He beamed as he went out, unwittingly leaving Maggy in Hal's company.

'Give me a shout when you're ready to leave, Maggy,' Hal said. 'I'll be out in the yard doing a job for Dad.'

Maggy was again able to ignore him when Anna asked her, 'Will you advise me what to take to Dalton? Then someone can bring my things down, when I know we are to leave.'

Being in no hurry to walk with Hal, and knowing that Anna had much to do and couldn't accompany them, Maggy was in no haste to finish her own packing. Seeing this, Anna remarked, 'You're very quiet today, do you think yourself well enough to go back to the keel?'

'Oh, yes,' Maggy quickly replied, 'I'm alright now, but perhaps a little despondent at leaving this house after receiving so warm a welcome, and after the excitement of London, but at least you will be coming with me.'

'Don't tell Michael, but I'm still nervous over travelling on that water,' Anna confessed. 'I know I must hide it from him but it won't be easy.'

Forgetting her own problems, Maggy smiled. 'You'll be safe enough and Michael can be very kind and considerate. Take your needlework and sit below with it when you feel anxious. You're going to see all sorts of things once we're on the canal and if the weather's good you'll soon grow to like it.'

Eventually Maggy could find no excuse for delaying further. She went to Ellen and kissed her on the cheek. 'You have done so much for me, and I will never be able to repay you.'

'You take care of yourself my dear, and if the keel remains here for some time you'll come and visit us, won't you? Come and stay too, when things have quietened down.' There was a tremor of emotion in Ellen's voice as she said this, which struck a responsive cord in Maggy's heart and she nodded, unable in her turn to say more. 'Shall I call Hal and tell him you're ready?' Ellen offered. Hal came in answer to her call and picked up some of the bags. At least this way, Maggy realised, with both hands occupied he would be harmless, so she picked up the remainder. 'Are you sure you can manage?' Ellen asked. 'Or shall Erik bring some tomorrow?'

'No, Mother, we'll manage,' Hal protested and set off, leaving Maggy to follow. They walked on, neither speaking, until Hal suddenly blurted out, 'What I did yesterday was unforgivable, Maggy. I don't know why I did what I did, except that some inner force drove me on. Will you ever forgive me?'

She stopped, a rising desire to hurt him returning. 'You took advantage of my predicament and the knowledge that…,'

'What, Maggy? The fact that I'd read in your eyes more than friendship? You can't deny that we both feel an attraction for each other.'

They were level with the cemetery now, and Maggy looked towards the gravestone where she had finally come to her senses. Had he followed her there yesterday she would most probably have succumbed to him, so overwhelming had been her desire to feel him touch her again. Now, walking along beside him, all passion was gone and in future she was determined to control her emotions at all costs.

'Please, Maggy, listen to me! I would never hurt you deliberately, you must know that!' His voice was anguished. 'For God's sake, I feel bad enough about it, without you crucifying me for it. I know you weren't really ill last night, you couldn't have been, not so suddenly. You made me feel ashamed of myself.'

'Your actions frightened me, and you *did* make me feel ill! I was tormented by my own feelings too, but that has all gone now,' she said flatly. 'Anyway, I must have looked sufficiently ill for your mother to think me so, but I can see it all dispassionately now.'

'I should never have done it, I will never forgive myself.' He stopped and turned to her, 'And neither will you, I think'. There was sad resignation in his eyes, 'I can say no more than ask if we can still be friends despite what has occurred'. His brown eyes softened as he pleaded with her, and she remembered his many kindnesses to her. It was a pity, for, had it not been for his moment of angry passion, she might have loved him dearly in time. However, had she given in to him yesterday all could have been lost forever; she might have carried his child and the disgrace for the rest of her life.

'You will always be my friend,' she replied firmly, 'but that is all.' Then in a softer voice, added, 'I will not forget your many kindnesses, though'.

He was relieved at this, although the feeling of guilt still remained. 'In my misery last night I tormented Ollie, telling him that I was going to fight for your affections,' he confessed, and seeing her disdain quickly went on, 'I'm not a vindictive man, Maggy, no matter what you think of me and I won't pester you again, but as we are destined to meet as a family, can we try to put this behind us, please?'

She was sensible enough to know how much it must have cost him emotionally to admit this, so she spoke frankly. 'I would never like to lose your friendship; we have too many ties to let rancour spoil our relationship, and I think enough has been said on the matter. I do forgive you, Hal, and will try to put it from my mind.' However, there was a lump in her throat which threatened her control, this stemming from the knowledge that their relationship could never be quite the same again.

'Thank you,' he answered huskily, 'I have nothing but admiration for you, never forget that.'

She walked on, all thought of revenge gone from her mind, leaving simply a longing to be back in her own familiar home again, and she called out to Michael with a relieved cry when she saw him at the dock-side.

He came eagerly towards them to ask, 'Is Anna coming down soon?'

'When she can,' Maggy replied, 'although she's already packed.'

'How long do you think you'll be here, Mike?' Hal asked.

'We hope to deliver this afternoon. Will you tell Ollie I took his advice to make contact with one of the sea merchants, and they've given me a contract to make regular runs with seeds and grain!' Michael could barely conceal his delight.

'That's excellent,' Hal responded. He didn't stay long on the keel, returning a little while later only to give Michael the sum of money he'd promised, and obtain a receipt for this until their agreement could be drawn up. Maggy kept out of the way so as not to cause embarrassment, and took no pride in having humbled and hurt him. When he finally left she came up on deck and looked at the jumble of vessels in the dock, and tried to let the familiar bustle of activity around her override her problems.

Seeing her pensive look, Michael joined her. 'Things are improving aren't they, and I'm looking forward to this trip, are you?'

Ignoring his question, she replied, 'You've done well to get the new contract. Now remember, Anna's not happy on water, so be patient, won't you!'

'Of course I will, but listen,' Michael said confidentially, 'Anna and I have discussed things with Erik and he's agreed that we can get married on our return from this next trip, before Ollie goes off to America; she would like that. What do you think? It's a bit quick, but I want her to spend as much of the summer with me as she can, otherwise I'll only see her a few days a month before winter comes. It'll mean a special licence, but it'll be quicker than reading the banns.'

'There's not really much point in waiting, is there? Not if you're sure. Why not see how this trip goes first—supposing she hates it?'

He'd obviously not thought of this possibility and his face fell. 'Don't say that, Maggy, or I'll have to spend my life like Erik, coming home only twice a month.'

'Would it matter that much? Mother didn't always come.'

'I suppose not if that's the only way. Just pray for good weather for us, won't you! It will make everything seem better.'

Later, after Ollie had collected his goods on a dray, and having suggested she call in on him when he'd had a chance to unpack a few items, Maggy left Michael and, with some reservations, set off for the warehouse,

Steeling herself against the hateful memories of the day before, she entered through the open door.

'It's just a small beginning,' Ollie said, welcoming her and waiting for her reaction.

'Even so, you've bought quite a lot of things already haven't you! Are you taking them all in this first shipment?' Maggy asked, her interest growing.

'Yes,' he replied, opening one of the parcels, 'and I'm waiting for more to come with Mike next time, items I ordered at the exhibition. They would not have been ready for collection before he left Sheffield.' He selected a slender brown package from amongst the parcels. 'Mostly these are practical commodities, but I'm taking a few luxury items as well, to see how they go.' He carefully unwrapped the protective paper to reveal a garter knife. 'These are used by certain women to protect themselves, they don't take up a lot of room.' He handed the knife to her. 'Don't touch the blade with your fingers, it's sharp, and the acid from your skin may do it harm.'

'It's quite beautiful,' Maggy said, noting the ivory handle and wondering if she might have been tempted to use one on Hal the day before, had she owned one. She simply remarked as she handed it carefully back to him, 'Before the handle was cut the ivory could quite easily have gone to Sheffield on the *Maggie Kelly*.'

He placed the knife back in its wrapper, his head bent forward and his hands hovered over the other packages, doing nothing in particular. Maggy became wary, worried over what would come next. Suddenly he turned and looked at her, his face tense and lined. 'Can I hold you, Maggy, just once! To give me hope?' he pleaded, holding his hands out encouragingly.

Maggy nodded, much as a mother would to a child. He drew her close and held her tight, his head pressed against her hair. Raising one hand he cradled her head against his. 'It's no good, is it, Maggy?' he murmured sadly. 'You don't love me, do you?' She made to draw back in protest, but he held her even tighter, 'It's true, I know it. Just let me hold you for a moment longer'.

She could feel him trembling. 'Oh, Ollie,' she cried, 'I do love you, but not the way you want me to.'

'I realised that when I saw the way Anna looked at Michael last night, the way you never look at me.' He slowly released her. 'I do understand,' he said forlornly. 'Go now, it's best that way!' He refused to look at her and turned his head away. 'Go, please go!'

Instinctively, and to comfort him, she raised her head and kissed him tenderly on the cheek. 'You're a good man, Ollie,' she said, 'such a good man!' Then, doing as he'd asked, she left the warehouse and with her head bowed, walked slowly along the street. She was suddenly aware of someone approaching and made to step aside when she heard a familiar voice.

'Is there something wrong?' Hal asked.

'It's Ollie,' she said sadly, without lifting her tear-stained face. 'Go to him, Hal, he needs you.' She heard him hurrying towards the warehouse, and was relieved that he chose not to question her further.

Ollie was standing at the bench, staring at his packages. 'I've just seen Maggy,' Hal said anxiously. 'What's wrong?'

Without looking up at him, Ollie replied, 'You win, Hal. You've won this time, Maggy doesn't love me!'

Hal shook his head when he realised what his brother was implying. 'I don't think so,' he said huskily, 'I don't think either of us has won.'

Chapter 7

he weather was kind to the *Maggie Kelly* as they wended their way along the rivers and canals towards Dalton.

Michael flexed his arms and legs, easing the stiffness caused by sleeping in Erik's cramped cabin, and watched proudly as Maggy explained to Anna the ways of the keel and described the benefits of life on the water. Where to spot mushrooms growing wild in a field, how to take a cabbage from where a farmer had planted extra knowing he would always lose a few from passing vessels, the way to catch sticklebacks and draw pictures of dragonflies. More importantly, when Michael said 'throw in a fender' he meant one of rope, and not the metal one from the stove, also to mind her head as they approached a bridge, rather than be knocked into the canal.

He was well pleased with his lot, his financial problems had been solved and business was picking up. He could see himself in the future, with Anna and oft times Erik, sitting in an evening with needle, pen, book and ivory in their hands, and hoped she might at some time share with him her enjoyment of the books she read. In simple truth he was looking forward to having Anna by his side, as his wife, but in all this he failed to notice Maggy's loss of weight and the sometimes haunted, distant look in her eyes when their days work was done.

Meanwhile, in Hull, Ellen and Ollie had been busy arranging matters for the wedding in addition to preparing for his imminent departure to America. Hal helped when he could but his new employment was much more demanding than he'd anticipated. 'I do hope they don't change their minds,' Ellen said one day as she fussed and bustled about, 'and I've just realised that Maggy will have to stay here for a couple of nights after the wedding, to leave Anna and Michael alone for a bit. Do you think she will want to stay any longer?'

'I really don't know, Mother!' Ollie replied, having tried not very successfully to avoid thinking of their next meeting, and at the same time concentrate on his business needs.

'You men take some understanding,' his mother complained without looking at him. 'This house isn't the same without Anna, and soon you will be gone as well.' She sat down wearily at the table. 'I'm happy for them of course, but something's changed, all this organising to do, and you and Hal moping about. What's happened, have you two had a fight?'

'We're too old for that, Mother, there's nothing wrong between us. It's just been a trying time, especially with Hal's new job. We're tired, that's all.'

'I shall be glad when your father returns,' Ellen sighed, and got up to carry on.

Several days later, the morning quiet was shattered by Johann as he rushed into the house. 'It's Anna, Mother, she's coming up the street!'

'My, you look fit, Anna,' Ellen cried, as they embraced, 'and judging by your face all has gone well, I can see. Where's your father?'

'He'll be along when he can, he's helping Michael at the moment.' She took a deep breath to quell her excitement. 'We're lucky to get back in time, Michael got held up in Doncaster which threw things out.'

'How did you get on with Michael's family, did they approve of you?' Ellen asked nervously.

'I think so, once they'd got over the shock, and Patrick taught me to ride a horse,' Anna said, laughing. 'Unfortunately Michael's mother can't travel now and Maggy's sister, Mary, can't leave her, so we're to manage without them for the wedding. Mary's sent a small present for you.' She gave a basket of eggs and produce to Ellen.

'How very kind, but what a pity they can't come, just so long as it's not an excuse. Where's Maggy, anyway?'

'She's coming later with Michael, to discuss things.'

'Did Mike pick up my orders?' Ollie asked. 'Shall I go down to the docks and sort them out?'

'That's a good idea,' Anna said. 'If they could empty the keel today I know it would be very convenient. It would give us a free day tomorrow then.'

When evening came, Maggy had no choice but to accompany Michael to Anna's; to have refrained would have appeared strange and inexplicable. Much to her relief Hal wasn't there when they arrived and stayed out much longer than expected. She had seen Ollie on the keel as he collected his orders, and he'd behaved like a gentleman; now at home he was attentive and as kind as ever, concealing his inner feelings and trying to put her at ease. As time went on and Michael was unwilling to leave, Maggy began to worry, knowing that Hal could return at any time. She became edgy, glancing frequently at the door, so, as a distraction, she went to help Ellen in the kitchen.

'You've lost weight, Maggy,' Ellen said, 'and your hair's been lightened by the sun; it's a really pretty colour.' As Maggy appeared disinclined to talk, she went on. 'You'll meet my mother tomorrow, perhaps one day I may meet yours. Will you thank your sister for her gift? I can't write myself, you know—at least, not very well.' She'd not found talking to Maggy difficult before, but somehow there seemed to be a reserve about her now, which she couldn't understand. 'I'll just go and see if there's any more crockery to wash, I'll not be a minute,' she said, leaving Maggy to wash up.

Maggy fidgeted with the pots, wishing that Michael would make a move, and jumped with alarm when the back door suddenly opened to admit Hal. She gasped, clutched at the brooch at her throat, and made to follow Ellen out of the kitchen, only to see her returning.

'Hal! You don't usually come in the back way,' Ellen said. 'You've frightened Maggy half to death, just look at her.'

'I'm sorry, how was I to know?' It was the first time Maggy had seen him since their chance meeting in Sewer Lane; he looked tired, subdued even, and she wondered if he was unwell.

'Hello!' she said, as Ellen went back out. 'How's the job?'

'It's different,' he replied lethargically as he took off his coat and hung it up. 'I thought you'd be gone by now!'

Maggy realised then that he'd deliberately stayed away to avoid seeing her. 'We would have but Michael is reluctant to leave Anna, it'll be a good thing when they're married.' Hal seemed not to know what to say to her at this, or even want to be near her. She bit her lip, wishing he'd leave the room, but knew she'd no right to think that in his own home.

'I'll join the others,' he said, as if reading her thoughts. 'Are you coming?'

She had no choice but to follow him, and although not afraid of him any more, she was uncomfortably aware that the feelings she thought conquered had returned unbidden. She seated herself as far away from Hal as possible, trying to ignore his presence, yet all the time conscious of his watchful eyes and of her growing desire to be near him. By the time Michael condescended to leave, Maggy was ashamed of the warmth of her feelings towards the man she had spurned.

The great day arrived and Anna and Maggy arrived together at the church to find Michael waiting nervously. They were dressed in the gowns made for their London trip, and it was as if they had stepped back in time, but whereas before only part of Anna's mind had been with them, today she was blissfully happy, her eyes shining, and her face aglow with love for Michael.

Maggy joined the rest of the family and sat motionless and quiet, somehow isolated in the crowd, and in a deeply reflective mood as she thought of Hal and Ollie. Once, she'd risked glancing in Hal's direction and found his eyes on her, yet he looked away quickly when he realised that she was observing him, such had been his own preoccupation.

When the happy couple left the church followed by all the guests, Maggy remained seated on the hard wooden pew, uncertain whether to join Ellen and Erik, their family and friends. After a few minutes she heard footsteps behind her and turned to see Ollie approaching.

He sat down beside her and said, 'Well, another milestone in our lives has been reached, and tomorrow I'm off on my travels again'.

This news, although expected, still saddened her for she found she could still talk to him with ease; his respect for her seemed undiminished and this pleased her greatly. 'How are things with you?' he asked with concern. 'What does the future offer now your chaperoning job is over, have you any plans?'

Nodding soberly, she explained. 'I have had an offer, better than anything I could have expected. My sister worked at one time as a servant in a large Hall not far from where I live. She visits her old employer there occasionally and, on telling her of my trip to the Exhibition, Miss Saunderson offered me a job as her companion, to read to her mainly and do little errands. She's a nice person, I have met her a few times when visiting with Mary.'

'And do you like the idea?' he asked, questioning not her good fortune but the monotonous sound of the job.

Trying to appear cheerful she replied, 'I would be ungrateful not to appreciate such an excellent opportunity, and there is a library there full of beautiful books'.

'I think you'll do well!' He didn't press her further, thinking sadly of the wonders he could have shown her. 'Could I write to tell you of my progress? It would be good to correspond with someone who might enjoy reading of my travels as I go, rather than keeping a journal.'

'Why, yes!' she cried, 'I would like that.'

'May I also ask a couple of favours before I go?' He saw a wariness in her eyes, and smiled. 'Don't be alarmed, I am not going to embarrass you, but I know you have a head for business. Would you keep an eye open for any new ideas which you think might be useful in a new country where there are few luxuries? Also, if I have any problems with my suppliers, do you think you could go with Michael to Sheffield and visit them? If you can spare the time, naturally!' He could see interest stirring in Maggy in this suggestion and took comfort in the knowledge that something of her old self still remained. 'You see, Hal will be doing such a lot for me here. I can't ask too much of him, and you have a greater understanding of my expectations than he.'

'I will be happy to assist you,' she replied, 'and I value your respect and faith in me.'

'I'll give you an address in San Francisco to write to, they will keep my correspondence until I can collect it. However, I warn you the first letter I send may be a long one when it arrives; the weeks at sea will be monotonous and I may exploit your kindness by writing of my experiences.'

'And in turn I will give you news of the family,' she replied. 'But you said two favours, or are both covered already?'

'Have I asked for so much?'

'No,' she laughed, 'I didn't mean that.' He looked at her quietly for a moment, and suddenly he seemed older than he was, much as he might look in later years, rather like his father.

'Maggy,' he said softly. 'It hurts me to say this, but will you go to Hal and make your peace with him? I fear he will never come to you and if you keep your distance this it could destroy so much for you both!'

Without thinking, she glanced towards the door where Hal was standing, and tried to suppress the wave of emotion which coursed through her. She looked again at Ollie, as if seeking help.

'You've never looked at me like that,' he said. 'Go to him!'

She turned towards Hal, unsure of herself, yet wanting to do as Ollie asked.

Hal hadn't moved. He made a sad and lonely figure standing there, and what had he done that was so terrible for her to have inflicted such pain on him? It would take only a moment to make peace. Swallowing her pride she went towards him, half expecting him to spurn her. 'Hal,' she said, her voice quivering, 'I've come to say how sorry I am for the harsh things I said.'

'That's alright,' he replied gruffly, 'I deserved it, Maggy.'

'No, Hal, you didn't,' she whispered. 'I was too shocked to appreciate how you felt. I didn't understand at all, then.'

He stared at her. 'Do you understand now, Maggy? Because if you don't I can't go through all that again. Do you really know how I feel?' His voice was hoarse and emotional, his face pale and drawn.

'I...'. Words wouldn't come. 'Please, Hal,' she pleaded, 'I don't really know anything anymore, but I believe I do love you, deep down!'

She saw him relax a little and placed a hand on his arm. 'Don't do that, Maggy, don't touch me unless you're sure,' he cried as if in torment.

'Maggy? Maggy? Where is she?'

Maggy's face fell as she heard Ellen's voice outside the church. 'Hal?' she whispered frantically, expecting his mother to appear at any moment.

'We'll talk later,' he answered, just as Ellen appeared.

Seeing the strange look on Maggy's face, she paused, and like all mothers sensed something was wrong, saying only, 'Oh, you're there! Come along, dear, everyone's waiting to go'.

They reluctantly followed Ellen and emerged from the cool interior of the church into the bright sunlight, Maggy blinking back a tear and shielding her eyes. 'The light is rather strong dear,' Ellen said, well aware that Maggy was distressed. 'Don't Michael and Anna look happy?' With that she moved on to reprimand Johann who was mischievously climbing on a tombstone.

Hal stared after his mother, needing to follow, but not wanting to miss this opportunity to be alone with Maggy. 'Will you wait here, Maggy?' he pleaded. 'I'll be back in a minute!' He hurried off after Ellen. 'Please, Mother,' he said. 'I want to talk to Maggy alone for a while, and it's important, it really is. Can you make the excuse that I want to show her around the church, or something?' He could see this puzzled her, so added, 'I'll explain later, you've no need to worry'.

There was no mistaking his seriousness, and Ellen nodded, remembering how moody he'd been of late, and how strange Maggy had seemed since her return. 'Don't come until things are sorted,' she said gently.

He retraced his steps to the church where, being unable to see Maggy where he'd left her feared she might have gone. However, as he walked inside he saw her seated in a pew near the lectern. He breathed a sigh of relief and joined her. 'I've asked Mother to go on, and said we'd follow later,' he said apologetically. 'I hope you don't mind, but I can't talk to you in the house, and you'll be leaving again soon. Do you feel safe enough with me, in here?' She nearly laughed at this remark, until she realised how serious he was. Even so he saw her amusement and his face relaxed.

He was closer to her now than at any other time since he'd kissed her in the warehouse, yet she felt quite comfortable at his nearness. 'Of course I feel safe,' she said softly.

Accepting her sincerity, he said, 'I hardly know what to say, Maggy, as I have such a lot on my conscience. If I hadn't interfered you would probably have married my brother and together you could have worked things out, lived a happy life, and even loved one another. I have little to offer, yet I may have spoilt it for you both.'

'Please, Hal,' she murmured, 'don't you know how it upsets me too, to think of him going so far away, and alone. I care very much for him, yet there is something missing. I don't desire to touch him, to...'. Her voice trailed off, and the silence in the church was heavy with unspoken words.

Eventually Hal spoke again. 'Anna says you have been offered a position as a lady's companion. Do you think you'll be happy with that?'

'Not entirely,' she told him truthfully. 'Although it is a wonderful opportunity, and I have to earn my keep somehow. It won't be exciting, nor will it be forever, but I shall be able to enjoy the wonderful library there.'

'It's a pity to bury yourself that way. You have such a lively mind, and I have robbed you of adventure, wealth perhaps, and given you nothing.'

'Don't keep saying that, Hal!' she cried. 'The only thing you have done is to wake me up to the truth. I know I couldn't have married Ollie. Always there would have been something missing; always at the back of my mind I would have been searching for whatever that was, and simply become dull and dutiful.'

'As you could do being a companion to an old lady. That's not for you, Maggy, not permanently, not dullness. You'd die inside, just as I will die without you!' The enormity of this admission brought him up short, and more quietly he added. 'We'd better go. This is not the way to spend Anna and Mike's wedding day.'

'No, Hal, don't run away, we need to talk.' She had rested her hand on his arm for several seconds before realising she'd done so. Hal was more than aware of her touch, and he looked questioningly at her.

Finally he asked, 'Do you really understand, Maggy, why I behaved as I did in the warehouse? I can't always promise to be a gentleman like Ollie, nor do I have his obsessions, I only have strong feelings, and strong hands to work with. Did you mean what you said earlier, that you might love me?'

'Yes,' she whispered shyly, her hand trembling nervously on his arm.

Hal placed his hand over hers. 'I want to marry you Maggy, but I think you should take this position you've been offered, just for a while. I want you to do it with joy and enthusiasm, then come to me willingly and happily.' He was searching her face now, all his hopes pinned on her response. 'Could you do that?' he asked anxiously. Maggy smiled, her eyes reflecting the gratitude and love she felt. 'Come on,' he said, understanding her well. 'I feel guilty of my feelings in this place.' He took her hand firmly in his and gently led her outside. 'We'd better join the others before our secret is out!'

'It's been a long day,' Erik complained when he and Ellen finally retired for the night. 'Work on the keel is not so bad compared with all this fuss! Now that Mike has the grain contract we'll be loading tomorrow, then we leave the next day.'

'So soon?' Ellen grumbled, getting into the bed beside him. 'You've only been home three nights, and I've hardly had time to see you. Besides, Michael and Anna need time to be alone.'

'Anna has Mike all day when we leave,' he consoled her. 'Next time I come we enjoy ourselves, yes?' He gave her a resounding kiss which made her smile.

'And where will Maggy sleep going back on the keel? Ellen protested. 'She'll be in the way.'

He laughed. 'There are two beds in the cabin, Mother. Have you forgotten, it's much more exciting when you're afraid someone hears you? But I think if that doesn't suit you, she'll have to sleep in my cabin. Which you want?' He chuckled and lay back, breathing contentedly, and much to Ellen's annoyance was snoring within minutes.

She looked at him with affection, her mind retracing the events of the day, her happiness overshadowed only by Ollie's impending departure. The difference she'd noticed in Hal and Maggy when they arrived home gave her a feeling of great satisfaction and she smiled, for this at least was one trick Erik had missed.

However, within minutes he rolled over, grunted, and then mumbled, 'Mother, there's something going on between Hal and Maggy. Did you notice?'